CHILTON'S Repair and Tune-Up Guide

Inboard/ Outdrives

ILLUSTRATED

Prepared by the

Automotive Editorial Department

Chilton Book Company
401 Walnut Street
Philadelphia, Pa. 19106
215—WA 5–9111

managing editor **JOHN D. KELLY;** assistant managing editor **PETER J. MEYER;** senior editor **KERRY A. FREEMAN;** technical editors **Robert J. Brown, Philip A. Canal;** copy editor **Eric J. Roberts**

CHILTON BOOK COMPANY   PHILADELPHIA NEW YORK LONDON

Copyright © 1973 by Chilton Book Company
First Edition
All rights reserved

Published in Philadelphia by Chilton Book Company
and simultaneously in Ontario, Canada, by Thomas
Nelson & Sons, Ltd.

Manufactured in the United States of America

Library of Congress Cataloging in Publication Data

Chilton Book Co. Automotive Editorial Dept.
   Chilton's repair and tune-up guide: inboard/
outdrives.

   1. Inboard-outboard engines—Maintenance and repair.
I. Title.   II. Title: Repair and tune-up guide:
inboard/outdrives.
VM771.C44   1973   623.87′23′4   73-1268
ISBN 0-8019-5781-8
ISBN 0-8019-5804-0 (pbk)

Contents

ACKNOWLEDGEMENTS

CHILTON BOOK COMPANY expresses appreciation to the following firms for their generous assistance and technical information:

BELK'S MARINE SUPPLY (MERCURY), *Holmes, Pennsylvania*

THE BOATING INDUSTRY ASSOCIATION, *Chicago, Illinois*

CHAMPION SPARK PLUG COMPANY, *Toledo, Ohio*

KIEKHAEFER MERCURY, *Fond du Lac, Wisconsin*

OUTBOARD MARINE CORPORATION, *Milwaukee, Wisconsin*

UNITED STATES COAST GUARD

VOLVO PENTA (Chrysler Marine Divison), *Marysville, Michigan*

The editorial content of this book has been prepared by skilled editors from authoritative sources. While every effort is made to attain accuracy, the Publisher cannot be held responsible for manufacturing changes, typographical errors or omissions.

1 · General Information, Safety, and Maintenance

Introduction

This book is intended to serve as a guide to the tune-up, repair, and maintenance of all of the most popular models of engines and outdrives manufactured by Kiekhaefer Mercury, Outboard Marine Corporation (Evinrude and Johnson), and Chrysler/Volvo Penta. All procedures in this book are recommended by the manufacturer, the Boating Industry Association, or the United States Coast Guard. In some cases it was necessary to substitute more common tools for special factory tools; however, the use of the special tool was kept in mind when selecting an alternate. If in doubt concerning any service procedures, consult a dealer or, in minor cases, the owner's manual.

The operator of a boat should read and become familiar with the "Troubleshooting a Breakdown at Sea" and "Safety Afloat" sections of this book. Familiarity with either of these sections could save your life or someone else's in an extreme emergency. Before beginning any service operation, read the procedures and be sure that you understand each one clearly. All necessary tools and equipment should be available and their use understood thoroughly. This will assure your boat's return to service as soon as possible, eliminating aggravating delays. You will notice that some service procedures have been omitted since they require very special tools and knowledge. These operations are best left to authorized service facilities or factory dealers. If used wisely and properly, this book will provide all the necessary information needed to keep your boat and engine in peak condition, and also save money on repair and maintenance bills.

Boating Safety Courses

Wise boatmen know the value of becoming involved in a voluntary education program so they will better understand their responsibilities on the water. The Coast Guard Auxiliary offers any boatman the opportunity to obtain instruction in Seamanship, smallcraft handling, and safety practices afloat. Qualified members of the Coast Guard Auxiliary present each of the following courses:

1. Outboard Motorboat Handling—primarily for outboard operators with the emphasis on safety. Covers the fundamental rules of boat handling, equipment requirements, and common-sense courtesy.

2. Safe Boating—provides instruction in the elements of seamanship, navigation,

rules of the road, and boating safety for outboards and inboards.

3. Basic Seamanship and Smallboat Handling—provides a practical and comprehensive study of boating, seamanship, navigation, piloting (charts and compass), rules of the road, safe motorboat operation, and accident prevention. Those who successfully complete this course are awarded the U.S. Coast Guard Auxiliary Basic Smallboat Seamanship Certificate.

To obtain information on any of the above courses, write to the director of the Auxiliary located in your district (see list of U.S. Coast Guard Districts) or contact any member of the Coast Guard Auxiliary Flotilla nearest you.

In addition to the above courses, U.S. Power Squadrons and the American National Red Cross offer free courses for any boater.

Troubleshooting Emergencies Afloat

SAFETY PRECAUTIONS

Wise boatmen take a tip from professional sailors, who know the value of being prepared for emergencies. By studying the following sections, and familiarizing yourself and at least one other person with them, your reactions in an emergency situation will be fast and may save a life. Before venturing into any waters, check the following items:

1. Check the weather.
2. Advise someone of your destination.
3. Check your fuel supply and be sure that you carry enough fuel for a round trip.
4. Be sure that you have lifesaving equipment for all hands.

Remember that it is not necessary to be on the open seas to encounter an emergency. Many boating accidents occur each year on protected waters, inland waterways, and lakes or rivers.

SAFE LOAD CAPACITIES

The Outboard Boating Club of America has calculated weight capacity specifica-

tions as a guide for smallcraft operators. Most manufacturers display this information on a plate somewhere on their boats. These are recommended weight capacities for cruising in good weather and calm water. It is still the responsibility of the operator to exercise caution and sound judgement regarding the capacity of his craft. In the absence of capacity plates, the following formulae will help to determine the capacity of boats of more or less standard design.

CAPACITY (NUMBER OF PERSONS)

The number of persons that your boat can carry without crowding in good weather conditions can be calculated as follows:

L = Length Overall (feet)
B = Maximum Width (feet)
$\frac{L \times B}{15}$ = number of persons (to the nearest whole number)

CAPACITY (WEIGHT)

The weight-carrying capacity of your boat, taking into account the weight of people, engine, fuel, and gear, can be calculated as follows:

L = Length Overall (feet)
B = Maximum Width (feet)
De = Minimum Effective Depth of Boat (feet). "De" should be measured at the lowest point that water can enter. This takes into account low transom cutouts or acceptable engine wells.
$7.5 \times L \times B \times De$ = pounds for persons, engines, fuel, and gear (Minimum Necessary Equipment)

The state and the Federal governments have established minimum equipment which, by law, must be carried at all times. The following chart sets down additional equipment which is recommended for various classes of boats and various types of waters. "D" designates items which are desirable and "E" indicates essential items. Common sense and experience will dictate any changes to this recommended equipment list.

Item	Class A (to 16')			Class I (16'–26')			Class 2 (26'–40')		
	Open waters	Semi-protected	Protected	Open waters	Semi-protected	Protected	Open waters	Semi-protected	Protected
Anchor(s)	E	E	E	E	E	E	E	E	E
Anchor cable (line, chain, etc.)	E	E	E	E	E	E	E	E	E
Bailing device (pump, etc.)	E	E	E	E	E	E	E	E	E
Boat hook	—	—	—	D	D	D	E	E	E
Bucket (fire fighting/ bailing)	E	E	E	E	E	E	E	E	E
Coast pilot	—	—	—	D	D	—	D	D	—
Compass	E	E	D	E	E	D	E	E	E
Course protractor or parallel rules	D	D	—	E	E	D	E	E	E
Deviation table	D	D	—	E	E	D	E	E	E
Distress signals	E	E	E	E	E	E	E	E	E
Dividers	D	D	—	E	E	D	E	E	E
Emergency rations	E	—	—	E	—	—	E	—	—
Emergency drinking water	E	D	—	E	D	—	E	D	—
Fenders	D	D	D	D	D	D	D	D	D
First-aid kit and manual (10- to 20-unit)	E	E	E	E	E	E	E	E	E
Flashlight	E	E	E	E	E	E	E	E	E
Heaving line	—	—	—	—	—	—	D	D	D
Lantern, kerosine	—	—	—	—	—	—	D	D	D
Light list	D	D	—	E	E	D	E	E	E
Local chart(s)	E	D	—	E	E	E	E	E	E
Megaphone or loud hailer	—	—	—	—	—	—	D	D	D
Mooring lines	E	E	E	E	E	E	E	E	E
Motor oil and grease (extra supply)	—	—	—	D	D	D	D	D	D
Nails, screws, bolts, etc.	D	D	D	D	D	D	D	D	D
Oars, spare	E	E	E	E	E	E	—	—	—

Item	Class A (to 16')			Class I (16'–26')			Class 2 (26'–40')		
	Open waters	Semi-protected	Protected	Open waters	Semi-protected	Protected	Open waters	Semi-protected	Protected
Radar, reflector, collapsible	D	D	—	D	D	—	D	D	—
Radio direction finder	—	—	—	D	—	—	D	—	—
Radio, telephone	D	—	—	D	D	—	D	D	—
Ring buoy(s) (additional)	D	D	D	D	D	D	D	D	D
RPM table	—	—	—	D	D	D	D	D	D
Sounding device, (lead line, etc.)	D	D	—	D	D	D	E	E	E
Spare batteries	D	D	D	D	D	D	D	D	D
Spare parts	E	D	—	E	E	D	E	E	D
Tables, current	—	—	—	—	—	—	—	D	D
Tables, tide	—	—	—	—	—	—	—	D	D
Tools	E	D	—	E	E	D	E	E	D

COAST GUARD COURTESY EXAMINATIONS

You are required, by law, to carry certain equipment on board at all times while underway—the equipment depending on the class of your boat and the method of power. While there is no obligation, any boat owner or operator may request a free Courtesy Motorboat Examination from the Coast Guard Auxiliary or U.S. Coast Guard. If your boat is properly equipped, you will receive the Auxiliary's Official Courtesy Motorboat Examination decal. If your boat is improperly equipped, you will be so advised.

NOTE: *If you are advised that your boat is improperly equipped, NO report is made to any law enforcement agency. You are advised of deficiencies, so that they can be corrected.*

U.S. COAST GUARD DISTRICT OFFICES, RESCUE COORDINATION AND MARINE INSPECTION OFFICES

In the event of an emergency or for some other reason, it becomes necessary to contact the Coast Guard, the following list should be used. Do not contact Rescue Coordination, except in an emergency.

1st DISTRICT

Commander, 1st C.G. District
1400 Customhouse
Boston, Mass.

Rescue Coordination Center
Office hours, 0800–1630: Capital 7-3710
Nights, Saturdays, holidays: Capital 7-3710

Marine Inspection Offices

447 Commercial Street
Boston, Mass.

76 Pearl Street
Portland, Maine

409 Federal Building
Providence, R.I.

2d DISTRICT

Commander, 2d C.G. District
815 Olive Street
St. Louis, Mo.

Rescue Coordination Center
Office hours, 0800–1630: Main 1-8100
Nights, Saturdays, holidays: Main 1-8845,
   Main 1-8847

Marine Inspection Offices

815 Olive Street
St. Louis, Mo.

426 Falls Building
Memphis, Tenn.

425–427 New Post Office Building
Cairo, Ill.

670 U.S. Courthouse, 801 Broadway
Nashville, Tenn.

301 Post Office and Courthouse Building
Dubuque, Iowa

1215 Park Building
Pittsburgh, Pa.

748 Federal Building, 5th and Maine
   Streets
Cincinnati, Ohio

328 Federal Building, 5th Avenue and
   Ninth Street
Huntington, W. Va.

254 Francis Building, 4th and Chestnut
   Streets
Louisville, Ky.

3d DISTRICT

Commander, 3d C.G. District
650 Customhouse
New York, N.Y.

Rescue Coordination Center
Office hours, 0830–1700: Hanover 2-5700
Nights, Saturdays, holidays: Hanover 2-5700

Marine Inspection Offices

720 Customhouse
New York, N.Y.

313 Federal Building
Albany, N.Y.

302 Post Office Building
New London, Conn.

801 Customhouse, 2d and Chestnut
   Streets
Philadelphia, Pa.

5th DISTRICT

Commander, 5th C.G. District
Box 540, Post Office and Courthouse
   Building
Norfolk, Va.

Rescue Coordination Center
Office hours, 0800–1630: Madison 2-2771
Nights, Saturdays, holidays: Madison
   2-2771

Marine Inspection Offices

204 Customhouse
Norfolk, Va.

Customhouse Wharf
Wilmington, N.C.

Customhouse
Baltimore, Md.

7th DISTRICT

Commander, 7th C.G. District
Pan American Bank Building
150 S.E. 3d Avenue
Miami, Fla.

Rescue Coordination Center
Office hours, 0800–1630: Franklin 9-1871
Nights, Saturdays, holidays: Franklin
   9-1871

Marine Inspection Offices

410 Calumet Building, 10 N.E. 3d Avenue
Miami, Fla.

1 East Bay Street
Savannah, Ga.

316 Franklin St.
Tampa 2, Fla.

210 Federal Building
Jacksonville, Fla.

32 Customhouse
Charleston, S.C.

302 Federal Building, P.O. Box 3666
San Juan, P.R.

8th DISTRICT

Commander, 8th C.G. District
332 Customhouse
New Orleans, La.

Rescue Coordination Center
Office hours, 0800–1630: Express 2411
Nights, Saturdays, holidays: Magnolia
3949

Marine Inspection Offices

310 Customhouse
New Orleans, La.

232 Customhouse
Galveston, Tex.

563 Federal Building
Mobile, Ala.

101 Federal Building
Corpus Christi, Tex.

General Delivery, 1601 Proctor Street
Port Arthur, Tex.

7300 Wingate Street
Houston, Tex.

9th DISTRICT

Commander, 9th C.G. District
Main Post Office Building, West 3d and
    Prospect Streets
Cleveland, Ohio

Rescue Coordination Center
Office hours, 0800–1630: Cherry 1-1757
Nights, Saturdays, holidays: Cherry
    1-1757

Marine Inspection Offices

1055 East Ninth Street
Cleveland, Ohio

401 Had Building, 429 Summit Street
Toledo, Ohio

440 Federal Building
Buffalo, N.Y.

Municipal Building
Saint Ignace, Mich.

205 Federal Building
Oswego, N.Y.

10101 S. Ewing Avenue
Chicago, Ill.

430 Federal Building
Detroit, Mich.

National Bank Building
Ludington, Mich.

311 Federal Building
Duluth, Minn.

551A Federal Building
Milwaukee, Wis.

11th DISTRICT

Commander, 11th C.G. District
706 Times Building
Long Beach, Calif.

Rescue Coordination Center
Office hours, 0800–1630: Hemlock 7-2941
Nights, Saturdays, holidays: Hemlock
    7-2941, Hemlock 7-2942

Marine Inspection Offices

1105 Times Building
Long Beach, Calif.

12th DISTRICT

Commander, 12th C.G. District
903 Appraisers Building, 630 Sansome
    Street
San Francisco, Calif.

Rescue Coordination Center
Office hours, 0800–1630: Yukon 6-3111
Nights, Saturdays, holidays: Yukon
    6-3873

Marine Inspection Offices

903 Appraisers Building, 630 Sansome
    Street
San Francisco, Calif.

13th DISTRICT

Commander, 13th C.G. District
618 2d Avenue
Seattle, Wash.

Rescue Coordination Center
Office hours, 0745–1615: Main 4-2902
Nights, Saturdays, holidays: Main 4-2902

Marine Inspection Offices

618 2d Avenue
Seattle, Wash.

202 Lincoln Building, 208 S.W. 5th
   Avenue
Portland, Oreg.

14th DISTRICT

Commander, 14th C.G. District
P.O. Box 4010, Seaboard Finance Build-
   ing, 1347 Kapiolani
Honolulu, Hawaii

Rescue Coordination Center
Office hours, 0800–1630: Honolulu
   6-3811
Nights, Saturdays, holidays: Honolulu
   5-8831

Marine Inspection Offices

P.O. Box 2997, Pier 11
Honolulu, Hawaii

17th DISTRICT

Commander, 17th C.G. District
P.O. Box 2631, 3d Street
Juneau, Alaska

Rescue Coordination Center
Office hours, 0800–1700: Juneau 6-2680
Nights, Saturdays, holidays: Juneau
   6-2680

Marine Inspection Offices

P.O. Box 2631, 3d Street
Juneau, Alaska

WEATHER AND STORM SIGNALS

Wise boatmen are always aware of the weather, since, for the most part, you are at the mercy of the prevailing conditions. Before venturing onto any body of water, it is wise to check the weather and sea condition as well as the forecast for your area. Weather forecasts are available from the U.S. Weather Bureau Office in your area, as well as from radio stations and newspapers. All Coast Guard stations and some yacht clubs fly storm signals on the Great Lakes, Atlantic, Gulf, and Pacific coasts. Smallcraft warnings, in particular, should never be ignored. Remember, also, that many areas of the country, especially coastal areas, are subject to sudden squalls and the dreaded "northeasters" even with an optimistic forecast. Since these squalls and northeast storms can arise suddenly, all smallcraft should seek the nearest shelter at the first sign of foul weather. It is poor practice to try to weather a storm when shelter is available. If it is impossible to reach shelter, however, the best practice is to keep the bow into the wind. Under no circumstances should you allow the craft to become broadside to large waves.

Storm Signals

The storm signals following are descriptive of the type of weather indicated. All boatmen should become familar with their meaning and the location (in your area) from which they are flown.

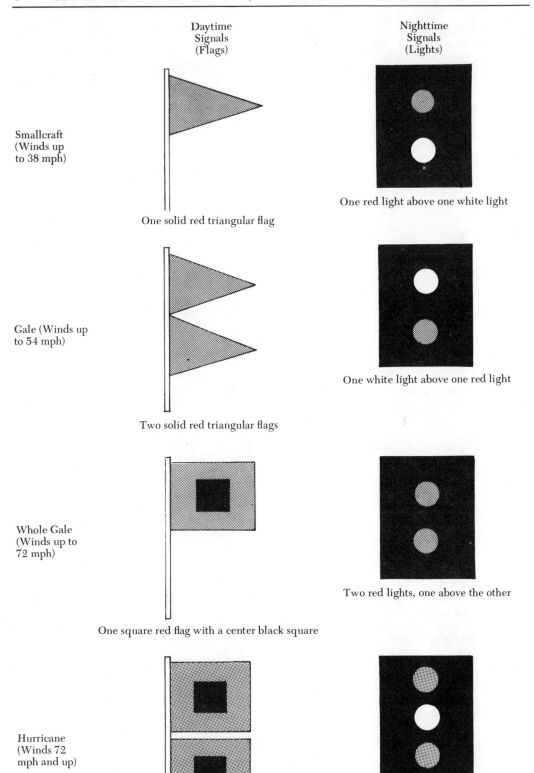

Daytime
Signals
(Flags)

Nighttime
Signals
(Lights)

Smallcraft
(Winds up
to 38 mph)

One solid red triangular flag

One red light above one white light

Gale (Winds up
to 54 mph)

Two solid red triangular flags

One white light above one red light

Whole Gale
(Winds up to
72 mph)

One square red flag with a center black square

Two red lights, one above the other

Hurricane
(Winds 72
mph and up)

Two square red flags with a center black square in
each flag

Two red lights with a white light in between

NOTE: *This table includes general statements about the weather and can be very useful. However, the latest Weather Bureau forecast should be used* *whenever available. These forecasts are available on scheduled marine radiotelephone broadcasts, commercial radio stations, and from Weather Bureau Offices.*

Wind Barometer Chart

Wind Direction	Barometer Reduced to Sea Level	Character of Weather
SW to NW	30.10 to 30.20 and steady	Fair, with slight temperature changes for 1 or 2 days.
SW to NW	30.10 to 30.20 and rising rapidly	Fair followed within 2 days by rain.
SW to NW	30.20 and above and stationary	Continued fair with no decided temperature change.
SW to NW	30.20 and above and falling slowly	Slowly rising temperature and fair for 2 days.
S to SE	30.10 to 30.20 and falling slowly	Rain in 12 to 18 hours.
S to SE	30.10 to 30.20 and falling rapidly	Wind increasing in force, with rain within 12 to 24 hours.
SE to NE	30.10 to 30.20 and falling slowly	Rain in 12 to 18 hours.
SE to NE	30.10 to 30.20 and falling rapidly	Increasing wind and rain within 12 hours.
E to NE	30.10 and above and falling slowly	In summer, with light winds, rain may not fall for several days. In winter, rain in 24 hours.
E to NE	30.10 and above and falling fast	In summer, rain probably in 12 hours. In winter, rain or snow with increasing winds will often set in when the barometer begins to fall and the wind set in NE.
SE to NE	30.00 or below and falling slowly	Rain will continue 1 or 2 days.
SE to NE	30.00 or below and falling rapidly	Rain with high wind, followed within 36 hours by clearing and, in winter, colder.
S to SW	30.00 or below and rising slowly	Clearing in a few hours and fair for several days.
S to E	29.80 or below and falling rapidly	Severe storm imminent, followed in 24 hours by clearing and, in winter, colder.
E to N	29.80 or below and falling rapidly	Severe NE gale and heavy rain; winter, heavy snow and cold wave.
Going to W	29.80 or below and rising rapidly	Clearing and colder.

Beaufort Wind Scale

Wind Force	Wind Velocity (knots)	Water Condition	Wind Condition
1	1–3	Ripples	Light air
2	4–6	Small wavelets	Light breeze
3	7–10	Wavelets crest	Gentle breeze
4	11–16	Small waves	Moderate breeze
5	17–21	Moderate waves	Fresh breeze
6	22–27	Many whitecaps	Strong breeze
7	28–33	Foam flies	Moderate gale
8	34–40	——	Fresh gale
9	41–47	——	Strong gale
10	48–55	——	Whole gale
11	56–66	——	Storm
12	66 and up	——	Hurricane

NOTE: *This is a traditional scale used to estimate wind force from wind and water conditions.*

Distress Procedures

DISTRESS SIGNALS

Searching for a vessel in distress is a time-consuming procedure when there is insufficient information on which to base the search. Your chances of receiving assistance are greatly increased if you know the recognized distress signals and have the proper equipment.

Radiotelephones are the best piece of equipment for communicating distress and should be carried by all vessels which are used for off-shore cruising. Pleasure craft, merchant vessels, Coast Guard ships, and monitoring stations listen on 2182 kilocycles, which is a calling and distress frequency. Occasionally, 2638 or 2738 kilocycles may not be busy and may bring assistance sooner. However, in an emergency, you may use any frequency available. In an extreme emergency, the spoken word MAYDAY (international code word for needing emergency assistance) stands a good chance of being heard in most areas. The spoken word MAYDAY should not be used unless immediate assistance is required.

Many search craft today are also equipped with radar, but wood and plastic boats do not make good radar targets. A small, collapsible radar reflector, positioned high on the craft, will infinitely increase your chances of radar detection.

The latest distress signal for smallcraft on waters of the United States is the act of standing as high as possible on the craft and SLOWLY RAISING AND LOWERING YOUR ARMS OUTSTRETCHED TO EACH SIDE. This is a distinctive signal, not likely to be mistaken for a greeting. It is important to remember that, when in need of emergency assistance, any signal that will attract attention is acceptable. Your chances are, however, enhanced by using any of the recognized distress signals, which are shown following.

Recognized Distress Signals

Signal	Inland rules	Great Lakes rules	Western rivers	International rules °
A gun or other explosive fired at intervals of about a minute.	Yes (day and night)	Yes (day and night)	Yes (day and night)	Yes
A continuous sounding with any fog-signal apparatus.	Yes (day and night)	Yes (day and night)	Yes (day and night)	Yes

Recognized Distress Signals (cont.)

Signal	Inland rules	Great Lakes rules	Western rivers	International rules °
Rockets or shells, throwing red stars fired one at a time at short intervals.				Yes
Signal made by radiotelegraphy or by any other signaling methods consisting of the group ···———··· (SOS) in Morse Code.				Yes
A signal sent by radiotelephony consisting of the spoken word "Mayday."				Yes
The International Code signal of distress indicated by N.C.			Yes (day)	Yes
A signal consisting of a square flag having above or below it a ball or anything resembling a ball.		Yes (day)	Yes (day)	Yes
Flames on the vessel (as from a burning tar barrel, oil barrel, etc.)	Yes (night)	Yes (night)	Yes (night)	Yes
A rocket parachute flare showing a red light.				Yes
Rockets or shells, bursting in the air with a loud report and throwing stars of any color or description, fired one at a time at short intervals.			Yes (day and night)	
A continuous sounding with steam whistle.			Yes (day and night)	
Rockets or shells, throwing stars of any color or description fired one at a time at short intervals.		Yes (day and night)		

* International rules do not distinguish between day and night us of signals.

REPORTING EMERGENCIES

The search and rescue responsibilities of the U.S. Coast Guard generally include conducting harbor checks, searches for missing craft, effecting emergency repairs, towing to the nearest port of safe anchorage, and furnishing emergency medical assistance or evacuation, depending on circumstances.

To assist the Coast Guard in search and rescue operations, remember the following points.

1. When requesting assistance by radio, provide information using the standard form on the following page.

2. Advise someone of your itinerary and, at the first opportunity, notify those concerned of any change in plans.

3. Do not use MAYDAY in voice distress communications unless immediate assistance is required.

MAN OVERBOARD

The following procedures are recommended in the event of a man overboard.

1. Keep calm. Do not panic or allow others to panic.

2. Swing the stern of the boat away from the man. This reduces the danger of his being injured by a propeller.

```
┌─────────────────────────────────────────────────────────────┐
│              DISTRESS INFORMATION SHEET                       │
│  When requesting assistance from the Coast Guard furnish the  │
│  following information after establishing communications      │
│              SPEAK SLOWLY AND CLEARLY                         │
│  _____ This is _____  │
│  (Coast Guard Station being called)  (Your boat's name and    │
│                                       radio call sign)        │
│  I am _____ in position _____ │
│       (Nature of distress—Disabled, sinking,    (Latitude and │
│        grounded, etc.)                                        │
│  _____   │
│  longitude bearing (True or Magnetic) and distance from a     │
│  prominent point of land)                                     │
│  I have _____ persons aboard. I am in _____   │
│            (Number)              (Immediate or no immediate   │
│                                   danger)                     │
│  My boat is _____, _____, _____, _____    │
│          (Length and type) (Type of rig) (Color of hull)      │
│                                        (Color of topside)     │
│  I request _____ assistance. │
│         (Source of assistance—Coast Guard or commercial)      │
│  I will standby _____                         OVER       │
│              (Radio frequency)                                │
└─────────────────────────────────────────────────────────────┘
```

3. Throw the man a lifesaving device as soon as possible. A ring buoy is best, since these are easiest to handle in the water. However, speed may be essential, and any device is better than none.

4. Keep the man in view at all times. If another person is available, have him act as a lookout. At night, direct the best possible light on the man in the water.

5. Maneuver to approach the man from downwind or into the sea. The particular maneuver that you use to approach the man will depend on circumstances (i.e., physical condition of the man in the water, availability of assistance, maneuvering room, etc.).

6. If capable assistance is available, it might be best to have that person put on a life jacket and go into the water to assist the person overboard. The person entering the water should not do so without attaching himself to the craft with a line.

7. Assist the man in boarding the boat. In small boats, the best way to take a person aboard from the water is over the stern. This will avoid capsizing and shipping water on smallcraft, which are sensitive to weight distribution. Common sense dictates that the propeller should be stopped or the engine shut off.

FIRE AFLOAT

Fire on the water is a terrifying experience. The person is trapped in a real sense. He has a choice of staying with a burning boat or jumping into unfamiliar surroundings. Either prospect is less than pleasant. The first thought should be to stay calm and assess the situation. More can be done in the first few minutes than in the next few hours.

Fire extinguishers such as dry chemical, carbon dioxide, and foam are most effective on oil or grease fires when the extinguisher is directed at the base of the flames. Vaporizing liquids (chlorobromomethane and carbon tetrachloride) should not be used in confined areas because of the danger to health. Burning items such as wood, mattresses, and rags should be extinguished by water. (Throwing them over the side is as good a method as any.)

If the fire occurs in a relatively closed space, it can be confined by closing all hatch doors, vents, and ports to cut off the oxygen supply.

Maneuvering the craft can also be a great aid in controlling fires. Reducing speed will help to minimize the fanning effect of the wind. To help in preventing the spread of the fire, keep the fire downwind by maneuvering the boat according to the position of the fire and direction of wind.

The following steps should be taken (not necessarily in order) in the event of fire.

1. Apply the extinguishing agent by:
   a. Fire extinguisher;

b. Discharging the fixed smothering system;

c. Applying water to wood or similar materials.

2. If practical, burning materials should be thrown over the side.

3. Reduce the air supply by:

a. Maneuvering the craft to reduce the effect of wind, and

b. Closing hatches, ports, vents and doors if the fire is in an area where this will be effective.

4. Make preparations for abandoning the craft by:

a. Putting on lifesaving devices, and

b. Signalling for assistance by radio or other means.

CAPSIZING

Many ships and boats involved in casualties have continued to float for long periods of time. If your boat capsizes, do not leave it. Generally, a damaged boat can be sighted more easily than a swimmer in the water. Aside from this, distances over water are deceiving. Keep your head and restrain the impulse to swim for shore. The actual distance is usually far more than the estimated distance.

Calmly weigh the facts of the situation such as injuries, proximity to shore, and swimming ability before deciding on a course of action. Get comfortable in your life preserver (which of course you have been wearing since the first sign of danger) and hang onto the boat. Almost all smallcraft built today have flotation characteristics built in. Since slick plastic hulls are hard to hang onto, tie a 6–10 ft length of rope to a cleat somewhere on the boat. It can be used for a temporary mooring line in the marina and can be useful as something to hang onto should you capsize.

NOTE: *The information pertaining to Minimum Necessary Equipment, Coast Guard District Offices, Weather and Storm Signals, Wind-Barometer Chart, and Distress Procedures, is taken from the* Recreational Boating Guide, CG 340, United States Coast Guard. *This pamphlet is for sale from the Superintendent of Documents, United States Government Printing Office, Washington 25, D.C. at 40 cents per copy.*

Mechanical Breakdowns

TOOLS

A few basic hand tools should be carried on board every boat. The number and type of tools carried depends on the boat's power source, how often the boat is used, and where the boat is used. Obviously, if you do a great deal of off-shore cruising, you will need more tools to remedy a breakdown than if you are stranded in a back bay or other protected water. The following list is not all-inclusive but it should give you an idea of what to carry. In addition, you should carry any special tools needed for effecting minor repairs on your particular engine.

A basic tool list should include:

1. Adjustable-end wrench (crescent type);

2. Slip-joint pliers;

3. Pipe wrench;

4. Vise grip;

5. Screwdrivers of various sizes and types (flathead, phillips);

6. Box-end wrench set;

7. Set of socker wrenches and ratchet (recommended but not essential);

8. Spark plug wrench;

9. Hammer;

10. Electrical tape;

11. Sealant (self-hardening type for repairing leaks);

12. Flashlight;

13. Test light (made from a socket and bulb compatible with boat's or motor's electrical system, 6 volt, 12 volt. Attach two lengths of wire and clean the ends for test probes.)

SPARE PARTS

Obviously it is not possible to carry a spare part for any part which could fail. However, there are some parts which prove troublesome more often than others. The following spares should be carried, since they are more likely to fail than other parts:

1. Distributor points;

2. Condenser;

3. Coil;

4. Spark plugs;

5. Fuel pump;

6. Spare propeller nut and cotter pin.

Mechanical Troubleshooting

In the event of mechanical breakdown, the best thing to do in order to find and correct the problem is to follow a logical troubleshooting procedure. More often than not, the trouble will be located quicker this way than by testing various parts at random. Follow the suggestions one at a time, and reset the adjustments before proceeding to the next step.

CAUTION: *Before performing any tests or repairs to the electrical system, be sure that the bilges and engine compartment are free of explosive vapors and fumes.*

Troubleshooting the Engine

ENGINE REACTION	*CHECK POINTS*
1. Starter will not turn engine.	A. Loose or corroded battery connections. B. Under-capacity or weak battery. C. Defective starter switch. D. Faulty starter solenoid. E. Open circuit in wiring. F. Broken or worn brushes in starter. G. Faulty starter armature or fields.
2. Starter turns but pinion does not engage.	A. Starter clutch slipping. B. Broken teeth on flywheel gear. C. Armature shaft rusted, dirty, or lacking lubrication. D. Broken bendix spring.
3. Solenoid plunger vibrates when starter switch is engaged.	A. Weak battery. B. Loose connections. C. Faulty solenoid.
4. Starter pinion jams or binds.	A. Starter mounting loose or misaligned. B. Broken or chipped teeth on flywheel gear or pinion.
5. Starter turns engine but hard to start or won't start.	A. Empty gas tank. B. Tank vent clogged. C. Shut-off valve closed. D. Clogged fuel filter. E. Dirt or water in fuel line or carburetor. F. Choke not operating. G. Faulty fuel pump. H. Carburetor flooded or out of adjustment. I. Vapor lock. J. Faulty coil, condenser, or CD ignition amplifier. K. Moisture on ignition wires or distributor cap. L. Fouled spark plugs or improper plug gap. M. Improper ignition timing. N. Ignition points improperly gapped, burned, or dirty, or CD ignition sensor faulty. O. Cracked distributor cap or rotor. P. Poor connections or damaged ignition wiring.
6. Poor idling.	A. Incorrect air idle adjustment. B. Carbonized idle tube or poor seating shoulder. C. Idle air bleed carbonized or of incorrect size. D. Idle discharge holes plugged or gummed. E. Throttle body carbonized or worn throttle shaft. F. Air leak at mounting between carburetor and manifold. G. Damaged or worn idle needle. H. Incorrect fuel or float level. I. Choke does not completely open. J. Loose main body-to-throttle body screws. K. Carburetor icing. L. Distributor vacuum advance leak. M. Loose distributor base plate bearing. N. Corroded wire ends or distributor towers. O. Incorrect distributor point gap.

Troubleshooting the Engine (cont.)

ENGINE REACTION	CHECK POINTS
6. Poor idling.	P. Fouled spark plugs, improper plug gap, or badly eroded plugs. Q. Incorrect ignition timing. R. Improper spark plugs. S. Incorrect valve timing. T. Compression not within limits. U. Intake manifold leak. V. Manifold heat control valve stuck. W. Internal coolant leak. X. Low boiling point fuel (winter fuel in summer). Y. Low grade fuel.
7. Engine misses while idling.	A. Dirty, eroded, or incorrectly gapped spark plugs; cracked porcelain. B. Broken or loose ignition wires. C. Burned or pitted contact points. D. Faulty coil, condenser, or CD ignition amplifier. E. Weak battery. F. Distributor cap or rotor cracked or burned. G. Distributor advance, point dwell, or CD ignition sensor adjustment incorrect. H. Moisture on ignition wires, distributor cap, or spark plugs. I. Excessive play in distributor shaft. J. Burned, warped, or pitted valves. K. Incorrect carburetor idle adjustment. L. Incorect carburetor float level. M. Low compression. N. Worn or damaged camshaft. O. Improper valve lash adjustment.
8. Engine has loss of power.	A. Incorrect ignition timing or CD ignition sensor adjustment. B. Defective coil, condenser, or CD ignition amplifier. C. Distributor rotor burned or cracked. D. Excessive play in distributor shaft. E. Worn distributor cam. F. Dirty, eroded, or incorrectly gapped spark plugs. G. Dirt or water in fuel line or carburetor. H. Improper carburetor float level. I. Defective fuel pump. J. Incorrect valve timing. K. Blown cylinder head gasket. L. Low compression. M. Burned, warped, or pitted valves. N. Faulty ignition cables. O. Worn or damaged camshaft. P. Improper valve lash adjustment.
9. Engine misses on acceleration.	A. Distributor contact points dirty, improperly gapped, or faulty CD ignition sensor. B. Coil or condenser defective. C. Spark plugs dirty, eroded, or gap too great. D. Incorrect ignition timing. E. Dirt in carburetor. F. Burned, warped, or pitted valves. G. Accelerator pump in carburetor faulty.
10. Engine misses at high speed.	A. Dirt or water in fuel line or carburetor. B. Dirty jets in carburetor. C. Defective coil, condenser, or CD ignition amplifier. D. Incorrect ignition timing. E. Distributor contact points dirty, incorrectly gapped, or faulty CD ignition sensor. F. Distributor rotor burned or cracked. G. Excessive play in distributor shaft. H. Spark plugs eroded, dirty, or gap set too wide. I. Distributor shaft cam worn. J. Faulty ignition wiring.

Troubleshooting the Engine (cont.)

ENGINE REACTION	*CHECK POINTS*
11. Noisy valves.	A. Worn tappets. B. Worn valve guides. C. Excessive run-out of valve seats or valve face. D. Broken spring or cocked springs. E. Clogged hydraulic valve lifters or oil gallery. F. Improper valve lash adjustment.
12. Connecting rod noise.	A. Low oil pressure. B. Insufficient oil supply. C. Thin or diluted oil. D. Misaligned connecting rods. E. Excessive bearing clearance. F. Crankpin journals out-of-round.
13. Main bearing noise.	A. Low oil pressure. B. Insufficient oil supply. C. Thin or diluted oil. D. Loose flywheel. E. Excessive bearing clearance. F. Excessive end-play. G. Crankshaft journals out-of-round. H. Sprung crankshaft. I. Loose vibration damper or pulley.
14. Oil pressure drop.	A. Low oil level. B. Clogged oil filter. C. Worn parts in oil pump. D. Excessive bearing clearance. E. Thin or diluted oil. F. Oil pump relief valve stuck. G. Oil pump suction tube not aligned or bent. H. Intake screen clogged. I. Defective or kinked oil lines.
15. Engine backfires.	A. Spark plug cables improperly installed. B. Intermittent fuel supply, dirt or water in system. C. Stuck intake valve. D. Improper distributor timing. E. Loose, improperly adjusted, or faulty CD ignition sensor.
16. Engine knocks or pings. (Most noticeable on quick acceleration or at full throttle)	A. Low-octane fuel. B. Excess deposits in combustion chambers. C. Overheated engine. D. Incorrect spark plugs. E. Ignition timing advanced too far.
17. Poor performance—mixture too lean.	A. Damaged main metering jet. B. Damaged tip or bad top shoulder seat of main discharge jet. C. Vacuum piston worn or stuck. D. Incorrect fuel or float level. E. Automatic choke not operating properly. F. Incorrect fuel pump pressure. G. Clogged fuel filters or lines. H. Clogged fuel tank vent.
18. Poor performance—mixture too rich.	A. Restricted flame arrestor. B. Excessive fuel pump pressure. C. High float or fuel level. D. Damaged needle and seat. E. Leaking float. F. Worn main metering jet. G. Sticking choke.

Troubleshooting the Engine (cont.)

ENGINE REACTION	*CHECK POINTS*
19. Excessive fuel consumption.	A. Overloading engine (wrong propeller). B. Cruising in high winds. C. Sticky choke. D. Incorrect ignition timing. E. Faulty distributor advance. F. Incorrect valve timing. G. High fuel level in carburetor. H. Stuck manifold heat control valve. I. Detonation or preignition. J. Fouled spark plugs. K. Low engine compression. L. Worn camshaft lobes. M. Sticking valves. N. Elevation and atmospheric conditions. O. Restricted exhaust system. P. Operating at excessive speeds.
20. Poor acceleration.	A. Step-up piston stuck in down position (lean mixture at wide open throttle). B. Accelerator pump piston (or plunger) leather too hard, worn, or loose on stem. C. Faulty accelerator pump discharge ball. D. Accelerator pump inlet check ball faulty. E. Incorrect fuel or float level. F. Worn accelerator pump and throttle linkage. G. Automatic choke not operating properly. H. Carburetor gummed up. I. Faulty coil or CD ignition amplifier. J. Loose distributor base plate bearing. K. Distributor not advancing properly. L. Incorrect ignition timing. M. Incorrect spark plug gap or badly eroded spark plugs. N. Fouled spark plugs. O. Overheated spark plugs. P. Manifold heat control valve stuck. Q. Low fuel pump pressure or vacuum. R. Compression not up to specifications. S. Incorrect valve timing. T. Low grade of fuel. U. Detonation or preignition.
21. Fouled spark plugs.	A. Carburetor mixture overly rich. B. Excessive oil consumption. C. Improper plug heat range. D. Improper plug gap adjustment. E. Faulty ignition.
22. Burned spark plugs.	A. Plugs loose in cylinder head. B. Carburetor mixture too lean. C. Improper plug heat range. D. Improper ignition timing. E. Leaking head gasket or cracked cylinder head.
23. Generator will not charge.	A. Battery condition. B. Connections loose or dirty. C. Drive belt loose or broken. D. Faulty regulator or cutout relay. E. Field fuse or fusible wire in regulator blown. F. Generator not polarized (DC generators). G. Open generator windings. H. Worn or sticking brushes and/or slip rings. I. Faulty rectifier diodes (AC generators). J. Faulty ammeter.

Troubleshooting the Engine (cont.)

ENGINE REACTION	CHECK POINTS
24. Low generator output and a low battery.	A. Drive belt loose. B. High resistance at battery terminals. C. High resistance in charging circuit. D. Faulty ammeter. E. Low regulator setting. F. Faulty rectifier diodes (AC generators). G. Faulty generator.
25. Excessive battery charging.	A. Regulator set too high. B. Regulator contacts stuck. C. Regulator voltage winding open. D. Regulator improperly grounded. E. High resistance in field coil.
26. Engine overheats.	A. Drive belt loose. B. Plugged water inlet (insufficient water in closed cooling system). C. Bad thermostat. D. Excessive deposits or obstructions in all water passages or jackets. E. Broken, pinched, collapsed, or leaking water lines. F. Improper ignition timing. G. Faulty heat indicator or indicator wiring. H. Worn water pump parts. I. Seals or gaskets (burned, cracked, or broken). J. Outboard drive not deep enough in water. K. Bad water pump impeller, plate, housing, or seal in outboard drive. (Recover any broken impeller blades.)
27. Insufficient engine heat.	A. Thermostat open.

Troubleshooting the Outdrive

DRIVE REACTION	CHECK POINTS
1. Oil level low.	A. Check inside boot for oil. B. Check for oil seepage at output shaft. C. Check case exterior for cracks. D. Check all cap gaskets.
2. Unit kicks up unnecessarily.	A. Interlock not adjusted properly. B. Return spring missing or broken. C. Interlock arm bent. D. Tilt adjusting pin bent.
3. Hard shift.	A. Bent shift cable. B. Bent interlock rod. C. Improperly adjusted control box.
4. Shifter dog jumps.	A. Worn shifter dog or gear dogs. B. Worn linkage. C. Remote control adjustment. D. Gearcase loose or sprung. E. Exhaust housing bent. F. Linkage out of adjustment.
5. Electric shift inoperative or slips.	A. Improper remote control installation. B. Faulty coils. C. Faulty springs. D. Faulty clutch and gear. E. Faulty bearings. F. Wrong lubricant. G. Loose or sprung gearcase. H. Shorted wiring. I. Corroded or poor wiring terminal connections.

Troubleshooting the Outdrive (cont.)

DRIVE REACTION	CHECK POINTS
6. Abnormal vibration.	A. Bent propeller shaft. B. Propeller unbalanced. C. Outdrive mounting loose. D. Worn pivot pin bearings. E. Gearcase sprung. F. Worn bearings.
7. Propeller cavitation.	A. Damaged propeller. B. Wrong tilt pin position. C. Unit or cavitation plate set too high for particular hull shape. D. Hull obstruction. E. Weeds on propeller. F. Wrong propeller. G. Slipping clutch. H. Wrong gear ratio.
8. Undesirable steering.	A. Trim tab deteriorated or position incorrect. B. Wrong gear ratio. C. Cavitation. D. Wrong propeller. E. Worn swivel bearings. F. Loose mountings.

NOTE: *The troubleshooting charts are taken from the Boating Industry Association's Marine Service Manual of Recommended Practices and reproduced with the permission of the Boating Industry Association.*

Troubleshooting Spark Plugs

The recommended spark plug and gap for a particular engine is given in the "Tune-Up Specifications" chart in each manufacturer's chapter. The particular designation of a spark plug gives the heat range, among other information. The hot or cold rating (heat range) refers to the ability of the spark plug to conduct heat away from the firing tip. The heat range has no bearing on the intensity of the spark. In general, cold plugs are required when the engine is subjected to large loads (pulling skiers, for example) and hot plugs are required for lower intensity operation (trolling).

CAUTION: *A spark plug that is too hot will not allow the electrode to cool sufficiently between power strokes and will cause the electrode to glow red-hot. This in turn causes excessively high temperatures, bringing about detonation and preignition.*

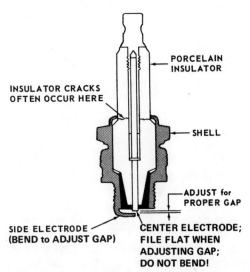

Cutaway view of typical conventional spark plug (© Champion Spark Plug Co.)

It is best to consult a dealer before installing plugs which differ from the manufacturer's recommendations.

CONVENTIONAL SPARK PLUGS

Each spark plug should be removed and inspected individually and compared to the spark plug diagnosis chart to determine the cause of malfunction and possible corrective measures. Replace spark plugs as necessary. In normal service, spark plugs are replaced in sets, corresponding

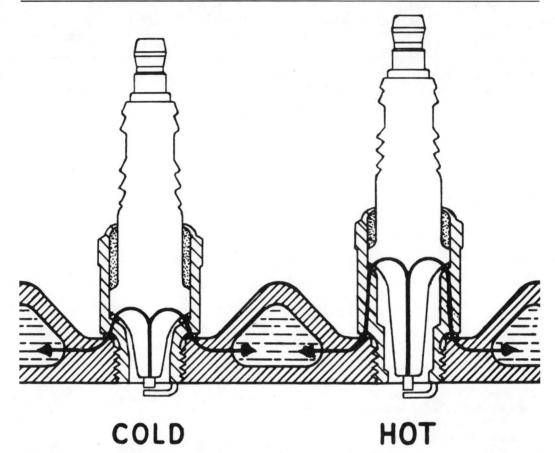

COLD   HOT

The heat range of a spark plug refers to its ability to conduct heat away from the firing tip (© Champion Spark Plug Co.)

to the number of cylinders. Inspect each spark plug for make, type, and heat range. All plugs must be of the same make and heat range. Adjust each spark plug gap (new or old) to the manufacturer's specification, using a round feeler gauge, as illustrated. Before adjusting the gap on used plugs, file the center electrode flat with a point file.

CAUTION: *Never bend the center electrode to adjust the gap; always adjust the gap by bending the side electrode.*

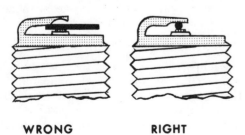

WRONG   RIGHT

Gapping conventional spark plugs (© Champion Spark Plug Co.)

SURFACE GAP SPARK PLUGS

Remove the spark plugs and inspect the center electrode as illustrated. If worn or burned back more than $1/32$ in. (0.8 mm) below the insulator, it will not function properly. Do not replace surface gap plugs for any reason other than this. Be sure that the plugs being replaced are definitely

Surface gap (polar gap) plug, illustrating proper gap (© Kiekhaefer Mercury)

misfiring; the accumulation of deposits can be deceiving.

CAUTION: *Due to the high voltage requirements with surface gap spark plugs, do not use this type of plug, unless specifically recommended by the manufacturer.*

SPARK PLUG INSTALLATION

Inspect the spark plug hole threads and clean them before installing the spark plugs. Crank the engine several times to blow out any material which might have been dislodged during the cleaning operation. Install the spark plugs in the powerhead with new gaskets and torque them to the manufacturer's specification. Improper installation is one of the largest single causes of unsatisfactory spark plug performance and is generally the result of one or more of the following practices.

Cause	Result
Insufficient torque (to fully seat gasket)	Compression loss— early plug failure
Excessive torque	Reduced operation life— complete destruction from inability to dissipate heat
Dirty gasket seal	High temperatures— early plug failure
Corroded hole threads	Excessively high temperatures—early failure (overheating)

Always use a new gasket seal and wipe the seats in the head clean. The gasket must be fully compressed on clean seats to ensure complete heat transfer and provide a gas-tight seal in the cylinder. For this reason, as well as the necessity of maintaining the proper plug gap, the correct torque when installing the spark plugs is extremely important.

Spark Plug Troubleshooting

PLUG CONDITION	FACTORS CAUSING	CORRECTIVE ACTION
Plug "Flash Over" (firing from upper terminal to base of plug)	Dirty insulator tops—oil, dirt and moisture on insulator will shunt current to base of plug. The above condition can be caused by failure of spark plug boot.	Keep plugs wiped clean with cloth moistened with cleaning solvent. Check spark plug boot and replace if necessary.
Lead Fouling (light and powdery or shiny glazed coating on firing end)	By-products of combustion and fuel additives, deposited as a powder which may later melt and glaze on insulator tip.	Remove deposits by blast cleaning. If this is not possible, plugs should be replaced.
Damaged Shell	Very seldom occurs, but cause is almost always due to mishandling by applying excessive torque during installation. This failure is usually in the form of a crack in the Vee of the thread next to the seat gasket or at the groove below the hex.	Replace with a new spark plug.
Oil or Carbon Fouling	Wet, black deposits on firing end of plug indicate oil pumping condition. This is usually caused by worn piston rings, pistons, cylinders or sticky valves. Soft, fluffy, dry black carbon deposits usually indicate a rich mixture operation, excessive idling, improper operation of automatic choke or faulty adjustment of carburetor. Hard, baked-on, black carbon deposits result from use of too cold a plug.	Correct engine condition. In most cases, plugs in this condition will be serviceable after proper cleaning and re-gapping. If troubles are not eliminated, use "hotter" type plug. Use "hotter" type plug.
Normal Electrode Wear	Due to intense heat, pressure and corrosive gases together with spark discharge, the electrode wears and gap widens.	Plugs should be regapped every 100 hours.

Spark Plug Troubleshooting (cont.)

PLUG CONDITION	FACTORS CAUSING	CORRECTIVE ACTION
Rapid Electrode Wear	Condition may be caused by (1) burned valves, (2) gas leakage past threads and seat gaskets, due to insufficient installation torque or damaged gasket, (3) too lean a mixture or (4) plug too "hot" for operating speeds and loads.	Correct engine condition. Install plugs to specified torque. Use a new spark plug seat gasket each time a new or cleaned spark plug is installed. Use "colder" type plug if condition continues to exist.
Broken Upper Insulator	Careless removal or installation of spark plug.	Replace with a new spark plug.
Broken Lower Insulator (Firing Tip)	The cause is usually carelessness in regapping by either bending of centerwire to adjust the gap or permitting the gapping tool to exert pressure against the tip of the center electrode or insulator when bending the side electrode to adjust the gap.	Replace with a new spark plug.
	Fracture or breakage of lower insulator also may occur occasionally if the engine has been operated under conditions causing severe and prolonged detonation or pre-ignition.	Use "colder" type plug for the particular type of operation.

Spark Plug Diagnosis

Plugs with even-colored tan or light gray deposits and moderate electrode wear.

Normal appearance (© Champion Spark Plug Co.)

Can be identified in a negative ground system by lack of wear at the center electrode and a semicircular wear pattern at the side electrode. The primary coil leads are reversed from proper position.

Reversed coil polarity (© Champion Spark Plug Co.)

Usually occurring in a relatively new set, splash deposits may form after a long delayed tune-up when accumulated cylinder deposits are thrown against the plugs at high rpm. Clean and install plugs.

Splash fouled (© Champion Spark Plug Co.)

If one or more plugs in a set have chipped insulators, severe detonation is the probable cause. Bending the center electrode to adjust the gap can also crack the insulator. Replace with new plugs of the correct gap and heat range. Check for overadvanced timing.

Chipped insulator (© Champion Spark Plug Co.)

Results from fused deposits which appear as tiny beads or glass-like bubbles; caused by improper oil/fuel ratio and high-speed operation following sustained slow speeds.

Gap bridged (© Champion Spark Plug Co.)

See "Gap Bridging."

Core bridged (© Champion Spark Plug Co.)

Oil or wet, black carbon covering the entire end of the plug, caused by excessive oil in the fuel, too rich fuel mixture, sustained slow-speed operation, or plugs of the incorrect heat range.

Oil fouled (© Champion Spark Plug Co.)

Usually caused by severe preignition or detonation. Likely causes are improper heat range of the plugs, low-octane gasoline, neglected engine maintenance (even with high-octane fuel), overadvanced ignition timing or inadequate engine cooling.

Mechanical damage (© Champion Spark Plug Co.)

If the set of plugs has dead white insulators and badly worn electrodes, check for overadvanced ignition timing. Install plugs of the next colder heat range.

Overheating (© Champion Spark Plug Co.)

Usually caused by an extremely rich air/fuel mixture and characterized by a dry, black appearance of the plug.

Cold fouled (© Champion Spark Plug Co.)

Boat Performance and Propeller Selection

There are many variables which influence and indeed dictate the performance characteristics of any given boat and engine combination, some, of course, having a greater influence than others. Assuming that the engine and outdrive are in good condition and the engine is properly tuned, the following factors must be considered (not necessarily in order) when attempting to evaluate or influence the performance of the boat and engine combination.

HULL DESIGN

Hull designs fall into two general classifications, displacement hulls and planing hulls, with many variations and combinations of the two. A displacement hull will displace its own weight in water, while a planing hull displaces its own weight while motionless, but displaces less than its own weight as it gains speed. A planing hull tends to move over the water, rather than through it.

Deep V

The deep V design, although not new, is presently the most popular due to its extraordinary success in off-shore power-boat racing. It is sometimes called a "Bertram design," after famed ocean racer Dick Bertram, or a "Hunt boat," after its designer Ray Hunt, who designed the first 31-ft version for Dick Bertram to race.

The most popular deep Vs are constructed of fiberglass and are usually recognizable by their deadrise (20° or more). Deadrise is the angle of inclination from the horizontal (where the bottom meets the side). The deadrise is usually present the full length of the keel and there are usually three or more spray rails which keep the water from running up the side of

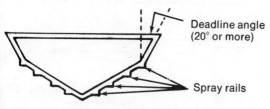

Deep V design showing spray rails and deadrise

the boat. The spray rails have the added advantage of tending to trap air bubbles under the hull, giving a smooth ride. The smooth (and relatively dry) ride in moderately rough seas is the most popular advantage of the design. When the boat leaves the water, its weight distribution causes it to come down stern first and the V shape cuts the water, eliminating the bone-jarring landings associated with flatter hulls. It is also easier to maintain a higher cruising speed in rough water, which has led to its success in off-shore racing.

Its inherent advantage more than offsets its disadvantages of being harder to move than flatter hulls, drawing more water, and requiring constant steering effort at slow speeds. Due to their steep hulls, these boats also pull a much larger wake at speed than flat-bottomed hulls pull.

Semi V

The semi V hull is a variation of the flat-bottomed hull and the deep V hull. The bottom consists of two flat planes set at an angle to each other with a deadrise of 5–15° from the horizontal. The angle of the flat planes is usually greatest at the bow and sometimes tapers off almost flat at the stern, to provide a better planing surface. Smaller examples of this design have a straight keel line, while larger examples have a longitudinal curve, called a rocker.

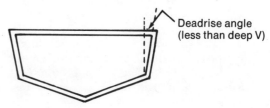

Semi V design

More research has gone into this type of hull than any other and boat builders have brought this design to the highest standards of the art. Most powerboat hulls fall into this classification and offer one major advantage: the semi V offers the best compromise between the riding comfort and stability of a deep V and the speed of a flat planing hull. If the local waters do not warrant a deep V design, this type of hull is the best compromise. The success of the semi V and deep V hulls are dependent on adequate power, and both are well suited for use with V drives or stern drives.

Planing

The flat-bottomed or planing hull is the simplest hull form today. It is used mainly for skiffs, bass boats, and prams, ranging in size from sea-going types to auxiliary craft.

Planing hulls are simply a box with straight sides or curved sides to throw spray aside. Some boats in this classification may have a curved bottom to make the hull stiffer.

Planing or flat hull design

Planing hulls are designed to gain speed by lifting out of the water. Because the lifting effect supports only part of the weight of the boat, displacement and frictional resistance are decreased, resulting in increased speed. In theory, planing hulls are perfectly flat, although perfect planing hulls do not exist in actuality, because of poor maneuverability and stability. They also tend to pound badly in rough seas and are considered safe only in calm protected waters. An exception to this is the true skiff, which was developed from boats used by the rum runners in New Jersey. These had a flat bottom and lapstrake sides, and were extremely fast and seaworthy.

Cathedral

Typical of this classification is the small Boston Whaler and the many copies of it. The hull has a deep V in the middle, flanked by shallower Vs on each side. The longitudinal axis is usually straight, with a very small rocker in some instances. The sides are usually vertical and the bow is squared off. The riding qualities are dependent on the center deep V and the side Vs are sometimes short, vaguely reminiscent of hydroplane sponsons. Air is trapped under the hull by the side Vs and

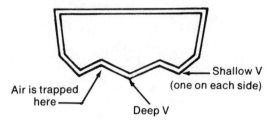

Cathedral hull design

provides flotation and stability. The side Vs also tend to make the craft ride flat in turns, unlike the tendency of the deep V configuration to bank in turns.

The great advantage offered by the cathedral hull is its inherent lateral stability and vast amount of useful space—especially in the bow. These hulls require considerable power to arrive at planing attitude; to maintain it in a chop requires even more power. These boats are definitely not meant to be underpowered. The hull is often noisy, even in a moderate sea, but its seaworthiness more than offsets any disadvantages.

Tunnel

The tunnel design was originally grouped as a special type, but Italian success with the design has catapulted it into popularity. These boats are mainly seen in the 16–24 ft range, with most constructed of fiberglass with a few custom plywood models. Many are powered by outboards, with stern drives becoming increasingly popular among those who desire speed.

These boats should not be mistaken for a catamaran type which is, essentially, two hulls joined by a wing section. A cross-section of a tunnel hull appears as the two-halves of a deep V hull, fore and aft, with a flat section in the middle. Closely resembling the early Hickman Sea Sled, they are characterized by a flat deck, non-trip sides, and light weight for speed. Most manufacturers of tunnel hulls prefer the light weight for speed rather than lavish accommodations for comfort.

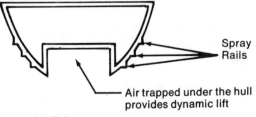

Tunnel hull design

The great advantage of the tunnel hull is speed and, when properly handled, stability. In good trim, they ride bow high on a stream of bubbles with little wetted surface. The rush of air trapped under the hull provides dynamic lift and the bow-high ride. Originally intended for racing, they are also good for out-running your neighbor, and aside from the high price and need for a large power plant, offer few disadvantages.

Displacement

Displacement hulls offer the only serious answer to long-range cruising when the weather and sea must be faced under all conditions. Its inherent advantages are seaworthiness and comfort, provided by a rounded bottom and rounded bilges, usually with a heavy skeg or keel to retard roll.

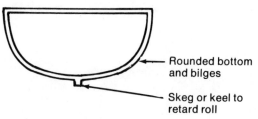

← Rounded bottom and bilges

← Skeg or keel to retard roll

Displacement hull design

The hull passes through the water, displacing its own weight, whether under way or at rest. One of the few disadvantages is a slow speed, which is fixed by the length of waterline. No matter how much horsepower is applied to drive the hull, the speed will not exceed 1½ the square root of its waterline, calculated by the following formula.

$$\text{Speed (mph)} = \frac{3 \text{ waterline length}}{2}$$

While displacement hulls are normally used on larger craft, semi-displacement hulls are also available. These combine many of the characteristics of a displacement hull, but feature a flat stern section which provides some planing ability with an increase in speed.

CENTER OF GRAVITY

For maximum speed, move the weight aft until the boat just begins to "porpoise." This will reduce wetted surface to a minimum, only the aft portion actually being in the water.

TILT PIN ADJUSTMENT

The tilt pin, controls the angle of the outdrive with relation to the transom. In general, the tilt pin should be adjusted so that the cavitation plate is about parallel to the water. The speed of boats with weight located forward will sometimes be improved by tilting the outdrive out one pin hole. This will tend to raise the bow of the boat and reduce wetted surface. If the motor is tilted in, the boat will ride with the bow down, wetting more of the bottom and reducing speed. This will generally improve operation in rough water. It should be noted that experimentation is necessary to determine the optimum tilt pin setting. Variations in design, power, weight distribution, and transom angle will dictate the correct tilt pin setting.

NOTE: *If it is found that the tilt pin cannot be satisfactorily adjusted, check for water in the bottom of the boat, since this will cause a constantly shifting mass of weight with a constantly changing weight distribution.*

BOTTOM CONDITION

Surface Roughness

Moss, barnacles, and other surface irregularities that increase friction will cause a considerable loss of speed. It was found in one specific test that a boat that was anchored in salt water for forty days suffered almost a 50 percent reduction in speed, due to marine growth on the hull.

Hook

The bottom is said to hook if it is concave in the fore and aft direction when viewed from below. When the boat is planing, this causes more lift on the bottom near the transom and allows the bow to drop. This greatly increases wetted surface and reduces speed. A hook will be more likely to occur near the transom and is the result of supporting the boat too

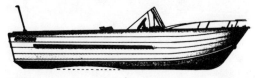

Extreme example of hook (© Kiekhaefer Mercury)

far forward of the transom while on a trailer or in storage.

Rocker

A boat is said to have a rocker if the bottom is convex in the fore and aft direction. A boat with a rocker will exhibit a strong tendency to porpoise.

Extreme example of rocker (© Kiekhaefer Mercury)

Propeller diameter

PROPELLER SELECTION

NOTE: *The following information on propeller selection is taken from the Boating Industry Association's* Marine Service Manual of Recommended Practices *and is reproduced with the permission of the Boating Industry Association.*

The only way to be absolutely sure that the engine will achieve its full horsepower, and will operate efficiently and safely, is to use a reliable tachometer to test the engine rpm at full throttle. Knowing that the engine will turn up to the manufacturer's recommended test wheel range, select a propeller from one of the many charts supplied by your engine or propeller supplier. Make a few test runs at full throttle, with the same load as the rig will normally carry, and note the average rpm reading indicated on the tachometer. If the reading is above or below the manufacturer's indicated operating range, it is imperative that you change propellers.

Since the diameter of the propeller is generally limited by the outdrive lower unit design, the pitch and blade area will be of the greatest concern. Pitch is the theoretical distance that the propeller will travel in a solid substance if it makes one complete revolution without slippage. Increasing the pitch reduces rpm at full throttle.

If the full-throttle tachometer reading is below the manufacturer's recommended operating range, you must try propellers of greater pitch until a propeller is found that will allow the engine to continually

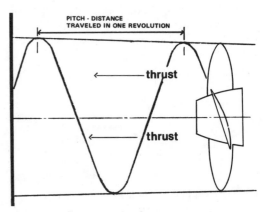

Propeller pitch (© Outboard Marine Corp.)

operate within the recommended full throttle operating range.

The number of blades for outdrive propellers generally varies from two to four. When selecting a propeller for a light boat, two, two-blade or three-blade props will give the best results. As the weight increases, the blade area should increase. On large, heavy boats, the blade area should be increased by using three or four blades, to obtain optimum performance.

In a situation where both a two-blade and three-blade prop or three-blade and four-blade prop will allow the engine to operate within the full throttle operating range, choose the one that will give the greatest forward speed.

Importance of Load Changes

To properly complete the job of propping, the rig should be checked with both the minimum and maximum expected loads—including skiers. It will often be necessary to have several propellers (or one variable-pitch propeller) available and information on when to use them and how to change them as loads vary.

Many times, however, a propeller operating at the high end of the recommended range with light loads will still operate within the range with a maximum load.

Propeller Care

A bent or nicked propeller will set up vibrations in the motor which will have a damaging effect on many of the operating parts. There will be a definite loss of power and efficiency with a damaged propeller. Propellers should be checked frequently to be sure that all blades are in good condition. Be sure to check the propeller for nicks and pitch on all service jobs. Consult your engine or propeller supplier for information on propeller repairs or familiarize yourself with the nearest repair service.

Boat Performance Troubleshooting

NOTE: *These are the most common problem areas affecting performance:*
1. Improper motor tilt angle or transom height.
2. Incorrect propeller selection.
3. Improper load distribution.
4. Water under cockpit floor.

BOAT REACTION	CHECK POINTS
1. Poor speed—light load.	A. Incorrect propeller selection. B. Load too far forward. C. Motor too low in water. D. Engine malfunction. E. Motor tilt too far in. F. Marine growth on hull or lower unit.
2. Poor speed—heavy load.	A. Underpowered. B. Engine malfunction. C. Incorrect propeller selection. D. Motor tilt too far out. E. Marine growth on hull or lower unit.
3. Slow to plane—heavy load.	A. Motor tilt too far out. B. Incorrect propeller selection. C. Too much load in stern. D. Water under cockpit floor. E. Hull has a hook.
4. Speed loss.	A. Water under cockpit floor. B. Marine growth on hull or lower unit. C. Weeds on propeller. D. Damaged propeller.
5. Hard ride in rough water.	A. Too much load in stern. B. Motor tilt too far out. C. Poor speed management.
6. Runs wet in rough water.	A. Load too far forward. B. Motor tilt too far in. C. Overloaded.
7. Lists on straight when heavily loaded.	A. Load not evenly distributed. B. Motor tilt too far in. C. Water under cockpit floor. D. Hull has a hook.
8. Lists or rolls on straight when lightly loaded.	A. Loose steering. B. Water under cockpit floor. C. Motor tilt too far in. D. Incorrect transom height. E. Load too far forward. F. Hull has a hook.
9. Nose heavy—catches on waves and in turns.	A. Motor tilt too far in. B. Load too far forward. C. Hull has a hook.

Boat Performance Troubleshooting (cont.)

BOAT REACTION	CHECK POINTS
10. Porpoises on straight run.	A. Motor tilt too far out. B. Motor too low in water. C. Too much load in stern. D. Hull has a rocker.
11. Porpoises on turns only.	A. Motor tilt too far out. B. Motor too low in water. C. Overpowered.
12. Banks too much in turns.	A. Overloaded. B. Load too far forward. C. Motor tilt too far in. D. Overpowered. E. Hull has a hook.
13. Excessive cavitation.	A. Incorrect propeller selection. B. Motor too high on transom. C. Motor tilt too far out. D. Overpowered. E. Load too far forward. F. Water under cockpit floor. G. Keel extends too far after thru-hull fittings disturb water flow. H. Weeds on propeller.

Periodic Maintenance

In order to prevent costly repair bills and to make sure that your boat will be kept in peak condition, the following checks should be made every 50 hours of operation time or at mid-season.

ENGINE

NOTE: *Before servicing the ignition system (particularly capacitive discharge types), disconnect the battery.*

1. Drain and refill the crankcase according to the manufacturer's specifications.

2. Remove and clean the fuel filter bowl and replace the filter bowl element. Always use a new gasket under the filter bowl.

3. Remove and clean the spark plugs. If necessary, these should be replaced. If serviceable, regap the plugs to the manufacturer's specification and install them. Pay particular attention to the manufacturer's specified torque and use new gaskets with plugs which require gaskets.

4. Lubricate all carburetor linkages with the recommended lubricant or white grease.

5. Check all fuel lines or fittings to be sure that they are tight.

6. Check all water lines and the level of closed cooling systems.

7. Clean the battery terminals and coat them with petroleum jelly or very light grease.

8. Lubricate the starter motor, generator or alternator, and distributor with the manufacturer's recommended lubricant.

9. Check the condition of the breaker points and replace if necessary. If serviceable, gap the points to the manufacturer's specification.

10. Check, and if necessary, adjust the ignition timing.

11. Check all electrical and ground connections to be sure that they are clean, tight, and waterproofed.

12. If possible, check and adjust the valve lash as recommended by the manufacturer.

OUTDRIVE

1. Drain and flush the gearcase and refill it to the correct level with the manufacturer's recommended lubricant.

2. Drain and refill the vertical drive gearbox to the correct level with the manufacturer's specified lubricant.

3. Check the operation of the water pump.

4. Lubricate all grease fittings with the manufacturer's recommended lubricant.

5. Clean and lubricate all steering connections.

6. Inspect the rubber bellows for deterioration and leaks and be sure that all mounting bolts are tight.

7. Check the condition of the self-sacrificing anti-electrolysis plate. This should be replaced if it is less than half its original size.

8. Touch up any areas where paint is chipped. Do not use a copper or bronze base paint on metal surfaces since this will promote the electrolytic process.

9. Check the propeller for nicks and gouges.

10. Check all fittings which pass through the hull or transom to be sure that they are tight and not corroded.

Salt Water Care

Engines and outdrives which are used in salt water present special problems and require meticulous care. Aluminum alloys used in outdrives are highly resistant to corrosion by oxidation (breakdown of metal, caused by its combination with oxygen) but very susceptible to galvanic action (electrical process of depositing atoms of one metal, in solution, on the surface of a different metal). Although oxidation cannot occur under water, it is prevalent in warm, humid climates. Aluminum parts are protected from galvanization by anodizing (the process of coating metal with a hard shell of aluminum oxide). However, this covering is only protective if it remains unbroken. Following are suggestions for care of all outdrives used in salt water.

1. After each use, tilt the outdrive out of the water and flush the entire unit with cool, fresh water.

2. If possible, periodically flush the outdrive following the manufacturer's recommendations in the appropriate chapter.

3. Be sure the outdrive is adequately protected with an *approved* paint.

NOTE: *Do not use antifouling paint, since these contain copper or mercury and can hasten galvanic corrosion.*

4. Check frequently to be sure that no aluminum parts are left unprotected. Bare metal should be protected quickly.

5. A small self-sacrificing block of susceptible metal placed near the part to be protected will sometimes spare a valuable part.

NOTE: *Consult a dealer before attempting to install such a device.*

Off-Season Storage

ENGINES

The following procedures should be followed to store an inboard/outdrive during the off-season to assure that the rig is kept in the best condition while in storage.

1. Before taking the boat out of water, run the engine to bring it to normal operating temperature. If equipped with a closed cooling system, check the condition of the antifreeze. If the antifreeze is more than one season old, a rust inhibitor should be added. If the solution is contaminated, replace it with a 50/50 solution of ethylene glycol and water.

2. Drain the crankcase completely. Remove the old filter and clean the filter housing. Install a new filter and refill the engine with the type and amount of oil specified by the manufacturer. Operate the engine at fast idle and check to be sure that the oil is well circulated.

3. Shut off the fuel supply at the tank and disconnect the line between the tank and the valve at the tank. Insert the end of the fuel line from the pump into a can of several ounces of approved rust-preventive oil. Run the engine at fast idle until the engine stalls from a lack of fuel.

4. Remove the spark plugs and inject a tablespoon of approved rust-preventive oil into each cylinder. Crank the engine for about 10–15 seconds to coat the cylinder walls. Check the condition of the spark plugs. If they are serviceable, then you should clean, regap, and install them. If they are not serviceable, install new plugs.

NOTE: *An alternative procedure is to remove the flame arrestor and shut off the fuel supply at the tank. Slowly pour a pint of rust-preventive oil into the carburetor intakes while running the engine at fast idle, using up the fuel remaining in the lines.*

5. Clean the fuel filter and sediment bowl. Install the bowl with a new gasket, and reconnect the fuel line.

6. For engines used in salt water, remove the boat from the water and flush the cooling system with fresh water, allowing it to circulate for about five minutes.

7. If equipped with a raw water cooling system, open all engine and water jacket drains. Allow the water to drain completely, making sure that inboard/outdrive engines are horizontal. Leave the drains open and disconnect all water hoses at the low end, allowing them to drain completely.

NOTE: *Horizontal oil coolers may not drain, requiring pump scavenging.*

8. Remove the drain plugs from the water pumps and drain these completely. If recommended by the manufacturer, remove the rubber impellers.

9. Lubricate all items such as the generator, starter, distributor, and control linkage as recommended by the manufacturer.

10. Seal off the carburetor and exhaust system openings to prevent the entry of foreign matter.

11. Remove the battery from the boat and store it in a cool, dry place. Be sure to keep it charged during storage.

SPECIFIC GRAVITY READING	CHARGED CONDITION
1.260-1.280	Fully Charged
1.230-1.250	Three Quarter Charged
1.200-1.220	One Half Charged
1.170-1.190	One Quarter Charged
1.140-1.160	Just About Flat
1.110-1.130	All The Way Down

Battery charge condition

12. For overhead valve engines, remove the rocker arm covers and inspect the valve train for wear or damage. Wipe out the inside of the rocker covers and liberally coat the valve train with clean crankcase oil. Reinstall the covers with new gaskets.

13. Clean the outside of the engine and wipe it off with a clean, lightly oiled cloth. Cover the engine but allow air to circulate around it.

OUTDRIVES

The following procedures should be used to winterize the outdrives.

1. Remove the boat from water and drain all the gearboxes and gearcases. Flush the gearcases with kerosine or a good grade of fuel oil.

NOTE: *Volatile solvents are not recommended.*

Refill the gearcase with fresh lubricant of the type recommended by the manufacturer. Grease all lubrication fittings as recommended.

2. Remove and inspect the propeller for nicks, scratches, and bent blades. If necessary, the propeller should be reconditioned by a shop equipped for this purpose. Clean and lubricate the propeller shaft and reinstall the propeller. If required, install a new drive pin. Replace the cotter pin or tab lockwasher.

3. Wipe the external surface of the drive unit with a clean, lightly oiled cloth.

4. Check all steering connections for tightness and lubricate all joints or pulleys.

Pre-Season Preparation

The power train should be checked and tuned at the start of each boating season.

ENGINE

1. The engine should be completely lubricated according to the manufacturer's recommendations. See the appropriate manufacturer's chapter.

2. If the spark plugs were not serviced when the engine was winterized, this should be done. Replace defective plugs and clean and regap old plugs that are still serviceable. Always use new gaskets under the plugs.

3. The ignition system should be checked thoroughly. Particularly check the points, coil, and condenser. Check the ignition timing and set the breaker point dwell and gap.

4. The fuel tank and all fuel lines, fittings, valves, and couplers should be examined for deterioration or leaks. Particularly check the filler pipe for a good ground connection. If the fuel was not drained during storage, check for gum

or varnish, which will quickly clog the carburetor and fuel lines.

5. Check the crankcase oil level. Change the oil if this was not done prior to storage.

6. Clean and inspect the flame arrestors.

7. Check and adjust the generator or alternator belt. Replace if it is frayed or worn.

8. Close all the water drains and lubricate the water pump impellers if recommended by the manufacturer. Check the water hoses, replacing those that are damaged. Check the cooling system sea-cocks and thru-hull fittings. Check the level of the closed cooling system, adding coolant if needed.

9. Check the battery for full charge and clean the battery terminals. Check the battery cables for broken insulation. When the battery is installed, cover the terminals with a light coat of petroleum jelly to prevent corrosion.

10. Check all electrical wiring and ground circuits.

11. If recommended by the manufacturer, prime the water pump and test-run the engine. Check all gauges for normal readings and particularly look for water discharge from the exhaust outlet. Be sure that there are no leaks of fuel, oil, or water.

12. When the engine has reached operating temperature, torque the cylinder head bolts according to the manufacturer's specifications.

INBOARD/OUTDRIVES

1. Check the gearbox and gearcase for the correct amount of lubricant.

2. Check all lubrication fittings and lubricate them as necessary.

3. Check the steering and tilt mechanism, and all other controls.

4. Check the gear train and controls for proper operation.

Engine Rebuilding

This section describes, in detail, the procedures involved in rebuilding a typical engine. The procedures specifically refer to an inline engine, however, they are basically identical to those used in rebuilding engines of nearly all design and configurations. Procedures for servicing atypical engines (i.e., horizontally opposed) are described in the appropriate section, although in most cases, cylinder head reconditioning procedures described in this chapter will apply.

The section is divided into two sections. The first, Cylinder Head Reconditioning, assumes that the cylinder head is removed from the engine, all manifolds are removed, and the cylinder head is on a workbench. The camshaft should be removed from overhead cam cylinder heads. The second section, Cylinder Block Reconditioning, covers the block, pistons, connecting rods and crankshaft. It is assumed that the engine is mounted on a work stand, and the cylinder head and all accessories are removed.

Procedures are identified as follows:

Unmarked—Basic procedures that must be performed in order to successfully complete the rebuilding process.

Starred (*)—Procedures that should be performed to ensure maximum performance and engine life.

Double starred (**)—Procedures that may be performed to increase engine performance and reliability. These procedures are usually reserved for extremely heavy-duty or competition usage.

In many cases, a choice of methods is also provided. Methods are identified in the same manner as procedures. The choice of method for a procedure is at the discretion of the user.

The tools required for the basic rebuilding procedure should, with minor exceptions, be those

TORQUE (ft. lbs.) *

U.S.

Bolt Diameter (inches)	Bolt Grade (SAE)				Wrench Size (inches)	
	1 and 2	5	6	8	Bolt	Nut
1/4	5	7	10	10.5	3/8	7/16
5/16	9	14	19	22	1/2	9/16
3/8	15	25	34	37	9/16	5/8
7/16	24	40	55	60	5/8	3/4
1/2	37	60	85	92	3/4	13/16
9/16	53	88	120	132	7/8	7/8
5/8	74	120	167	180	15/16	1
3/4	120	200	280	296	1-1/8	1-1/8
7/8	190	302	440	473	1-5/16	1-5/16
1	282	466	660	714	1-1/2	1-1/2

Metric

Bolt Diameter (mm)	Bolt Grade				Wrench Size (mm)
	5D	8G	10K	12K	Bolt and Nut
6	5	6	8	10	10
8	10	16	22	27	14
10	19	31	40	49	17
12	34	54	70	86	19
14	55	89	117	137	22
16	83	132	175	208	24
18	111	182	236	283	27
22	182	284	394	464	32
24	261	419	570	689	36

*—Torque values are for lightly oiled bolts. CAUTION: Bolts threaded into aluminum require much less torque.

General Torque Specifications

34

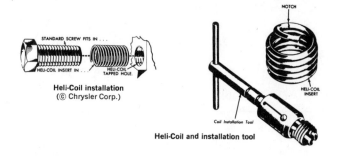

Heli-Coil installation
(© Chrysler Corp.)

Heli-Coil and installation tool

Heli-Coil Insert			Drill	Tap	Insert. Tool	Extracting Tool
Thread Size	Part No.	Insert Length (In.)	Size	Part No.	Part No.	Part No.
1/2 -20	1185-4	3/8	17/64(.266)	4 CPB	528-4N	1227-6
5/16-18	1185-5	15/32	Q(.332)	5 CPB	528-5N	1227-6
3/8 -16	1185-6	9/16	X(.397)	6 CPB	528-6N	1227-6
7/16-14	1185-7	21/32	29/64(.453)	7 CPB	528-7N	1227-16
1/2 -13	1185-8	3/4	33/64(.516)	8 CPB	528-8N	1227-16

Heli-Coil Specifications

included in a mechanic's tool kit. An accurate torque wrench, and a dial indicator (reading in thousandths) mounted on a universal base should be available. Bolts and nuts with no torque specification should be tightened according to size (see chart). Special tools, where required, all are readily available from the major tool suppliers (i.e., Craftsman, Snap-On, K-D). The services of a competent automotive machine shop must also be readily available.

When assembling the engine, any parts that will be in frictional contact must be pre-lubricated, to provide protection on initial start-up. Vortex Pre-Lube, STP, or any product specifically formulated for this purpose may be used. NOTE: *Do not use engine oil.* Where semi-permanent (locked but removable) installation of bolts or nuts is desired, threads should be cleaned and coated with Loctite. Studs may be permanently installed using Loctite Stud and Bearing Mount.

Aluminum has become increasingly popular for use in engines, due to its low weight and excellent heat transfer characteristics. The following precautions must be observed when handling aluminum engine parts:

—Never hot-tank aluminum parts.

—Remove all aluminum parts (identification tags, etc.) from engine parts before hot-tanking (otherwise they will be removed during the process).

—Always coat threads lightly with engine oil or anti-seize compounds before installation, to prevent seizure.

—Never over-torque bolts or spark plugs in aluminum threads. Should stripping occur, threads can be restored according to the following procedure, using Heli-Coil thread inserts:

Tap drill the hole with the stripped threads to the specified size (see chart). Using the specified tap (NOTE: *Heli-Coil tap sizes refer to the size thread being replaced, rather than the actual tap size*), tap the hole for the Heli-Coil. Place the insert on the proper installation tool (see chart). Apply pressure on the insert while winding it clockwise into the hole, until the top of the insert is one turn below the surface. Remove the installation tool, and break the installation tang from the bottom of the in-

sert by moving it up and down. If the Heli-Coil must be removed, tap the removal tool firmly into the hole, so that it engages the top thread, and turn the tool counter-clockwise to extract the insert.

Snapped bolts or studs may be removed, using a stud extractor (unthreaded) or Vise-Grip pliers (threaded). Penetrating oil (e.g., Liquid Wrench) will often aid in breaking frozen threads. In cases where the stud or bolt is flush with, or below the surface, proceed as follows:

Drill a hole in the broken stud or bolt, approximately ½ its diameter. Select a screw extractor (e.g., Easy-Out) of the proper size, and tap it into the stud or bolt. Turn the extractor counter-clockwise to remove the stud or bolt.

Magnaflux and Zyglo are inspection techniques used to locate material flaws, such as stress cracks. Magnafluxing coats the part with fine magnetic particles, and subjects the part to a magnetic field. Cracks cause breaks

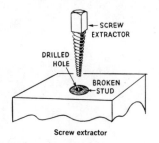

Screw extractor

in the magnetic field, which are outlined by the particles. Since Magnaflux is a magnetic process, it is applicable only to ferrous materials. The Zyglo process coats the material with a fluorescent dye penetrant, and then subjects it to blacklight inspection, under which cracks glow bright-

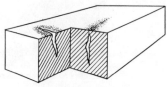

Magnaflux indication of cracks

ly. Parts made of any material may be tested using Zyglo. While Magnaflux and Zyglo are excellent for general inspection, and locating hidden defects, specific checks of suspected cracks may be made at lower cost and more readily using spot check dye. The dye is sprayed onto the suspected area, wiped off, and the area is then sprayed with a developer. Cracks then will show up brightly. Spot check dyes will only indicate surface cracks; therefore, structural cracks below the surface may escape detection. When questionable, the part should be tested using Magnaflux or Zyglo.

CYLINDER HEAD RECONDITIONING

Procedure	Method
Identify the valves:  **Valve identification** (© SAAB)	Invert the cylinder head, and number the valve faces front to rear, using a permanent felt-tip marker.
Remove the rocker arms:	Remove the rocker arms with shaft(s) or balls and nuts. Wire the sets of rockers, balls and nuts together, and identify according to the corresponding valve.
Remove the valves and springs:	Using an appropriate valve spring compressor (depending on the configuration of the cylinder head), compress the valve springs. Lift out the keepers with needlenose pliers, release the compressor, and remove the valve, spring, and spring retainer.
Check the valve stem-to-guide clearance: **Checking the valve stem-to-guide clearance** (© American Motors Corp.)	Clean the valve stem with lacquer thinner or a similar solvent to remove all gum and varnish. Clean the valve guides using solvent and an expanding wire-type valve guide cleaner. Mount a dial indicator so that the stem is at 90° to the valve stem, as close to the valve guide as possible. Move the valve off its seat, and measure the valve guide-to-stem clearance by moving the stem back and forth to actuate the dial indicator. Measure the valve stems using a micrometer, and compare to specifications, to determine whether stem or guide wear is responsible for excessive clearance.
De-carbon the cylinder head and valves: **Removing carbon from the cylinder head** (© Chevrolet Div. G.M. Corp.)	Chip carbon away from the valve heads, combustion chambers, and ports, using a chisel made of hardwood. Remove the remaining deposits with a stiff wire brush. NOTE: *Ensure that the deposits are actually removed, rather than burnished.*

Procedure	Method
Hot-tank the cylinder head:	Have the cylinder head hot-tanked to remove grease, corrosion, and scale from the water passages. NOTE: *In the case of overhead cam cylinder heads, consult the operator to determine whether the camshaft bearings will be damaged by the caustic solution.*
Degrease the remaining cylinder head parts:	Using solvent (i.e., Gunk), clean the rockers, rocker shaft(s) (where applicable), rocker balls and nuts, springs, spring retainers, and keepers. Do not remove the protective coating from the springs.
Check the cylinder head for warpage:  ① ③ CHECK DIAGONALLY ② CHECK ACROSS CENTER A 2895-A **Checking the cylinder head for warpage** (© Ford Motor Co.)	Place a straight-edge across the gasket surface of the cylinder head. Using feeler gauges, determine the clearance at the center of the straight-edge. Measure across both diagonals, along the longitudinal centerline, and across the cylinder head at several points. If warpage exceeds .003″ in a 6″ span, or .006″ over the total length, the cylinder head must be resurfaced. NOTE: *If warpage exceeds the manufacturers maximum tolerance for material removal, the cylinder head must be replaced.* When milling the cylinder heads of V-type engines, the intake manifold mounting position is altered, and must be corrected by milling the manifold flange a proportionate amount.
** Porting and gasket matching:  **Marking the cylinder head for gasket matching** (© Petersen Publishing Co.)  **Port configuration before and after gasket matching** (© Petersen Publishing Co.)	** Coat the manifold flanges of the cylinder head with Prussian blue dye. Glue intake and exhaust gaskets to the cylinder head in their installed position using rubber cement and scribe the outline of the ports on the manifold flanges. Remove the gaskets. Using a small cutter in a hand-held power tool (i.e., Dremel Moto-Tool), gradually taper the walls of the port out to the scribed outline of the gasket. Further enlargement of the ports should include the removal of sharp edges and radiusing of sharp corners. Do not alter the valve guides. NOTE: *The most efficient port configuration is determined only by extensive testing. Therefore, it is best to consult someone experienced with the head in question to determine the optimum alterations.*

Procedure	*Method*

** Polish the ports:

Relieved and polished ports
(© Petersen Publishing Co.)

Polished combustion chamber
(© Petersen Publishing Co.)

** Using a grinding stone with the above mentioned tool, polish the walls of the intake and exhaust ports, and combustion chamber. Use progressively finer stones until all surface imperfections are removed. NOTE: *Through testing, it has been determined that a smooth surface is more effective than a mirror polished surface in intake ports, and vice-versa in exhaust ports.*

* Knurling the valve guides:

Cut-away view of a knurled valve guide
(© Petersen Publishing Co.)

* Valve guides which are not excessively worn or distorted may, in some cases, be knurled rather than replaced. Knurling is a process in which metal is displaced and raised, thereby reducing clearance. Knurling also provides excellent oil control. The possibility of knurling rather than replacing valve guides should be discussed with a machinist.

Replacing the valve guides: NOTE: *Valve guides should only be replaced if damaged or if an oversize valve stem is not available.*

A-VALVE GUIDE I.D.
B-SLIGHTLY SMALLER THAN VALVE GUIDE O.D.

Valve guide removal tool

WASHERS

A-VALVE GUIDE I.D.
B-LARGER THAN THE VALVE GUIDE O.D.

Valve guide installation tool (with washers used during installation)

Depending on the type of cylinder head, valve guides may be pressed, hammered, or shrunk in. In cases where the guides are shrunk into the head, replacement should be left to an equipped machine shop. In other cases, the guides are replaced as follows: Press or tap the valve guides out of the head using a stepped drift (see illustration). Determine the height above the boss that the guide must extend, and obtain a stack of washers, their I.D. similar to the guide's O.D., of that height. Place the stack of washers on the guide, and insert the guide into the boss. NOTE: *Valve guides are often tapered or beveled for installation.* Using the stepped installation tool (see illustration), press or tap the guides into position. Ream the guides according to the size of the valve stem.

Procedure	Method
Replacing valve seat inserts:	Replacement of valve seat inserts which are worn beyond resurfacing or broken, if feasible, must be done by a machine shop.
Resurfacing (grinding) the valve face:  **Grinding a valve** (ⓒ Subaru) 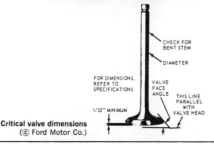 **Critical valve dimensions** (ⓒ Ford Motor Co.)	Using a valve grinder, resurface the valves according to specifications. CAUTION: *Valve face angle is not always identical to valve seat angle.* A minimum margin of 1/32″ should remain after grinding the valve. The valve stem tip should also be squared and resurfaced, by placing the stem in the V-block of the grinder, and turning it while pressing lightly against the grinding wheel.
Resurfacing the valve seats using reamers:  **Reaming the valve seat** (ⓒ S.p.A. Fiat)  **Valve seat width and centering** (ⓒ Ford Motor Co.)	Select a reamer of the correct seat angle, slightly larger than the diameter of the valve seat, and assemble it with a pilot of the correct size. Install the pilot into the valve guide, and using steady pressure, turn the reamer clockwise. CAUTION: *Do not turn the reamer counter-clockwise.* Remove only as much material as necessary to clean the seat. Check the concentricity of the seat (see below). If the dye method is not used, coat the valve face with Prussian blue dye, install and rotate it on the valve seat. Using the dye marked area as a centering guide, center and narrow the valve seat to specifications with correction cutters. NOTE: *When no specifications are available, minimum seat width for exhaust valves should be 5/64″, intake valves 1/16″.* After making correction cuts, check the position of the valve seat on the valve face using Prussian blue dye.
* Resurfacing the valve seats using a grinder:  **Grinding a valve seat** (ⓒ Subaru)	Select a pilot of the correct size, and a coarse stone of the correct seat angle. Lubricate the pilot if necessary, and install the tool in the valve guide. Move the stone on and off the seat at approximately two cycles per second, until all flaws are removed from the seat. Install a fine stone, and finish the seat. Center and narrow the seat using correction stones, as described above.

Procedure	Method
Checking the valve seat concentricity: 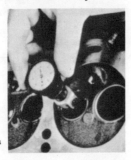 Checking the valve seat concentricity using a dial gauge (© American Motors Corp.)	Coat the valve face with Prussian blue dye, install the valve, and rotate it on the valve seat. If the entire seat becomes coated, and the valve is known to be concentric, the seat is concentric.
	* Install the dial gauge pilot into the guide, and rest the arm on the valve seat. Zero the gauge, and rotate the arm around the seat. Run-out should not exceed .002″.
* Lapping the valves: NOTE: *Valve lapping is done to ensure efficient sealing of resurfaced valves and seats. Valve lapping alone is not recommended for use as a resurfacing procedure.*  Hand lapping the valves  HAND DRILL ROD SUCTION CUP Home made mechanical valve lapping tool	* Invert the cylinder head, lightly lubricate the valve stems, and install the valves in the head as numbered. Coat valve seats with fine grinding compound, and attach the lapping tool suction cup to a valve head (NOTE: *Moisten the suction cup*). Rotate the tool between the palms, changing position and lifting the tool often to prevent grooving. Lap the valve until a smooth, polished seat is evident. Remove the valve and tool, and rinse away all traces of grinding compound.
	** Fasten a suction cup to a piece of drill rod, and mount the rod in a hand drill. Proceed as above, using the hand drill as a lapping tool. CAUTION: *Due to the higher speeds involved when using the hand drill, care must be exercised to avoid grooving the seat.* Lift the tool and change direction of rotation often.
Check the valve springs: 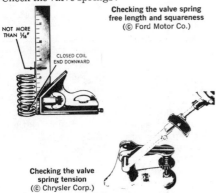 Checking the valve spring free length and squareness (© Ford Motor Co.) NOT MORE THAN 1/16″ CLOSED COIL END DOWNWARD Checking the valve spring tension (© Chrysler Corp.)	Place the spring on a flat surface next to a square. Measure the height of the spring, and rotate it against the edge of the square to measure distortion. If spring height varies (by comparison) by more than 1/16″ or if distortion exceeds 1/16″, replace the spring.
	** In addition to evaluating the spring as above, test the spring pressure at the installed and compressed (installed height minus valve lift) height using a valve spring tester. Springs used on small displacement engines (up to 3 liters) should be ± 1 lb. of all other springs in either position. A tolerance of ± 5 lbs. is permissible on larger engines.

Procedure	*Method*

* Install valve stem seals:

Valve stem seal installation
(ⓒ Ford Motor Co.)   SEAL

* Due to the pressure differential that exists at the ends of the intake valve guides (atmospheric pressure above, manifold vacuum below), oil is drawn through the valve guides into the intake port. This has been alleviated somewhat since the addition of positive crankcase ventilation, which lowers the pressure above the guides. Several types of valve stem seals are available to reduce blow-by. Certain seals simply slip over the stem and guide boss, while others require that the boss be machined. Recently, Teflon guide seals have become popular. Consult a parts supplier or machinist concerning availability and suggested usages. NOTE: *When installing seals, ensure that a small amount of oil is able to pass the seal to lubricate the valve guides; otherwise, excessive wear may result.*

Install the valves:

Lubricate the valve stems, and install the valves in the cylinder head as numbered. Lubricate and position the seals (if used, see above) and the valve springs. Install the spring retainers, compress the springs, and insert the keys using needlenose pliers or a tool designed for this purpose. NOTE: *Retain the keys with wheel bearing grease during installation.*

Checking valve spring installed height:

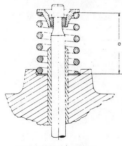 

Valve spring installed height dimension
(ⓒ Porsche)

Measuring valve spring installed height
(ⓒ Petersen Publishing Co.)

Measure the distance between the spring pad and the lower edge of the spring retainer, and compare to specifications. If the installed height is incorrect, add shim washers between the spring pad and the spring. CAUTION: *Use only washers designed for this purpose.*

** CC'ing the combustion chambers:

** Invert the cylinder head and place a bead of sealer around a combustion chamber. Install an apparatus designed for this purpose (burette mounted on a clear plate; see illustration) over the combustion chamber, and fill with the specified fluid to an even mark on the burette. Record the burette reading, and fill the combustion chamber with fluid. (NOTE: *A hole drilled in the plate will permit air to escape*). Subtract the burette reading, with the combustion chamber filled, from the previous reading, to determine combustion chamber volume in cc's. Duplicate this procedure in all combustion

Procedure	*Method*

CC'ing the combustion chamber
(© Petersen Publishing Co.)

chambers on the cylinder head, and compare the readings. The volume of all combustion chambers should be made equal to that of the largest. Combustion chamber volume may be increased in two ways. When only a small change is required (usually), a small cutter or coarse stone may be used to remove material from the combustion chamber. NOTE: *Check volume frequently.* Remove material over a wide area, so as not to change the configuration of the combustion chamber. When a larger change is required, the valve seat may be sunk (lowered into the head). NOTE: *When altering valve seat, remember to compensate for the change in spring installed height.*

Inspect the rocker arms, balls, studs, and nuts (where applicable):

Stress cracks in rocker nuts
(© Ford Motor Co.)

Visually inspect the rocker arms, balls, studs, and nuts for cracks, galling, burning, scoring, or wear. If all parts are intact, liberally lubricate the rocker arms and balls, and install them on the cylinder head. If wear is noted on a rocker arm at the point of valve contact, grind it smooth and square, removing as little material as possible. Replace the rocker arm if excessively worn. If a rocker stud shows signs of wear, it must be replaced (see below). If a rocker nut shows stress cracks, replace it. If an exhaust ball is galled or burned, substitute the intake ball from the same cylinder (if it is intact), and install a new intake ball. NOTE: *Avoid using new rocker balls on exhaust valves.*

Replacing rocker studs:

Reaming the stud bore for oversize rocker studs
(© Buick Div. G.M. Corp.)

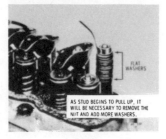

Extracting a pressed in rocker stud
(© Buick Div. G.M. Corp.)

In order to remove a threaded stud, lock two nuts on the stud, and unscrew the stud using the lower nut. Coat the lower threads of the new stud with Loctite, and install.

Two alternative methods are available for replacing pressed in studs. Remove the damaged stud using a stack of washers and a nut (see illustration). In the first, the boss is reamed .005-.006″ oversize, and an oversize stud pressed in. Control the stud extension over the boss using washers, in the same manner as valve guides. Before installing the stud, coat it with white lead and grease. To retain the stud more positively, drill a hole through the stud and boss, and install a roll pin. In the second method, the boss is tapped, and a threaded stud installed. Retain the stud using Loctite Stud and Bearing Mount.

Procedure	*Method*
Inspect the rocker shaft(s) and rocker arms (where applicable) :  Disassembled rocker shaft parts arranged for inspection (ⓒ American Motors Corp.) 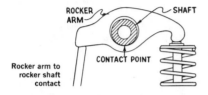 Rocker arm to rocker shaft contact	Remove rocker arms, springs and washers from rocker shaft. NOTE: *Lay out parts in the order they are removed.* Inspect rocker arms for pitting or wear on the valve contact point, or excessive bushing wear. Bushings need only be replaced if wear is excessive, because the rocker arm normally contacts the shaft at one point only. Grind the valve contact point of rocker arm smooth if necessary, removing as little material as possible. If excessive material must be removed to smooth and square the arm, it should be replaced. Clean out all oil holes and passages in rocker shaft. If shaft is grooved or worn, replace it. Lubricate and assemble the rocker shaft.
Inspect the camshaft bushings and the camshaft (overhead cam engines) :	See next section.
Inspect the pushrods:	Remove the pushrods, and, if hollow, clean out the oil passages using fine wire. Roll each pushrod over a piece of clean glass. If a distinct clicking sound is heard as the pushrod rolls, the rod is bent, and must be replaced.
	* The length of all pushrods must be equal. Measure the length of the pushrods, compare to specifications, and replace as necessary.
Inspect the valve lifters: 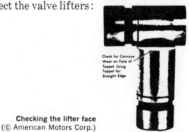 Checking the lifter face (ⓒ American Motors Corp.)	Remove lifters from their bores, and remove gum and varnish, using solvent. Clean walls of lifter bores. Check lifters for concave wear as illustrated. If face is worn concave, replace lifter, and carefully inspect the camshaft. Lightly lubricate lifter and insert it into its bore. If play is excessive, an oversize lifter must be installed (where possible). Consult a machinist concerning feasibility. If play is satisfactory, remove, lubricate, and reinstall the lifter.
* Testing hydraulic lifter leak down: 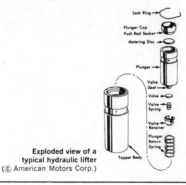 Exploded view of a typical hydraulic lifter (ⓒ American Motors Corp.)	Submerge lifter in a container of kerosene. Chuck a used pushrod or its equivalent into a drill press. Position container of kerosene so pushrod acts on the lifter plunger. Pump lifter with the drill press, until resistance increases. Pump several more times to bleed any air out of lifter. Apply very firm, constant pressure to the lifter, and observe rate at which fluid bleeds out of lifter. If the fluid bleeds very quickly (less than 15 seconds), lifter is defective. If the time exceeds 60 seconds, lifter is sticking. In either case, recondition or replace lifter. If lifter is operating properly (leak down time 15-60. seconds), lubricate and install it.

CYLINDER BLOCK RECONDITIONING

Procedure	*Method*
Checking the main bearing clearance:	Invert engine, and remove cap from the bearing to be checked. Using a clean, dry rag, thoroughly clean all oil from crankshaft journal and bearing insert. NOTE: *Plastigage is soluble in oil; therefore, oil on the journal or bearing could result in erroneous readings.* Place a piece of Plastigage along the full length of journal, reinstall cap, and torque to specifications. Remove bearing cap, and determine bearing clearance by comparing width of Plastigage to the scale on Plastigage envelope. Journal taper is determined by comparing width of the Plastigage strip near its ends. Rotate crankshaft 90° and retest, to determine journal eccentricity. NOTE: *Do not rotate crankshaft with Plastigage installed.* If bearing insert and journal appear intact, and are within tolerances, no further main bearing service is required. If bearing or journal appear defective, cause of failure should be determined before replacement.

Plastigage installed on main bearing journal
(© Chevrolet Div. G.M. Corp.)

Measuring Plastigage to determine
main bearing clearance
(© Chevrolet Div. G.M. Corp.)

Causes of bearing failure
(© Ford Motor Co.)

* Remove crankshaft from block (see below). Measure the main bearing journals at each end twice (90° apart) using a micrometer, to determine diameter, journal taper and eccentricity. If journals are within tolerances, reinstall bearing caps at their specified torque. Using a telescope gauge and micrometer, measure bearing I.D. parallel to piston axis and at 30° on each side of piston axis. Subtract journal O.D. from bearing I.D. to determine oil clearance. If crankshaft journals appear defective, or do not meet tolerances, there is no need to measure bearings; for the crankshaft will require grinding and/or undersize bearings will be required. If bearing appears defective, cause for failure should be determined prior to replacement.

Checking the connecting rod bearing clearance:	Connecting rod bearing clearance is checked in the same manner as main bearing clearance, using Plastigage. Before removing the crankshaft, connecting rod side clearance also should be measured and recorded.

Plastigage installed on connecting rod
bearing journal
(© Chevrolet Div. G.M. Corp.)

* Checking connecting rod bearing clearance, using a micrometer, is identical to checking main bearing clearance. If no other service

Procedure	Method
 **Measuring Plastigage to determine connecting rod bearing clearance** (© Chevrolet Div. G.M. Corp.)	is required, the piston and rod assemblies need not be removed.
Removing the crankshaft:  **Connecting rod matching marks** (© Ford Motor Co.)	Using a punch, mark the corresponding main bearing caps and saddles according to position (i.e., one punch on the front main cap and saddle, two on the second, three on the third, etc.). Using number stamps, identify the corresponding connecting rods and caps, according to cylinder (if no numbers are present). Remove the main and connecting rod caps, and place sleeves of plastic tubing over the connecting rod bolts, to protect the journals as the crankshaft is removed. Lift the crankshaft out of the block.
Remove the ridge from the top of the cylinder: 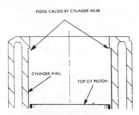 **Cylinder bore ridge** (© Pontiac Div. G.M. Corp.)	In order to facilitate removal of the piston and connecting rod, the ridge at the top of the cylinder (unworn area; see illustration) must be removed. Place the piston at the bottom of the bore, and cover it with a rag. Cut the ridge away using a ridge reamer, exercising extreme care to avoid cutting too deeply. Remove the rag, and remove cuttings that remain on the piston. CAUTION: *If the ridge is not removed, and new rings are installed, damage to rings will result.*
Removing the piston and connecting rod:  **Removing the piston** (© SAAB)	Invert the engine, and push the pistons and connecting rods out of the cylinders. If necessary, tap the connecting rod boss with a wooden hammer handle, to force the piston out. CAUTION: *Do not attempt to force the piston past the cylinder ridge* (see above).

Procedure	Method
Service the crankshaft:	Ensure that all oil holes and passages in the crankshaft are open and free of sludge. If necessary, have the crankshaft ground to the largest possible undersize.
	** Have the crankshaft Magnafluxed, to locate stress cracks. Consult a machinist concerning additional service procedures, such as surface hardening (e.g., nitriding, Tuftriding) to improve wear characteristics, cross drilling and chamfering the oil holes to improve lubrication, and balancing.
Removing freeze plugs:	Drill a hole in the center of the freeze plugs, and pry them out using a screwdriver or drift.
Remove the oil gallery plugs:	Threaded plugs should be removed using an appropriate (usually square) wrench. To remove soft, pressed in plugs, drill a hole in the plug, and thread in a sheet metal screw. Pull the plug out by the screw using pliers.
Hot-tank the block:	Have the block hot-tanked to remove grease, corrosion, and scale from the water jackets. NOTE: *Consult the operator to determine whether the camshaft bearings will be damaged during the hot-tank process.*
Check the block for cracks:	Visually inspect the block for cracks or chips. The most common locations are as follows: Adjacent to freeze plugs. Between the cylinders and water jackets. Adjacent to the main bearing saddles. At the extreme bottom of the cylinders. Check only suspected cracks using spot check dye (see introduction). If a crack is located, consult a machinist concerning possible repairs.
	** Magnaflux the block to locate hidden cracks. If cracks are located, consult a machinist about feasibility of repair.
Install the oil gallery plugs and freeze plugs:	Coat freeze plugs with sealer and tap into position using a piece of pipe, slightly smaller than the plug, as a driver. To ensure retention, stake the edges of the plugs. Coat threaded oil gallery plugs with sealer and install. Drive replacement soft plugs into block using a large drift as a driver.
	* Rather than reinstalling lead plugs, drill and tap the holes, and install threaded plugs.

Procedure	*Method*

Check the bore diameter and surface:

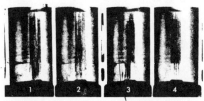

1, 2, 3 Piston skirt seizure resulted in this pattern. Engine must be rebored

4. Piston skirt and oil ring seizure caused this damage. Engine must be rebored

5, 6 Score marks caused by a split piston skirt. Damage is not serious enough to warrant reboring

7. Ring seized longitudinally, causing a score mark 1 3/16" wide, on the land side of the piston groove. The honing pattern is destroyed and the cylinder must be rebored

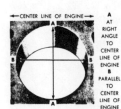 

8. Result of oil ring seizure. Engine must be rebored

9. Oil ring seizure here was not serious enough to warrant reboring. The honing marks are still visible

Cylinder wall damage
(© Daimler-Benz A.G.)

Visually inspect the cylinder bores for roughness, scoring, or scuffing. If evident, the cylinder bore must be bored or honed oversize to eliminate imperfections, and the smallest possible oversize piston used. The new pistons should be given to the machinist with the block, so that the cylinders can be bored or honed exactly to the piston size (plus clearance). If no flaws are evident, measure the bore diameter using a telescope gauge and micrometer, or dial gauge, parallel and perpendicular to the engine centerline, at the top (below the ridge) and bottom of the bore. Subtract the bottom measurements from the top to determine taper, and the parallel to the centerline measurements from the perpendicular measurements to determine eccentricity. If the measurements are not within specifications, the cylinder must be bored or honed, and an oversize piston installed. If the measurements are within specifications the cylinder may be used as is, with only finish honing (see below). NOTE: *Prior to submitting the block for boring, perform the following operation(s).*

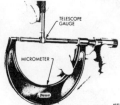 

Cylinder bore measuring positions
(© Ford Motor Co.)

Measuring the cylinder bore with a telescope gauge
(© Buick Div. G.M. Corp.)

Determining the cylinder bore by measuring the telescope gauge with a micrometer
(© Buick Div. G.M. Corp.)

Measuring the cylinder bore with a dial gauge
(© Chevrolet Div. G.M. Corp.)

Procedure	*Method*
Check the block deck for warpage:	Using a straightedge and feeler gauges, check the block deck for warpage in the same manner that the cylinder head is checked (see Cylinder Head Reconditioning). If warpage exceeds specifications, have the deck resurfaced. NOTE: *In certain cases a specification for total material removal (Cylinder head and block deck) is provided. This specification must not be exceeded.*
* Check the deck height:	The deck height is the distance from the crankshaft centerline to the block deck. To measure, invert the engine, and install the crankshaft, retaining it with the center main cap. Measure the distance from the crankshaft journal to the block deck, parallel to the cylinder centerline. Measure the diameter of the end (front and rear) main journals, parallel to the centerline of the cylinders, divide the diameter in half, and subtract it from the previous measurement. The results of the front and rear measurements should be identical. If the difference exceeds .005″, the deck height should be corrected. NOTE: *Block deck height and warpage should be corrected concurrently.*
Check the cylinder block bearing alignment: 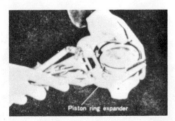 **Checking main bearing saddle alignment** (© Petersen Publishing Co.)	Remove the upper bearing inserts. Place a straightedge in the bearing saddles along the centerline of the crankshaft. If clearance exists between the straightedge and the center saddle, the block must be align-bored.
Clean and inspect the pistons and connecting rods: **Removing the piston rings** (© Subaru)	Using a ring expander, remove the rings from the piston. Remove the retaining rings (if so equipped) and remove piston pin. NOTE: *If the piston pin must be pressed out, determine the proper method and use the proper tools; otherwise the piston will distort.* Clean the ring grooves using an appropriate tool, exercising care to avoid cutting too deeply. Thoroughly clean all carbon and varnish from the piston with solvent. CAUTION: *Do not use a wire brush or caustic solvent on pistons.* Inspect the pistons for scuffing, scoring, cracks, pitting, or excessive ring groove wear. If wear is evident, the piston must be replaced. Check the connecting rod length by measuring the rod from the inside of the large end to the inside of the small end using calipers (see

Procedure	Method

 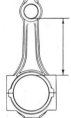

Cleaning the piston ring grooves
(© Ford Motor Co.)

Connecting rod length checking dimension

illustration). All connecting rods should be equal length. Replace any rod that differs from the others in the engine.

* Have the connecting rod alignment checked in an alignment fixture by a machinist. Replace any twisted or bent rods.

* Magnaflux the connecting rods to locate stress cracks. If cracks are found, replace the connecting rod.

Fit the pistons to the cylinders:

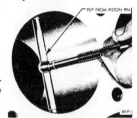

Measuring the cylinder with a telescope gauge for piston fitting
(© Buick Div. G.M. Corp.)

Measuring the piston for fitting
(© Buick Div. G.M. Corp.)

Using a telescope gauge and micrometer, or a dial gauge, measure the cylinder bore diameter perpendicular to the piston pin, $2\frac{1}{2}''$ below the deck. Measure the piston perpendicular to its pin on the skirt. The difference between the two measurements is the piston clearance. If the clearance is within specifications or slightly below (after boring or honing), finish honing is all that is required. If the clearance is excessive, try to obtain a slightly larger piston to bring clearance within specifications. Where this is not possible, obtain the first oversize piston, and hone (or if necessary, bore) the cylinder to size.

Assemble the pistons and connecting rods:

Installing piston pin lock rings
(© Nissan Motor Co., Ltd.)

Inspect piston pin, connecting rod small end bushing, and piston bore for galling, scoring, or excessive wear. If evident, replace defective part(s). Measure the I.D. of the piston boss and connecting rod small end, and the O.D. of the piston pin. If within specifications, assemble piston pin and rod. CAUTION: *If piston pin must be pressed in, determine the proper method and use the proper tools; otherwise the piston will distort.* Install the lock rings; ensure that they seat properly. If the parts are not within specifications, determine the service method for the type of engine. In some cases, piston and pin are serviced as an assembly when either is defective. Others specify reaming the piston and connecting rods for an oversize pin. If the connecting rod bushing is worn, it may in many cases be replaced. Reaming the piston and replacing the rod bushing are machine shop operations.

Procedure	*Method*

Clean and inspect the camshaft:

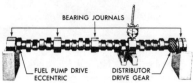

BEARING JOURNALS

FUEL PUMP DRIVE ECCENTRIC   DISTRIBUTOR DRIVE GEAR

Checking the camshaft for straightness
(© Chevrolet Motor Div. G.M. Corp.)

Camshaft lobe measurement
(© Ford Motor Co.)

Degrease the camshaft, using solvent, and clean out all oil holes. Visually inspect cam lobes and bearing journals for excessive wear. If a lobe is questionable, check all lobes as indicated below. If a journal or lobe is worn, the camshaft must be reground or replaced. NOTE: *If a journal is worn, there is a good chance that the bushings are worn.* If lobes and journals appear intact, place the front and rear journals in V-blocks, and rest a dial indicator on the center journal. Rotate the camshaft to check straightness. If deviation exceeds .001″, replace the camshaft.

* Check the camshaft lobes with a micrometer, by measuring the lobes from the nose to base and again at 90° (see illustration). The lift is determined by subtracting the second measurement from the first. If all exhaust lobes and all intake lobes are not identical, the camshaft must be reground or replaced.

Replace the camshaft bearings:

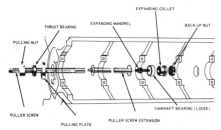

EXPANDING COLLET
THRUST BEARING   EXPANDING MANDREL   BACK-UP NUT
PULLING NUT
PULLER SCREW   CAMSHAFT BEARING (LOOSE)
PULLING PLATE   PULLER SCREW EXTENSION

Camshaft removal and installation tool (typical)
(© Ford Motor Co.)

If excessive wear is indicated, or if the engine is being completely rebuilt, camshaft bearings should be replaced as follows: Drive the camshaft rear plug from the block. Assemble the removal puller with its shoulder on the bearing to be removed. Gradually tighten the puller nut until bearing is removed. Remove remaining bearings, leaving the front and rear for last. To remove front and rear bearings, reverse position of the tool, so as to pull the bearings in toward the center of the block. Leave the tool in this position, pilot the new front and rear bearings on the installer, and pull them into position. Return the tool to its original position and pull remaining bearings into position. NOTE: *Ensure that oil holes align when installing bearings.* Replace camshaft rear plug, and stake it into position to aid retention.

Finish hone the cylinders:

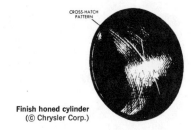

CROSS-HATCH PATTERN

Finish honed cylinder
(© Chrysler Corp.)

Chuck a flexible drive hone into a power drill, and insert it into the cylinder. Start the hone, and move it up and down in the cylinder at a rate which will produce approximately a 60° cross-hatch pattern (see illustration). NOTE: *Do not extend the hone below the cylinder bore.* After developing the pattern, remove the hone and recheck piston fit. Wash the cylinders with a detergent and water solution to remove abrasive dust, dry, and wipe several times with a rag soaked in engine oil.

Procedure	*Method*
Check piston ring end-gap:  **Checking ring end-gap** (© Chevrolet Motor Div. G.M. Corp.)	Compress the piston rings to be used in a cylinder, one at a time, into that cylinder, and press them approximately 1″ below the deck with an inverted piston. Using feeler gauges, measure the ring end-gap, and compare to specifications. Pull the ring out of the cylinder and file the ends with a fine file to obtain proper clearance. CAUTION: *If inadequate ring end-gap is utilized, ring breakage will result.*
Install the piston rings: 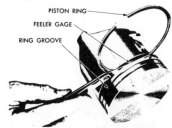 **Checking ring side clearance** (© Chrysler Corp.) 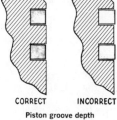 CORRECT INCORRECT **Piston groove depth** **Correct ring spacer installation**	Inspect the ring grooves in the piston for excessive wear or taper. If necessary, recut the groove(s) for use with an overwidth ring or a standard ring and spacer. If the groove is worn uniformly, overwidth rings, or standard rings and spacers may be installed without recutting. Roll the outside of the ring around the groove to check for burrs or deposits. If any are found, remove with a fine file. Hold the ring in the groove, and measure side clearance. If necessary, correct as indicated above. NOTE: *Always install any additional spacers above the piston ring.* The ring groove must be deep enough to allow the ring to seat below the lands (see illustration). In many cases, a "go-no-go" depth gauge will be provided with the piston rings. Shallow grooves may be corrected by recutting, while deep grooves require some type of filler or expander behind the piston. Consult the piston ring supplier concerning the suggested method. Install the rings on the piston, lowest ring first, using a ring expander. NOTE: *Position the ring markings as specified by the manufacturer (see car section).*
Install the camshaft:	Liberally lubricate the camshaft lobes and journals, and slide the camshaft into the block. CAUTION: *Exercise extreme care to avoid damaging the bearings when inserting the camshaft.* Install and tighten the camshaft thrust plate retaining bolts.
Check camshaft end-play:  **Checking camshaft end-play with a feeler gauge** (© Ford Motor Co.)	Using feeler gauges, determine whether the clearance between the camshaft boss (or gear) and backing plate is within specifications. Install shims behind the thrust plate, or reposition the camshaft gear and retest end-play.

Procedure	Method

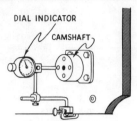

DIAL INDICATOR

CAMSHAFT

Checking camshaft end-play with a
dial indicator

* Mount a dial indicator stand so that the stem of the dial indicator rests on the nose of the camshaft, parallel to the camshaft axis. Push the camshaft as far in as possible and zero the gauge. Move the camshaft outward to determine the amount of camshaft end-play. If the end-play is not within tolerance, install shims behind the thrust plate, or re-position the camshaft gear and retest.

Install the rear main seal (where applic-able):

Seating the rear
main seal
(© Buick Div. G.M. Corp.)

Position the block with the bearing saddles facing upward. Lay the rear main seal in its groove and press it lightly into its seat. Place a piece of pipe the same diameter as the crankshaft journal into the saddle, and firmly seat the seal. Hold the pipe in position, and trim the ends of the seal flush if required.

Install the crankshaft:

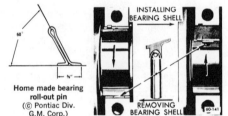

60°

Home made bearing
roll-out pin
(© Pontiac Div.
G.M. Corp.)

INSTALLING
BEARING SHELL

REMOVING
BEARING SHELL

Removal and installation of upper
bearing insert using a roll-out pin
(© Buick Div. G.M. Corp.)

Thoroughly clean the main bearing saddles and caps. Place the upper halves of the bearing inserts on the saddles and press into position. NOTE: *Ensure that the oil holes align.* Press the corresponding bearing inserts into the main bearing caps. Lubricate the upper main bearings, and lay the crankshaft in position. Place a strip of Plastigage on each of the crankshaft journals, install the main caps, and torque to specifications. Remove the main caps, and compare the Plastigage to the scale on the Plastigage envelope. If clearances are within tolerances, remove the Plastigage, turn the crankshaft 90°, wipe off all oil and retest. If all clearances are correct, remove all Plastigage, thoroughly

PRY FORWARD

THRUST BEARING

PRY CRANKSHAFT FORWARD

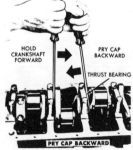

HOLD
CRANKSHAFT
FORWARD

PRY CAP
BACKWARD

THRUST BEARING

PRY CAP BACKWARD

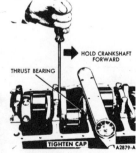

HOLD CRANKSHAFT
FORWARD

THRUST BEARING

TIGHTEN CAP

A2879-A

Aligning the thrust bearing
(© Ford Motor Co.)

Procedure	Method
	lubricate the main caps and bearing journals, and install the main caps. If clearances are not within tolerance, the upper bearing inserts may be removed, without removing the crankshaft, using a bearing roll out pin (see illustration). Roll in a bearing that will provide proper clearance, and retest. Torque all main caps, excluding the thrust bearing cap, to specifications. Tighten the thrust bearing cap finger tight. To properly align the thrust bearing, pry the crankshaft the extent of its axial travel several times, the last movement held toward the front of the engine, and torque the thrust bearing cap to specifications. Determine the crankshaft end-play (see below), and bring within tolerance with thrust washers.
Measure crankshaft end-play:  **Checking crankshaft end-play with a dial indicator** (© Ford Motor Co.)  **Checking crankshaft end-play with a feeler gauge** (© Chevrolet Div. (G.M. Corp.)	Mount a dial indicator stand on the front of the block, with the dial indicator stem resting on the nose of the crankshaft, parallel to the crankshaft axis. Pry the crankshaft the extent of its travel rearward, and zero the indicator. Pry the crankshaft forward and record crankshaft end-play. NOTE: *Crankshaft end-play also may be measured at the thrust bearing, using feeler gauges* (see illustration).
Install the pistons:	Press the upper connecting rod bearing halves into the connecting rods, and the lower halves into the connecting rod caps. Position the piston ring gaps according to specifications (see car section), and lubricate the pistons. Install a ring compresser on a piston, and press two long (8″) pieces of plastic tubing over the rod bolts. Using the plastic tubes as a guide, press the pistons into the bores and onto the crankshaft with a wooden hammer handle. After seating the rod on the crankshaft journal, remove the tubes and install the cap finger tight. Install the remaining pistons in the same man-

Procedure	*Method*

Tubing used as guide when installing
a piston
(© Oldsmobile Div. G.M. Corp.)

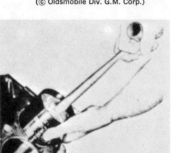

Installing a piston
(© Chevrolet Div. G.M. Corp.)

ner. Invert the engine and check the bearing clearance at two points (90° apart) on each journal with Plastigage. NOTE: *Do not turn the crankshaft with Plastigage installed.* If clearance is within tolerances, remove *all* Plastigage, thoroughly lubricate the journals, and torque the rod caps to specifications. If clearance is not within specifications, install different thickness bearing inserts and recheck. CAUTION: *Never shim or file the connecting rods or caps.* Always install plastic tube sleeves over the rod bolts when the caps are not installed, to protect the crankshaft journals.

Check connecting rod side clearance:

Checking connecting rod side clearance
(© Chevrolet Div. G.M. Corp.)

Determine the clearance between the sides of the connecting rods and the crankshaft, using feeler gauges. If clearance is below the minimum tolerance, the rod may be machined to provide adequate clearance. If clearance is excessive, substitute an unworn rod, and recheck. If clearance is still outside specifications, the crankshaft must be welded and reground, or replaced.

Inspect the timing chain:

Visually inspect the timing chain for broken or loose links, and replace the chain if any are found. If the chain will flex sideways, it must be replaced. Install the timing chain as specified. NOTE: *If the original timing chain is to be reused, install it in its original position.*

Procedure	Method
Check timing gear backlash and runout:  **Checking camshaft gear backlash** (© Chevrolet Div. G.M. Corp.)  **Checking camshaft gear runout** (© Chevrolet Div. G.M. Corp.)	Mount a dial indicator with its stem resting on a tooth of the camshaft gear (as illustrated). Rotate the gear until all slack is removed, and zero the indicator. Rotate the gear in the opposite direction until slack is removed, and record gear backlash. Mount the indicator with its stem resting on the edge of the camshaft gear, parallel to the axis of the camshaft. Zero the indicator, and turn the camshaft gear one full turn, recording the runout. If either backlash or runout exceed specifications, replace the worn gear(s).

Completing the Rebuilding Process

Following the above procedures, complete the rebuilding process as follows:

Fill the oil pump with oil, to prevent cavitating (sucking air) on initial engine start up. Install the oil pump and the pickup tube on the engine. Coat the oil pan gasket as necessary, and install the gasket and the oil pan. Mount the flywheel and the crankshaft vibrational damper or pulley on the crankshaft. NOTE: *Always use new bolts when installing the flywheel.* Inspect the clutch shaft pilot bushing in the crankshaft. If the bushing is excessively worn, remove it with an expanding puller and a slide hammer, and tap a new bushing into place.

Position the engine, cylinder head side up. Lubricate the lifters, and install them into their bores. Install the cylinder head, and torque it as specified in the car section. Insert the pushrods (where applicable), and install the rocker shaft(s) (if so equipped) or position the rocker arms on the pushrods. If solid lifters are utilized, adjust the valves to the "cold" specifications.

Mount the intake and exhaust manifolds, the carburetor(s), the distributor and spark plugs. Adjust the point gap and the static ignition timing. Mount all accessories and install the engine in the car. Fill the radiator with coolant, and the crankcase with high quality engine oil.

Break-in Procedure

Start the engine, and allow it to run at low speed for a few minutes, while checking for leaks. Stop the engine, check the oil level, and fill as necessary. Restart the engine, and fill the cooling system to capacity. Check the point dwell angle and adjust the ignition timing and the valves. Run the engine at low to medium speed (800-2500 rpm) for approximately ½ hour, and retorque the cylinder head bolts. Road test the car, and check again for leaks.

Follow the manufacturer's recommended engine break-in procedure and maintenance schedule for new engines.

2 · Kiekhaefer Mercury

General Information and Specifications

INTRODUCTION

Kiekhaefer Mercury entered the stern drive market in 1962 with the Mercruiser package which, by the end of the first year, had exceeded the sales of the total market in the year 1961. To continually improve Mercruisers, Mercury operates complete marine proving facilities at Lake X, Mercabo, Florida and at Oshkosh, Wisconsin. From these proving facilities have come such features as computer-matched gears for long life and quiet service, a shock-absorbing propeller hub with a live rubber safety clutch to prevent shock damage, corrosion-proof water pump, and a one-piece driveshaft and lower unit housing, providing rigid support for gears and bearings. With power trim, you can adjust the angle of the drive unit for best performance as load and water conditions vary, even while under way.

MerCruisers are available to suit almost any purpose, from the 90 hp four-cylinder engine up to the 482 cu in., V8 powerplant capable of propelling heavy cruisers.

Serial Number Identification

ENGINE

MerCruiser 120, 140, 160, 165, and 225

The engine serial number is located on the right rear side of the engine block, above the starter motor.

MerCruiser 120 and 225 serial number location

MerCruiser 215

The serial number is located on the left rear side of the engine.

MerCruiser 215 serial number location

MerCruiser I outdrive serial number location

MerCruiser 325

The serial number is located on the rear of the engine on the flywheel housing.

MerCruiser 325 serial number location

OUTDRIVE

MerCruiser I

The serial number of early model Mer-Cruiser I stern drive models is located beneath the shoulder of the MerCruiser decal on the right side of the driveshaft housing. On later models the serial number is located on the left side of the driveshaft housing on the driveshaft housing-to-bell housing mounting flange, on or under the decal. All MerCruiser I stern drives are right-hand rotation.

MerCruiser II

The stern drive serial number is stamped on a plate on the front of the steerting lever housing. MerCruiser II units (through serial number 1778953) are right-hand rotation, unless Marked "L". From serial number 1778954, stern drive units are left-hand rotation.

MerCruiser II outdrive serial number location

MerCruiser III and 215

The serial number is embossed on the Mercruiser decal, which is located on the left side of the driveshaft housing. This number is also stamped on the driveshaft housing, directly below the decal.

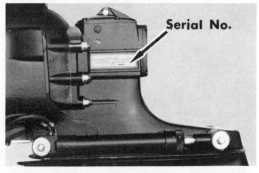

MerCruiser III and 215 outdrive serial number location

General Engine Specifications

Engine Model	Engine Displacement (cu in.)	No. of Cyls	Advertised Horsepower	Wide Open Throttle (rpm) ▲	Bore and Stroke (in.)	Advertised Compression Ratio	Oil Pressure @ rpm (psi)
110–120	153	4	120	3900–4300	3.87 x 3.25	8.5:1	35 @ 2,000
140	181	4	140	4200–4600	4.00 x 3.60	8.5:1	30–55 @ 2,000
140	194	6	140	3700–4100	3.56 x 3.25	8.5:1	35 @ 2,000
160	250	6	160	3900–4300	3.87 x 3.53	8.5:1	30–55 @ 2,000
165	250	6	165	3900–4300	3.87 x 3.53	8.5:1	30–55 @ 2,000
888	302	V8	188	3800–4200	4.00 x 3.00	8.5:1	30–55 @ 2,000
200	292	6	200	3900–4300	3.87 x 4.12	8.1:1	30–55 @ 2,000
215	302	V8	215	3800–4200	4.00 x 3.00	9.0:1	30–55 @ 2,000
225	327	V8	225	3800–4200	4.00 x 3.25	8.1:1	30–55 @ 2,000
250	327	V8	250	3800–4200	4.00 x 3.25	8.8:1	30–55 @ 2,000
270	350	V8	270	3800–4200	4.00 x 3.48	8.8:1	30–55 @ 2,000
325	427	V8	325	3800–4200	4.25 x 3.76	8.8:1	30–70 @ 2,000
390	482	V8	390	3800–4200	4.25 x 4.25	10.0:1	30–70 @ 2,000

▲ Maximum RPM at wide open throttle.

Tune-Up Specifications

When analyzing compression test results, look for uniformity among cylinders rather than specific pressures.

ENGINE		SPARK PLUGS		DISTRIBUTOR					IDLE SPEED
Engine Model	Displace-ment (cu in.)	Type	Gap (in.)	Point Dwell (deg)	Point Gap (in.)	Ignition Timing (deg)	Compression Pressure	Fuel Pump Pressure (psi)	(rpm)
120	153	AC-CR44N①	0.035	31–34	0.022	8B②	140	3.5–4.5	500–600
140	181	AC-CR44N①	0.035	31–34	0.016	6B	140	3–5	500–600
140	194	AC-CR44N	0.035	31–34	0.016	10B	140	3.5–4.5	500–600
160	250	AC-CR44N①	0.035	31–34	0.016	6B	140	3.5–4.5	500–600
165	250	AC-CR44N③	0.035	31–34	0.016	6B	140	3.5–4.5	500–600
888	302	Au-BTF-3M	0.030	26–31	0.017	10B	150	3–6	550–600

Tune-Up Specifications (cont.)

ENGINE		SPARK PLUGS		DISTRIBUTOR					Fuel Pump	IDLE SPEED
Engine Model	Displacement (cu in.)	Type	Gap (in.)	Point Dwell (deg)	Point Gap (in.)	Ignition Timing (deg)	Compression Pressure	Pressure (psi)		(rpm)
200	292	AC-CR44N①	0.035	31–34	0.016	8B	140	3–5		500–600
215	302	Au-BTF-3M	0.030	28–32	0.016	12B	150	3–6		550–600
225	327	AC-CR43K④	0.035	28–32	0.016	⑤	140	4–7		550–600
250	327	AC-V40K⑥	——	——	——	10B	150	4–7		550–600
270	350	AC-V40K⑥	——	——	——	10B	150	4–7		550–600
325	427	AC-V40NK⑥	——	——	——	10B	150	4–7		550–600
390	482	AC-WR41N	0.035	——	——	10B	170	4–7		550–600

① May be equipped with AC-C44N, which is interchangeable with AC-CR44N.
② Engines with distributor No.s 1112467 are timed at 6B.
③ 165 HP may be equipped with AC-CR44T, which has a tapered seat.
④ May be equipped with AC-C43. Service replacement is AC-CR43K.
⑤ Engines with distributor No.s 1111076 and 1111249—8B.
   Engines with distributor No.s 1111297—4B.
   All others—12B.
⑥ May be equipped with AC-V40N.
AC—AC Spark Plugs.
Au—Autolite Spark Plugs.
—— Not applicable; surface gap spark plugs or transistorized ignition.

Crankshaft and Connecting Rod Specifications

All measurements are given in in.

Engine Model	Engine Displacement (cu in.)	CRANKSHAFT			CONNECTING ROD		
		Main Brg. Journal Dia	Main Brg. Oil Clearance	Shaft End-Play	Journal Diameter	Oil Clearance	Side Clearance
120	153	2.2983–2.2993	0.004 (Max)	0.002–0.006	1.999–2.000	0.004 (Max)	0.0085–0.0135
140	181	2.2983–2.2993	0.004 (Max)	0.002–0.006	2.099–2.100	0.004 (Max)	0.009–0.013
140	194	2.2983–2.2993	0.004 (Max)	0.002–0.006	1.999–2.000	0.004 (Max)	0.0008–0.0014
160	250	2.2983–2.2993	0.004 (Max)	0.002–0.006	1.999–2.000	0.004 (Max)	0.0085–0.0135
165	250	2.2983–2.2993	0.004 (Max)	0.002–0.006	1.999–2.000	0.004 (Max)	0.0085–0.0135
888	302	2.2482–2.2490	①	0.004–0.012	2.1228–2.1236	0.0008–0.0015	0.010–0.020
200	292	2.2983–2.2993	0.004 (Max)	0.002–0.006	1.999–2.000	0.004 (Max)	0.0085–0.0135
215	302	2.2482–2.2490	①	0.004–0.012	2.1228–2.1236	0.0008–0.0026	0.010–0.020

Crankshaft and Connecting Rod Specifications (cont.)

All measurements are given in in.

Engine Model	Engine Displacement (cu in.)	CRANKSHAFT			CONNECTING ROD		
		Main Brg. Journal Dia	Main Brg. Oil Clearance	Shaft End-Play	Journal Diameter	Oil Clearance	Side Clearance
225	327	②	0.004 (Max)	0.003–0.011	③	0.004 (Max)	0.009–0.013
250	327	②	0.004 (Max)	0.003–0.011	2.099–2.100	0.004 (Max)	0.009–0.013
270	350	②	0.004 (Max)	0.003–0.011	2.099–2.100	0.004 (Max)	0.009–0.013
325	427	④	0.004 (Max)	0.006–0.010	2.199–2.200	0.004 (Max)	0.019–0.025
390	482	* ④	0.004 (Max)	0.006–0.010	2.199–2.200	0.004 (Max)	0.019–0.025

① No. 1 bearing: 0.0001–0.0018; All others: 0.0005–0.0024.
② No.s 1, 2, 3, and 4: 2.4484–2.4493; No. 5: 2.4479–2.4488.
③ S/N 239937 and below: 1.999–2.000; S/N 239938 and up: 2.099–2.100.
④ No.s 1, 2, 3, and 4: 2.7481–2.7490; No. 5: 2.7478–2.7488.

Ring Gap Specifications

Engine Model	Engine Displacement (cu. in.)	Top Compression	Bottom Compression	Oil Control
120	153	0.010–0.030	0.010–0.030	0.015–0.065
140	181	0.010–0.030	0.010–0.030	0.015–0.065
140	194	0.010–0.030	0.010–0.030	0.015–0.065
160	250	0.010–0.030	0.010–0.030	0.015–0.065
165	250	0.010–0.030	0.010–0.030	0.015–0.065
888	302	0.010–0.020	0.010–0.020	0.015–0.069
200	292	0.010–0.020	0.010–0.030	0.015–0.065
215	302	0.002–0.004	0.002–0.004	0.015–0.069
225	327	0.013–0.033	0.013–0.035	0.015–0.065
250	327	0.010–0.030	0.013–0.035	0.015–0.065
270	350	0.010–0.030	0.013–0.040	0.015–0.065
325	427	0.010–0.030	0.010–0.030	0.010–0.033
390	482	0.010–0.030	0.010–0.030	0.010–0.033

Ring Side Clearance Specifications

Engine Model	Engine Displacement (cu. in.)	Top Compression	Bottom Compression	Oil Control
120	153	0.0012–0.0037	0.0012–0.0042	0.000–0.006
140	181	0.0012–0.0037	0.0012–0.0042	0.000–0.006
140	194	0.0012–0.0037	0.0012–0.0042	0.000–0.006
160	250	0.0012–0.0037	0.0012–0.0042	0.000–0.006
165	250	0.0012–0.0037	0.0012–0.0042	0.000–0.006
888	302	0.002–0.004	0.002–0.004	"Snug"
200	292	0.0012–0.0032	0.0012–0.0042	0.0005–0.0065
215	302	0.002–0.004	0.002–0.004	"Snug"
225	327	0.0012–0.0037	0.0012–0.0042	0.000–0.006
250	327	0.0012–0.0042	0.0012–0.0042	0.002–0.008
270	350	0.0012–0.0042	0.0012–0.0037	0.000–0.006
325	427	0.0018–0.0048	0.0018–0.0048	0.002–0.0045
390	482	0.0018–0.0048	0.0018–0.0048	0.002–0.0045

Valve Specifications

Engine Model	Engine Displacement (cu in.)	Seat Angle (deg.)	Face Angle (deg.)	Spring Pressure (lbs. @ in.)	Spring Installed Height (in.) $1\frac{1}{32}$ in.	Stem to Guide Clearance (in.)	
						Intake	Exhaust
120	153	46	45	170–180 @ 1.26	1.6562	0.0037 (Max)	0.0052 (Max)
140	181	46	45	175 @ 1.26	1.6562	0.0037 (Max)	0.0052 (Max)
140	194	46	45	163–173 @ 1.33	1.6562	0.0037 (Max)	0.0052 (Max)
160	250	46	45	180–192 @ 1.27	1.6562	0.0037 (Max)	0.0052 (Max)
165	250	46	45	180–192 @ 1.27	1.6562	0.0037 (Max)	0.0052 (Max)
888	302	45	44	184–226 @ 1.340	1.781	0.0010–0.0045	0.0015–0.0055
200	292	46	46	174–184 @ 1.30	1.6562②	0.0037 (Max)	0.0052 (Max)
215	302	45	44	184–226 @ 1.34	1.781	0.0010–0.0045	0.0015–0.0055
225	327	46	45	194–206 @ 1.25	1.1562	0.0037	0.0047
250	327	46	45	194–206 @ 1.25	1.1562	0.0037	0.0047
270	350	46	45	170–180 @ 1.26	1.6562	0.0037	0.0047
325	427	46	①	303–372 @ 1.38	1.8750	0.0035	0.0047
390	482	46	46	——	1.8750	0.0037	0.0047

① 46° Exhaust; 45° Intake
② Exhaust: 1.625 in.

Inline Engine Torque Specifications

Fastener Location	MerCruiser 110, 120, 140, 150, 160, 165, 200 HP	
	Size	Torq Ft Lbs
Camshaft Thrust Plate	1/4-20	6
Carburetor Mounting	5/16-24	12
Crankshaft Pulley	5/16-24	18
Connecting Rod Cap	11/32-24	33
Connecting Rod Cap	3/8-24	40
Coupling to Flywheel	7/16-20	60
Cylinder Head	1/2-13	93
Distributor Clamp	3/8-16	20
Flywheel Housing to Block	3/8-16	21
Front Mount to Block	3/8-16	21
Main Bearing Cap	7/16-14	65
Manifold to Head	3/8-24	23
Oil Pan (Side)	1/4-20	7
Oil Pan (End)	5/16-18	10
Oil Pan Drain Plug	1/2-20	23
Oil Pump Cover	1/4-20	6
Oil Pump to Block	5/16-18	10
Oil Pump Pick-up	1/4-20	5
Rocker Arm Cover	1/4-20	4
Spark Plugs ▲	14 mm	25
Starter Motor	3/8-16	37
Timing Gear Cover	1/4-20	6
Water Pump to Block	5/16-18	15

▲ Torque Tapered Seat Spark Plugs without Gaskets to 15 Ft Lbs.

V8 Engine Torque Specifications
(215 hp–250 hp)

Fastener Location	MerCruiser 215 888		MerCruiser 225		MerCruiser 250	
	Size	Torq Ft Lbs	Size	Torq Ft Lbs	Size	Torq Ft Lbs
Camshaft Sprocket	3/8-16	43	5/16-18	20	5/16-18	20
Camshaft Thrust Plate	1/4-20	8				
Crankshaft Damper	3/8-16	80	7/16-20	60	7/16-20	60
Carburetor	5/16-24	22	5/16-24	20		
Connecting Rod Cap			11/32-24	33	3/8-24	45
Coupler			7/16-20	60		
Cylinder Head	7/16-14	70	7/16-14	65	7/16-14	65
Distributor Hold-Down			3/8-16	20	3/8-16	20
Exhaust Manifold			3/8-16	21		
Flywheel	7/16-20	80	7/16-20	60	7/16-20	60
Flywheel Housing to Block			3/8-16	21	3/8-16	20
Flywheel Cover to Housing			1/4-20	6	1/4-20	6
Front Mount			3/8-16	21	3/8-16	21
Fuel Pump			3/8-16	30	3/8-16	30
Intake Manifold			3/8-16	30	3/8-16	30
Main Bearing Cap	7/16-14	65	7/16-14	75	7/16-14	75
Oil Cooler to Housing			5/16-18	11	5/16-18	11
Oil Filter Bolt			1/2-20	23		
Oil Drain Plug			1/2-20	20	1/2-20	20
Oil Pump	3/8-16	25	7/16-14	65	7/16-14	65
Oil Pump Cover	1/4-20	10	1/4-20	6	1/4-20	6
Oil Pump Pick-up Tube	5/16-18	14				

V8 Engine Torque Specifications (cont.)
(215 hp–250 hp)

Fastener Location	MerCruiser 215 888 Size	Torq Ft Lbs	MerCruiser 225 Size	Torq Ft Lbs	MerCruiser 250 Size	Torq Ft Lbs
Rocker Arm Cover	1/4-20	4	1/4-20	5		
Spark Plugs	18 mm	18	14 mm	25	14 mm	25
Timing Chain or Gear Cover	5/16-18	13	1/4-20	6	1/4-20	6
Water Pump	5/16-18	14	3/8-16	30	3/8-16	30

V8 Engine Torque Specifications
(270 hp–390 hp)

Fastener Location	MerCruiser 270 Size	Torq Ft Lbs	MerCruiser 325 Size	Torq Ft Lbs	MerCruiser 390 Size	Torq Ft Lbs
Camshaft Sprocket	5/16-18	20	5/16-18	20	5/16-18	20
Camshaft Thrust Plate			5/16-18	20	5/16-18	20
Camshaft Damper	7/16-20	60	1/2-20	85	1/2-20	85
Carburetor			5/16-18	11	5/16-18	11
Connecting Rod Cap	3/8-24	45	3/8-24	50	7/16-20	65
Cylinder Head	7/16-14	65	7/16-14	80	7/16-14	80
Distributor Hold-Down	3/8-16	20	3/8-16	20	3/8-16	20
Drive Plate			3/8-16	35	3/8-16	35
Exhaust Manifold	3/8-16	20	3/8-16	20	3/8-16	20
Flywheel	7/16-20	60	7/16-20	65	7/16-20	65
Flywheel Housing to Block	3/8-16	20	3/8-16	20	3/8-16	20
Front Mount	1/4-20	6	1/4-20	6	1/4-20	6
Fuel Pump	3/8-16	30	3/8-16	20	3/8-16	20
Intake Manifold	3/8-16	30	3/8-16	30	3/8-16	30

V8 Engine Torque Specifications (cont.)
(270 hp–390 hp)

Fastener Location	MerCruiser 270 Size	Torq Ft Lbs	MerCruiser 325 Size	Torq Ft Lbs	MerCruiser 390 Size	Torq Ft Lbs
Main Bearing Cap	7/16-14	75	1/2-13	110	1/2-13	110
Oil Cooler to Housing			5/16-18	11	5/16-18	11
Oil Pan	1/4-20	7	5/16-18	11	5/16-18	11
Oil Pan	5/16-18	10				
Oil Pan Drain Plug	1/2-20	20				
Oil Pump	7/16-14	65	7/16-14	65	7/16-14	65
Oil Pump Cover	1/4-20	6	1/4-20	6	1/4-20	6
Rear Mount			7/16-14	50	7/16-14	50
Rocker Arm Cover			1/4-20	4	1/4-20	4
Spark Plugs ▲	14 mm	25	14 mm	25	14 mm	25
Starter Motor			7/16-14	50	7/16-14	50
Timing Chain or Gear Cover			1/4-20	6	1/4-20	6
Transmission Support Bearing			7/16-14	50	7/16-14	50
Transmission Support Bearing			7/16-14	50	7/16-14	50
Water Pump	3/8-16	30	3/8-16	30	3/8-16	30

▲ Torque Tapered Seat Spark Plugs without Gaskets to 15 Ft. Lbs.

Driveshaft Housing Torque Specifications

Driveshaft Housing Location	MerCruiser I-thru-165-888		MerCruiser II-thru-225		MerCruiser 215		MerCruiser III-thru-390	
	Thread	Torque Ft Lbs	Thread	Torque Ft Lbs	Thread	Torque Ft Lbs	Thread	Torque Ft Lbs
Driveshaft Housing-to-Gear Housing Stud, Nut	7/16-20	35 (5)	7/16-20	40 (8)	7/16-20	35 (6)	9/16-18	60 (6)
Bellhousing-to-Driveshaft Housing Stud, Nut	7/16-20	50 (6)	N.A.	N.A.	N.A.	N.A.	N.A.	N.A.
Crankshaft Cover, Screw	N.A.	N.A.	N.A.	N.A.	1/4-28	15 (3)	N.A.	N.A.
Gearshift Stop, Screw	N.A.	N.A.	1/4-20	12 (6)	8-32 ■	Tight (1)	3/8-16 °	20 (2)
Driveshaft Housing Back (Rear) Cover, Screw °	N.A.	N.A.	N.A.	N.A.	3/8-16 °	20 (4)	7/16-20	Snug (4)
Driveshaft Housing Back Cover Stud, Nut	N.A.	N.A.	N.A.	N.A.	N.A.	N.A.	7/16-14	30 (2)
Driveshaft Housing Front Cover, Screw	N.A.	N.A.	N.A.	N.A.	3/8-16 °	20 (4)	3/8-24	20 (7)
Driveshaft Housing Front Cover Stud, Nut	N.A.	N.A.	N.A.	N.A.	N.A.	N.A.	N.A.	N.A.
Driveshaft Housing Top Cover, Screw °	3/8-16	20 (4)	3/8-16	30 (5)	3/8-16 °	20 (4)	7/16-20	30 (4)
Driveshaft Housing Bearing Retainer Stud, Nut °	N.A.	N.A.	N.A.	N.A.	N.A.	N.A.	4 1/4-16 ° ■	200 (1)
Driveshaft Housing Threaded Retainer °	N.A.	N.A.	N.A.	N.A.	N.A.	N.A.	1 3/4-16 ■ ·	♦ 250 (1) ||
Driveshaft Housing Bearing Cone Retainer, Nut ■	N.A.	N.A.	N.A.	N.A.	3/8-16 ■	Tight (1)	N.A.	N.A.
Driveshaft Housing Socket Head, Setscrew ■	5/8-18	85 (1)	7/8-14	200 (1)	3/4-16 §	150 (1)	1-14	200 (1)
Universal Joint Shaft Pinion, Nut	N.A.	N.A.	3/4-16	150 (1)	3/4-16 §	150 (1)	N.A.	N.A.
Universal Joint Shaft, Nut	N.A.	N.A.	N.A.	N.A.	N.A.	N.A.	N.A.	N.A.
Universal Joint Cover, Retainer °	3 7/8-16	200 (1)	N.A.	N.A.	N.A.	N.A.	N.A.	N.A.
Driveshaft Pinion, Nut	N.A.	N.A.	N.A.	250	N.A.	N.A.	N.A.	N.A.
Driveshaft Housing Assembly, Nut	N.A.	N.A.	N.A.	N.A.	N.A.	N.A.	N.A.	N.A.
Driveshaft Gear Retainer, Nut	N.A.	N.A.	N.A.	N.A.	N.A.	N.A.	N.A.	N.A.
Driveshaft Preload	N.A.	N.A.	N.A.	N.A.	7/8-14 §	75 (1) :	N.A.	25 ± 5 ▲
Driveshaft Ball Bear. Ret. to Gear Hsg., Screw	N.A.	N.A.	5/16-18	20 (4)	N.A.	N.A.	N.A.	N.A.
Upper Driveshaft Gear, Nut (Up to 1970 Models)	5/8-18	85 (1)	3/8-16	30 (8)	N.A.	N.A.	N.A.	N.A.
Upper Driveshaft Preload △	N.A.	26-44 *	N.A.	N.A.	N.A.	N.A.	N.A.	N.A.
Pinion Bear. Retainer to Driveshaft Hsg., Screw □	N.A.	N.A.	1/4-20	12 (4)	N.A.	N.A.	N.A.	N.A.
Rack Guide-to-Driveshaft Housing, Screw □ ■	N.A.	N.A.	N.A.	N.A.	10-32 ■	30 * (3)	N.A.	N.A.
Valve Guide-to-Driveshaft Housing, Screw ■	N.A.	N.A.	N.A.	N.A.	N.A.	N.A.	N.A.	N.A.
Rear Pinion Bearing Retainer, Special Nut ■	N.A.	N.A.	N.A.	N.A.	2 3/8-16 ■	250 (1)	N.A.	N.A.
Front Pinion Bearing Retainer, Special Nut	N.A.	N.A.	N.A.	N.A.	2 3/8-16 ■	250 (1)	N.A.	N.A.
Ratchet Screw Nut	N.A.	N.A.	N.A.	N.A.	1/4-28	15 (1)	N.A.	N.A.
Shift Shaft to Driveshaft Hsg., Threaded Bushing	N.A.	N.A.	N.A.	N.A.	9/16-12 §	50 (2)	N.A.	N.A.
Shift Link Rod Assembly, Nut	N.A.	N.A.	N.A.	N.A.	1/4-28	15 (1)	N.A.	N.A.
Water Pocket Cover, Screw	N.A.	N.A.	N.A.	N.A.	N.A.	N.A.	N.A.	N.A.
Water Pump Body, Screw	N.A.	30-40 * (4)	N.A.	N.A.	N.A.	N.A.	N.A.	N.A.
Upper Drive Impeller Shaft	N.A.	N.A.	N.A.	N.A.	N.A.	N.A.	N.A.	N.A.
Trim Tab Bolt	N.A.	180 * (1)	N.A.	180 * (1)	N.A.	N.A.	N.A.	180 * (1)
Driveshaft Locknut ■	N.A.	N.A.	N.A.	N.A.	N.A.	N.A.	N.A.	N.A.

N.A.—Not Applicable

* In. Lbs   ° Use with Anti-Corrosion Grease (C-92-45134A1)   ■ Use with Loctite A (C-92-32609)   ( ) = Quantity

△ Use with New Multipurpose Lubricant (C-92-49588)   · Left-Hand Thread   ▲ New: 15 ± 5 Serviceable

□ Tab Washered   § Use with Loctite Grade "35"   : Back Off ⅛-Turn   ♦ Or 1¼-16°   \|\| Or 200 (1)   ■

Gimbal Housing Torque Specifications

Gimbal Housing Location	MerCruiser I-thru-165-888 Thread	Torque Ft Lbs	MerCruiser II-thru-225 Thread	Torque Ft Lbs	MerCruiser 215 Thread	Torque Ft Lbs	MerCruiser III-270-325-390 Thread	Torque Ft Lbs
Gimbal Housing Seal Retaining Covers, Screw	N.A.	N.A.	N.A.	N.A.	1/4-20	12 (4)	N.A.	N.A.
Steering Lever Coupler Screw, Nut	3/8-24	20 (1)	5/16-24	20 (1)	7/16-20	35 (1)	3/8-24	30 (1)
Gimbal Ring to Upper Swivel Shaft, Screw	5/16-18	20 (1)	N.A.	N.A.	7/16-18 °	20 (1)	3/8-16 °	20 (1)
Steering Lever to Upper Swivel Shaft, Nut	7/16-20	45-50	N.A.	N.A.	N.A.	N.A.	N.A.	N.A.
Hydraulic Connector to Gimbal Housing Stud, Nut	1/4-28	10 (2)	1/4-28	10 (2)	1/4-28	10 (2)	1/4-28	10 (2)
Top Hydraulic Connector to Gimbal Housing, Screw	N.A.	N.A.	N.A.	N.A.	1/4-20	12 (1)	N.A.	N.A.
Hydraulic Connector to Top Connector, Tubing	N.A.	N.A.	N.A.	N.A.	3/8-24	140-160 (2)	N.A.	N.A.
Oil Hose Retaining Clamp	N.A.	N.A.	N.A.	N.A.	N.A.	10-15 * (4)	N.A.	25 * (4)
Exhaust Bellows Retaining Clamp	N.A.	35-38 *	N.A.	12 (2)	N.A.	35 * (2)	N.A.	N.A.
Universal Joint Bellows Retaining Clamp	N.A.	35-38 *	N.A.	12 (1)	N.A.	35 * (2) z	N.A.	35 * (2)
Shift Bellows Clamp	N.A.	35-38 *	N.A.	N.A.	N.A.	35 * (1) z	N.A.	N.A.
Valve Guide Cover to Bell Housing, Screw	N.A.	N.A.	N.A.	N.A.	1/4-28	15 (3)	1/4-28	15 (4)
Bell Housing to Gimbal Ring, Hinge Pin	7/16-20	50 (6)	N.A.	N.A.	5/8-18 ■	60 ° (2)	3/4-16 ■	75 ° (2)
Bell Housing Stud to Driveshaft Housing, Nut	N.A.	N.A.	N.A.	N.A.	1/2-20	75-85 (6)	5/8-18	100 (6)
Reservoir Cover to Transom Plate, Screw	N.A.	N.A.	N.A.	N.A.	5/16-18	20 (8)	5/16-18	20 (11)
Exhaust Cover to Transom Plate, Screw	N.A.	N.A.	N.A.	N.A.	5/16-24	20 (15)	N.A.	N.A.
Exhaust Cover to Transom Plate, Screw	N.A.	N.A.	N.A.	N.A.	5/8-18 ■	20 (2)	N.A.	N.A.
Mount Brackets to Flywheel Housing, Screw	5/16-24	14 (3)	5/16-24	20 (3)	5/16-24	100 (2)	N.A.	N.A.
Hydraulic Pump Bracket, Screw	3/8-24	20 (1)	N.A.	N.A.	3/8-24	20 (6)	5/16-18 ·	20 (4)
Steering Link Rod, Nut or Bolt to Ride-Guide	N.A.	N.A.	N.A.	N.A.	10-32	20 (1)	N.A.	N.A.
Trim Limit Switch and Trim Sender, Screw	N.A.	N.A.	N.A.	N.A.	N.A.	Tight	N.A.	N.A.
Gimbal Housing Stud to Transom Plate, Nut	1/2-13	20-25 (2)	1/2-20	20-25 (8)	1/2-20	25-30 (8)	1/2-20	25-30 (6)
Transom Plate Carriage Bolt, Nut	1/2-13	20-25 (2)	N.A.	N.A.	N.A.	N.A.	1/2-20	25-30 (2)
Transom Plate to Gimbal Housing, Screw	7/16-14	20-25 (2)	N.A.	N.A.	N.A.	N.A.	N.A.	N.A.
Gimbal Housing Stud, Nut	7/16-20	20-25 (2)	N.A.	N.A.	N.A.	N.A.	N.A.	N.A.
Bearing Support Housing to Transmission, Screw	N.A.	N.A.	N.A.	N.A.	N.A.	N.A.	7/16-14	40-45 (8)
Transmission to Flywheel Housing, Screw	N.A.	N.A.	N.A.	N.A.	N.A.	N.A.	7/16-14	40-45 (6)
Mount Brackets to Transmission, Screw	N.A.	N.A.	N.A.	N.A.	N.A.	N.A.	7/16-14	40-45 (2)
Gimbal Housing to Steering Lever Housing, Screw	N.A.	N.A.	1/2-13	75 (6)	N.A.	N.A.	N.A.	N.A.
Steering Link Rod Bolts, Steering Lever Housing	N.A.	N.A.	1/2-20	75 (2)	N.A.	N.A.	N.A.	N.A.
Top Pivot Bolt, Nut	N.A.	N.A.	5/8-18	100 (1)	N.A.	N.A.	N.A.	N.A.
Shift Cable to Core Wire Support, Nut	5/16	15 (1)	5/16	15 (1)	N.A.	N.A.	N.A.	N.A.
Tilt Pin Bolt, Nut	7/16-20 §	Snug (2)	7/16-20 §	Snug (2)	N.A.	N.A.	N.A.	N.A.
Upper and Lower Steering Arm, Screw	N.A.	N.A.	3/8-24	30 □ (2)	N.A.	N.A.	N.A.	N.A.
Clamp Nut Cover to Inner Transom Plate, Screw	3/8-16	20-25 (3)	5/16-18	20 (6)	N.A.	N.A.	N.A.	N.A.
Exhaust Elbow, Screw	1/2-20	60 (2)	N.A.	N.A.	N.A.	N.A.	N.A.	N.A.
Engine Mount Nut, Bolt	7/8-14	Tight (2)	7/8-14	Tight (1)	7/8-14	Tight (2)	7/8-14	Tight (1)
Steering Cable Guide, Jam Nut	5/16-18	14 (2)	7/8-14	14 (2)	7/8-14	14 (2)	7/8-14	14 (2)
Reverse Lock Valve, Screw	5/16-18	50-75 (1)	N.A.	50-75 *	N.A.	N.A.	N.A.	N.A.
Shift Cutout Lever Arm Spring Retainer, Screw	5/16-18	50-75 (1)	N.A.	N.A.	N.A.	N.A.	N.A.	N.A.

N.A.—Not Applicable
* In. Lbs   ° Use with Anti-Corrosion Grease (C-92-45134A1)   □ Tab Washered   ■ Use with Grade "A" Loctite (C-92-32609)
▲Tight   · Or 5/16-24   § Early Model, ¼-Turn Loose   ( ) = Quantity
z Use with Bellows Adhesive (C-92-36340)

Gear Housing Torque Specifications

Gear Housing Location	MerCruiser I-thru-165-888		MerCruiser II-thru-225		MerCruiser 215		MerCruiser III-thru-390	
	Thread	Torque Ft Lbs	Thread	Torque Ft Lbs	Thread	Torque Ft Lbs	Thread	Torque Ft Lbs
Gear Housing to Driveshaft Housing Screw	3/8-16	28 (1)	7/16-14	50 (7)	1/2-13	50 (1)	1/2-13	50 (1)
	N.A.	N.A.	7/16-14	50 (1)	N.A.	N.A.	N.A.	N.A.
Gear Housing Stud to Driveshaft Housing, Nut	N.A.	N.A.	1/4-20	12 (3)	7/16-20	35 (1)	N.A.	N.A.
Gearcase Cover, Retainer Spool	4-3/8-16	250° wo/Tab	N.A.	N.A.	5-1/8-16 °	250 ■ (1)	5-1/2-16 °	250 ■ (1)
	N.A.	150° w/Tab	4-3/8-16	250 ° (1)	N.A.	N.A.	N.A.	N.A.
Gear Housing Stud Bearing Retainer, Nut	N.A.	N.A.	N.A.	N.A.	N.A.	N.A.	3/8-24	30 (4)
Gear Housing to Driveshaft Housing Stud, Nut	N.A.	N.A.	N.A.	N.A.	N.A.	N.A.	9/16-18	60 (1)
	N.A.	N.A.	N.A.	N.A.	N.A.	N.A.	7/16-20	35 (1)
Gear Housing Preload at Driveshaft	N.A.	N.A.	N.A.	N.A.	N.A.	N.A.	(New)	35 ± 5
	N.A.	N.A.	N.A.	N.A.	N.A.	N.A.	(Serviceable)	15 ± 5
Trim Tab to Gear Housing, Screw	7/16-14	180 * (1)	N.A.	N.A.	7/16-14	180 * (1)	7/16-14	180 * (1)
Lower Gear Bearing Cups, Retainer	N.A.	N.A.	3-7/8-16	200 (1)	N.A.	N.A.	N.A.	N.A.
Forward and Reverse Gear, Locknut	N.A.	N.A.	1-3/4-16	150 · (2)	3/4-16 □	150 (1)	N.A.	N.A.
Gear Housing Pinion, Nut	5/8-18	60-80 (1)	1-1/4-1	150 (1)	N.A.	N.A.	7/8-14	175 (1)
Water Pump Housing Stud, Nut	1/4-28	50-60 * (2)	N.A.	N.A.	N.A.	N.A.	N.A.	N.A.
	5/16-24	50-60 * (1)	N.A.	N.A.	N.A.	N.A.	N.A.	N.A.
Water Pump Housing Screw	1/4-20	50-60 * (1)	N.A.	N.A.	N.A.	N.A.	N.A.	N.A.
Propeller Shaft, Nut	3/4-16	40 ± 5 § (1)	N.A.	40 ± 5 (1)	N.A.	40 ± 5 (1)	N.A.	40 ± 5 (1)
Oil and Water Adaptor, Screw	N.A.	N.A.	N.A.	N.A.	N.A.	N.A.	N.A.	N.A.

N.A.—Not Applicable
* In. Lbs   ° Use with Anti-Corrosion Grease (C-92-45134A1)   · Swagged   □ Tab Washered   § Adjusted to Tab Space
■ Use with Grade "A" Loctite (C-92-32609)   ▼ 50 Ft Lbs for "60" Model; 60 Ft Lbs for "80" and "90"   ( ) = Quantity

Torque Sequences

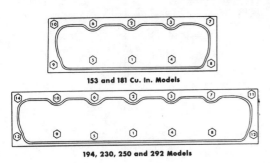

153 and 181 Cu. In. Models

194, 230, 250 and 292 Models

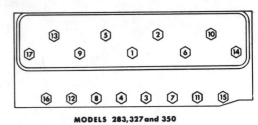

MODELS 283, 327 and 350

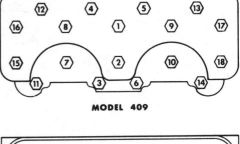

MODEL 409

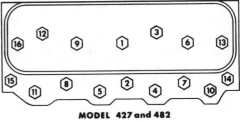

MODEL 427 and 482

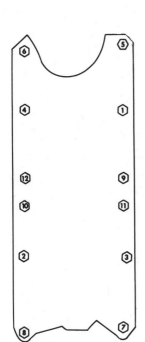

Ford V-8 intake manifold

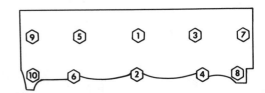

Ford V-8 cylinder head

Alternator Specifications

Identification Number	Ground	Rotation °	Field Current		Cold Output 5000 rpm	Hot Output
			Amperes	Volts		
1100619	N	CCW	1.9–2.3	12	40 Amps	42 Amps
1100721	N	CCW	2.2–2.6	12	30 Amps	32 Amps
1100806	N	CCW	2.2–2.6	12	30 Amps	32 Amps
1100912	N	CCW	4.1–4.5	12	37 Amps	42 Amps

* Rotation is dependent upon engine rotation and fan type.

Starter Specifications

| Identification Number | Volts | No Load Test | | | | Pinion Clearance | Brush Spring Tension |
		Min Amps	Max Amps	Min rpm	Max rpm		
1107259	10.6	49	76	6200	9400	0.005–0.050	40
1107274	10.6	65	100	3600	5100	0.005–0.050	35
1108361	9	55	85	3100	4900	0.010–0.140	35
1108365	9	53	69	6400	8600	0.010–0.140	35
1108391	9	55	85	3100	4900	0.010–0.140	35
215E *	——	70	——	——	——	——	40

* Autolite Positive-Engagement Drive
—— Not Available

Carburetor Specifications

Carburetor Model		B-BC	BC	2GC	2GC	2GC
Carburetor No.		7025183 7025184	7020994 7020996 7024180 7024181	7020993 7028086	7025188 7026088	7028188 7040080 7040081
Adjustment		See "Fuel System"				
Float Level	Primary	①	$1\frac{9}{32}$	$\frac{5}{8}$	$\frac{5}{8}$	$\frac{5}{8}$
	Secondary					
Float Drop	Primary	$1\frac{3}{4}$	$1\frac{3}{4}$	$1\frac{29}{32}$	$1\frac{29}{32}$	$1\frac{24}{32}$
	Secondary					
Pump Rod				$1\frac{5}{32}$	$1\frac{1}{8}$	$1\frac{5}{32}$
Fast Idle (Bench)			②	②		
Vacuum Break						Flush
Unloader		0.230	0.230	0.160	0.080	0.080
Choke Setting		Index	Index	Index	Index	Index

① $1\frac{9}{32}$ in. with $\frac{1}{32}$ in. shim between needle and float.
② Turn screw in to contact low step of cam.

Carburetor Specifications

Carburetor Model		*4GC*	*4GC*	*4GC*	*4GC*	*4MV*	*4MV*	*4MV*	*Holley*	*Holley*
Carburetor No.		*7020995*	*7023180*	*7023183*	*7025180*	*7027080*	*7029280* *7029285* *7040283*	*7037082*	*4160*	*2300C*
Adjustment						See "Fuel System"				
Float Level	Primary	1 3/8	1 1/2	1 3/8	1 11/32	1/4	1/4	1/4	Bottom of Hole	Sight Plug ±1/32"
	Secondary	1 11/32	1 9/16	1 11/32	1 3/8					
Float Toe	Primary	11/16		11/16						
	Secondary	9/16		9/16						
Float Drop	Primary	1 3/8	2 1/4	1 3/8	1 3/8					
	Secondary	1 3/8	2 1/4	1 3/8	1 3/8					
Pump Rod Location		Outer	Outer	Outer		Inner		Inner		
Pump Rod		1 1/32	1 3/32	1 1/16	1	9/32		9/32		0.015–0.062
Fast Idle (Bench)		①	①	①		2 Turns		2 Turns	0.081	
Choke Rod		Flush	Flush	Flush	0.050	0.100	0.100	0.100	1 23/32 Bench	
Air Valve Dashpot						0.030	0.030	0.030		
Vacuum Break					Flush	0.150	0.150	0.150	0.110	
Unloader		0.120	0.230	0.130	0.120	0.300		0.300	0.015–0.062	0.270–0.160
Air Valve Lockout						0.015		0.015	0.015	

					Electric	Index	Index
Throttle Valve Lockout			0.110–0.015				
Secondary Opening	0.015	0.020	0.015		0.070	0.070	
Secondary Closing	0.110	0.020	0.030		0.020	0.020	
Second Metering Rod					7/8	7/8	
A.V. Spring Windup					5/8	3/4	
Choke Setting	3 N.L.	Index	Index	3 N.L.	1 Rod Diameter Interference	1 Rod Diameter Interference	Index

N.L. = Notches Lean.
①—Turn screw in to contact low step of cam.

Main Metering Jet Sizes
Up to 5000 Ft Elevation

Engine Model	Type Carburetor	Size (in.)	Approach Angle	Part No.	Quan.	Adjustment
120	2GC	0.063	Full 60°	B-1397-2448	2	
140 and 150	B (less choke) BC (with choke)	0.060 0.061	Full 60° Full 60°	B-1397-2446 B-1397-2447	1 1	
150	2GC (single carb.)	0.063	Full 60°	B-1397-2448	2	
160	2GC	0.065	Full 60°	B-1397-2994	1	Set choke 2 notches lean.
225	4GC (no. 7020995)	Primary 0.054 Secondary 0.073	Partial 60° Full 60°	B-1397-2453 B-1397-2451	2 2	

5000 Ft to 10,000 Ft Elevation

Engine Model	Type Carburetor	Size (in.)	Approach Angle	Part No.	Quan.	Adjustment
120	2GC	0.061	Full 60°	B-1397-2213 (kit)	1	Set choke 2 notches lean.
140 and 150	B (less choke) BC (with choke)	0.059 0.060	Partial 60° Partial 60°	B-1397-2219 (kit) B-1397-2215 (kit)	1 1	Also change power spring. Use kit listed. Set automatic choke (BC only) 2 notches lean.
150	2GC (single carb.)	0.061	Full 60°	B-1397-2213	1	Set choke 2 notches lean.
160	2GC	0.063	Full 60°	B-1397-2292	1	Set choke 2 notches lean.
225	4GC (no. 7020995)	Primary 0.051 Secondary 0.070	Partial 60° Full 60°	B-1397-2217 (kit)	1	Also change power piston & spring. Use kit listed. Set choke 5 notches lean.

Main Metering Jet Sizes (cont.)
10,000 Ft Elevation and Up

Engine Model	Type Carburetor	Size (in.)	Approach Angle	Part No.	Quan.	Adjustment
120	2GC	0.060	Partial 60°	B-1397-2214 (kit)	1	Set choke 2 notches lean.
140 and 150	B (less choke) BC (with choke)	0.056 0.057	Partial 60° Partial 60°	B-1397-2220 (kit) B-1397-2216 (kit)	1 1	Also change power spring. Use kit listed. Set automatic choke (BC only) 2 notches lean.
150	2GC (single carb.)	0.060	Partial 60°	B-1397-2214	1	Set choke 2 notches lean.
160	2GC	0.060	Partial 60°	B-1397-2214	1	Set choke 2 notches lean.
225	4GC (no. 7020995)	Primary 0.049 Secondary 0.067	Partial 60° Full 60°	B-1397-2218 (kit)	1	Also change power piston & spring. Use kit listed. Set choke 5 notches lean.

METRIC CONVERSION: 1 inch is equal to 25.4 mm (millimeter)

NOTE: *Do not identify main metering jets by the orifice size which is stamped on front of jet. It is possible to have three different jets with the same size orifice, as jets are available with three different approach angles. Figures, shown below, illustrate the approach angles that a jet may have. All three could have the same size orifice, although each one will allow a different amount of fuel to flow thru the carburetor. When ordering replacement jets, order by part number and not by orifice size.*

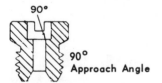

90°
Approach Angle

Partial 60°
Approach Angle

Full 60°
Approach Angle

Wiring Diagrams

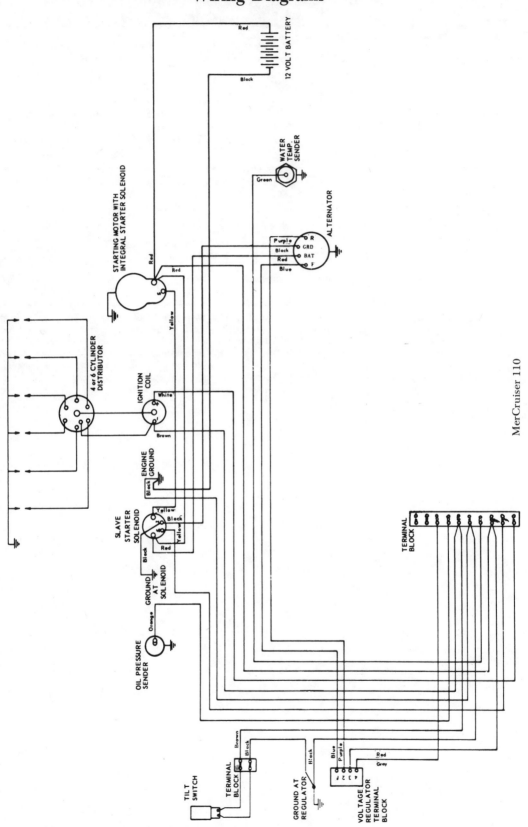

MerCruiser 110

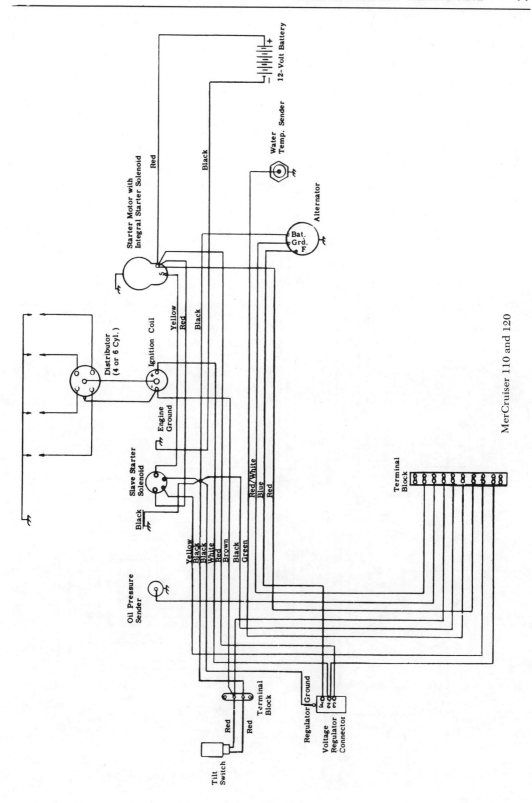

MerCruiser 110 and 120

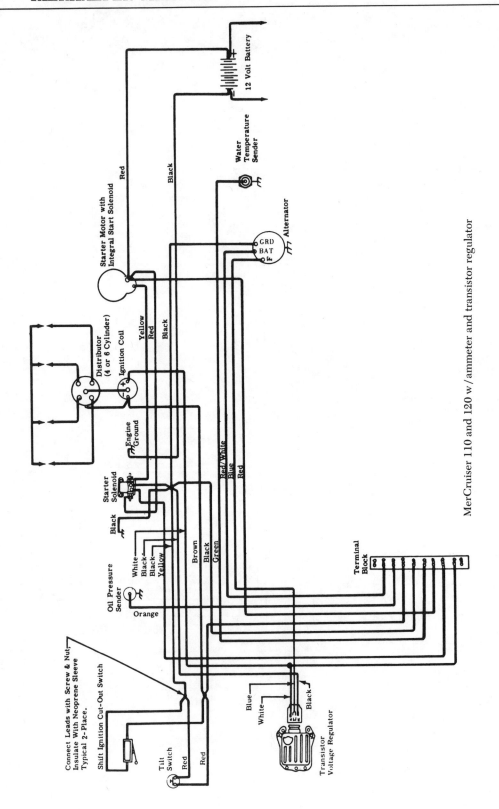

12 Volt Battery

Water Temperature Sender

Starter Motor with Integral Start Solenoid

Red

Black

Alternator

GRD
BAT
F

Distributor (4 or 6 Cylinder)

Ignition Coil

Yellow

Red

Black

Engine Ground

Red/White

Blue

Red

Starter Solenoid

Black

Oil Pressure Sender

White

Black

Black

Yellow

Brown

Black

Green

Orange

Terminal Block

Connect Leads with Screw & Nut, Insulate With Neoprene Sleeve Typical 2-Place.

Shift Ignition Cut-Out Switch

Tilt Switch

Red

Red

Blue

White

Black

Transistor Voltage Regulator

MerCruiser 110 and 120 w/ammeter and transistor regulator

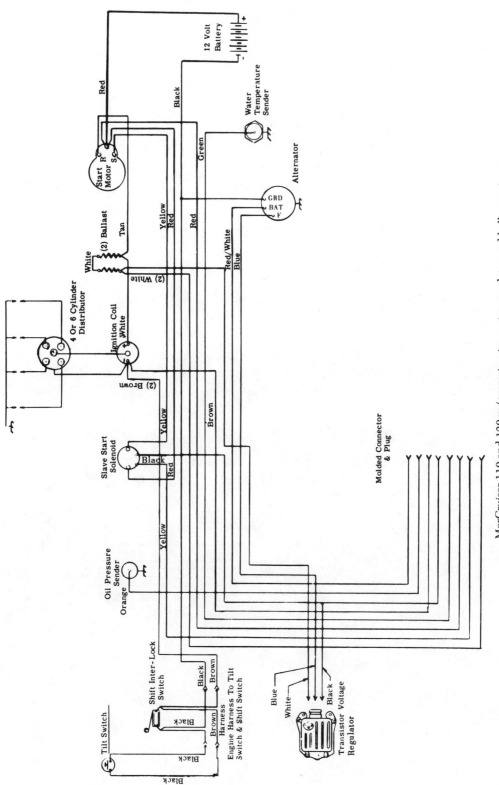

MerCruiser 110 and 120 w/ammeter, transistor regulator and ballast resistor

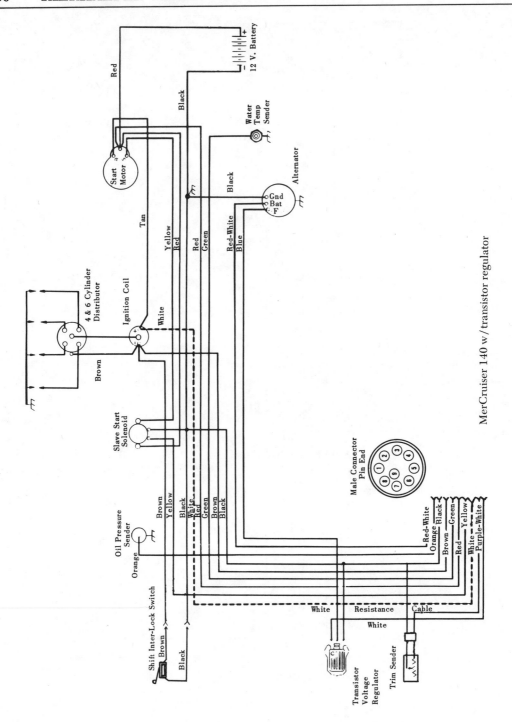

MerCruiser 140 w/ transistor regulator

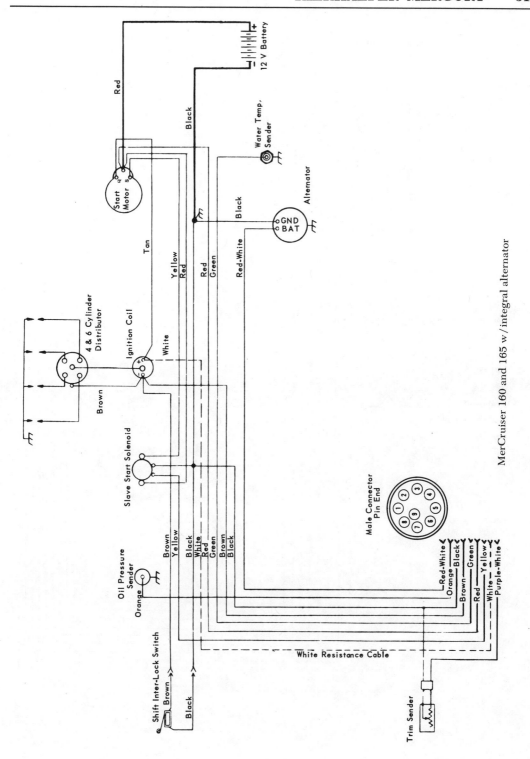

MerCruiser 160 and 165 w/integral alternator

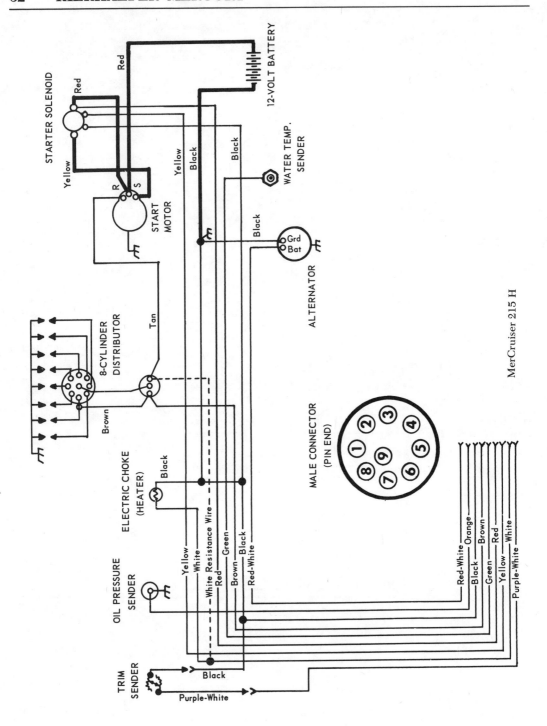

MerCruiser 215 H

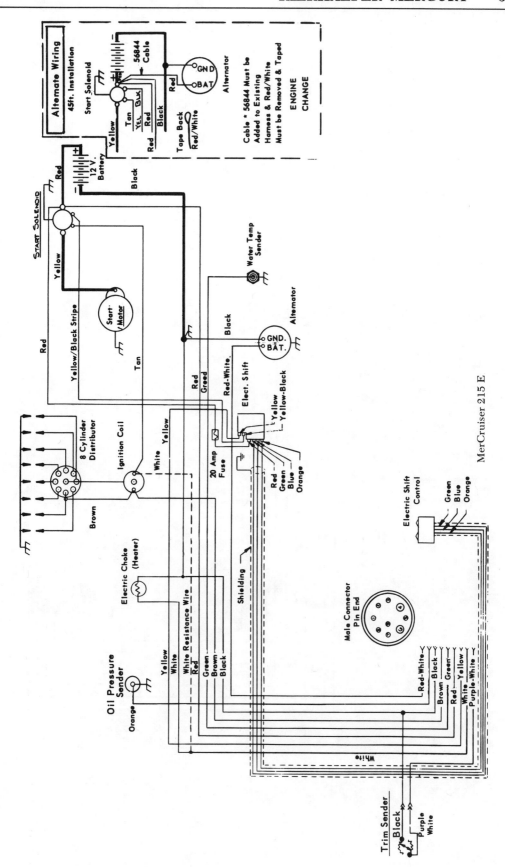

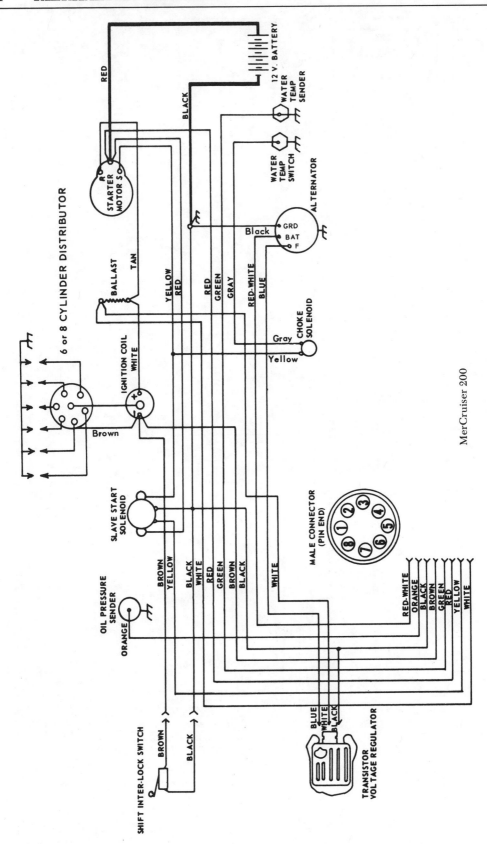

MerCruiser 200

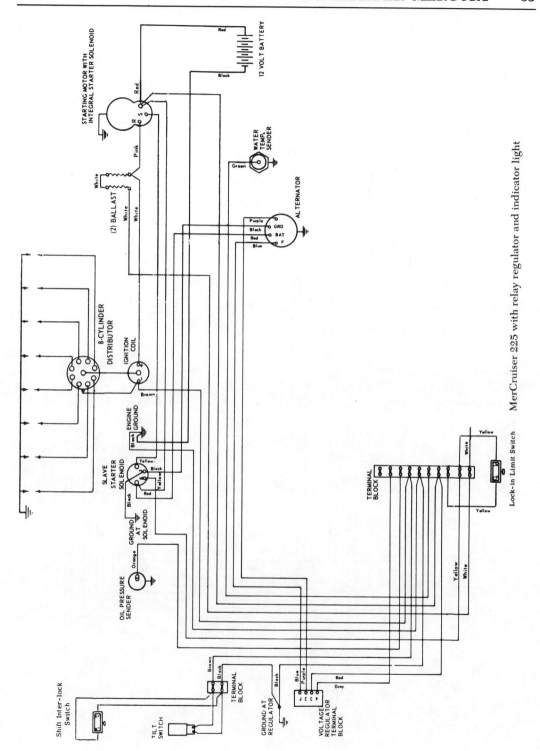

MerCruiser 225 with relay regulator and indicator light

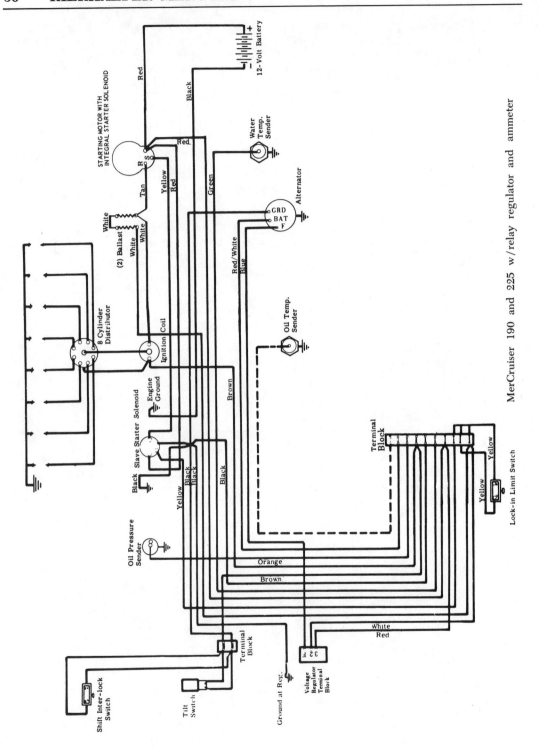

MerCruiser 190 and 225 w/relay regulator and ammeter

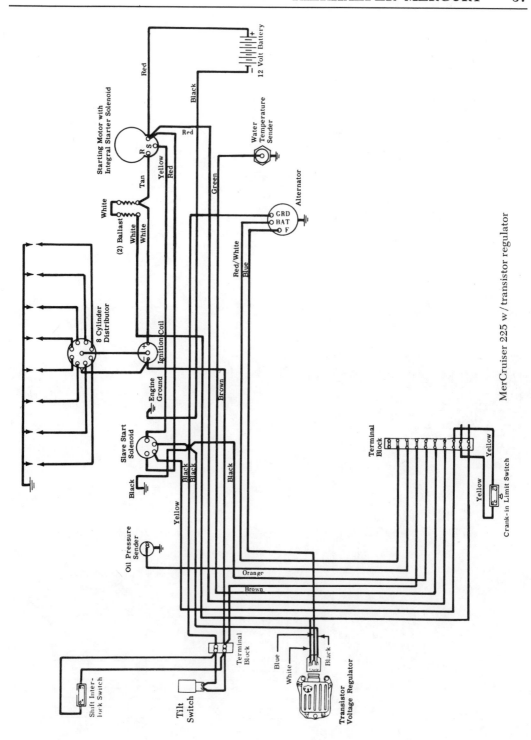

MerCruiser 225 w/transistor regulator

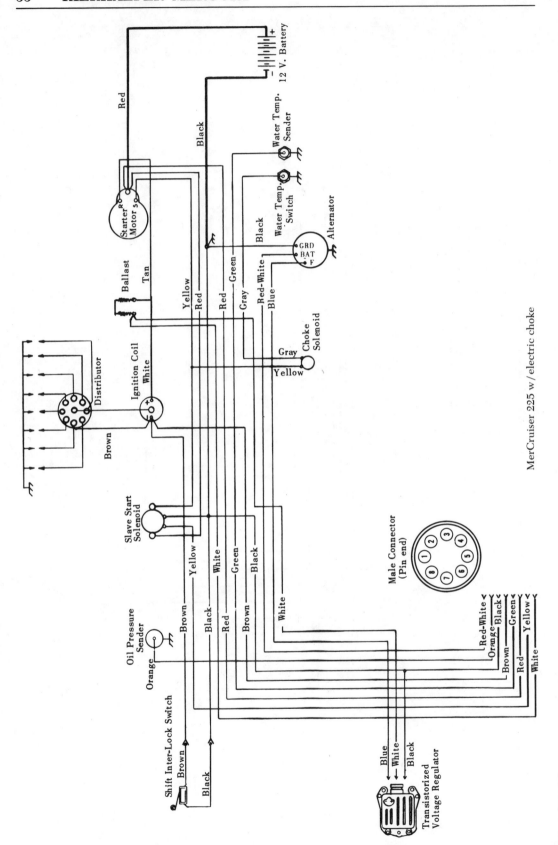

MerCruiser 225 w/electric choke

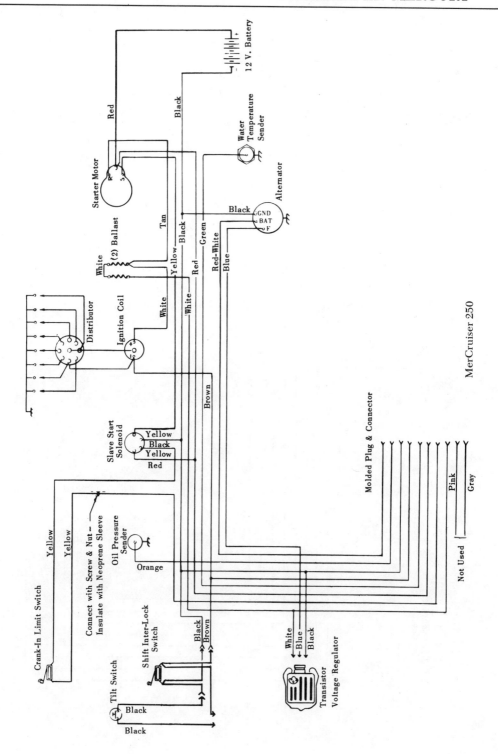

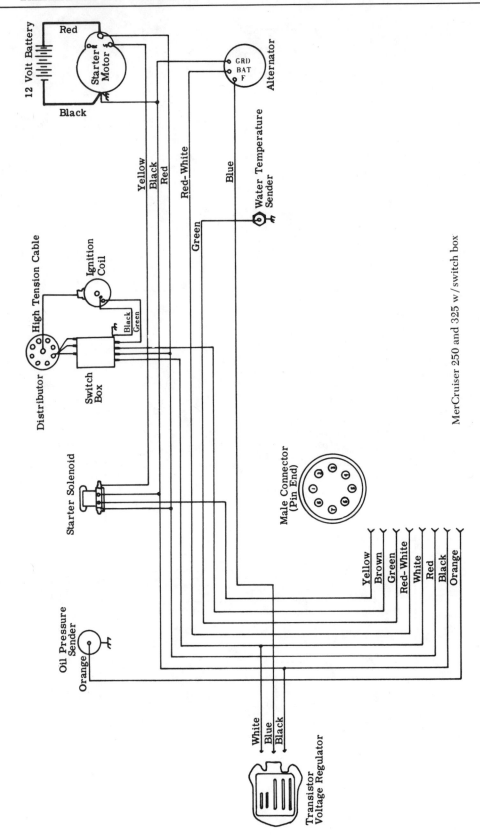

MerCruiser 250 and 325 w/switch box

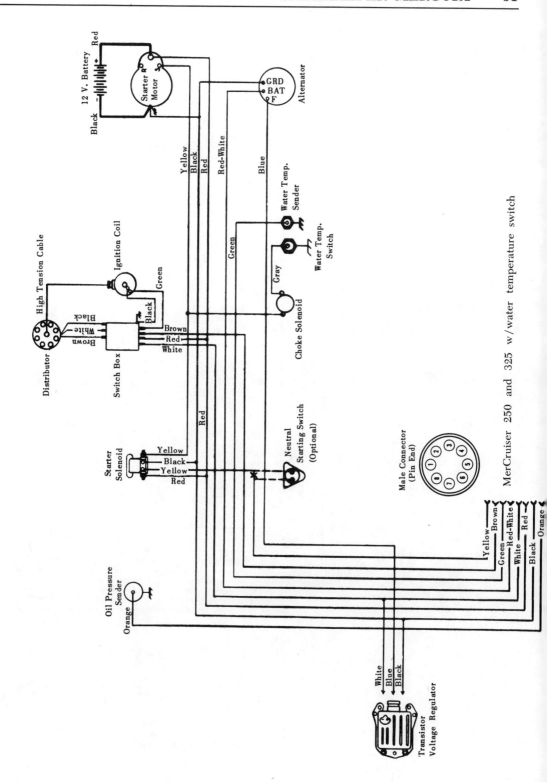

MerCruiser 250 and 325 w/water temperature switch

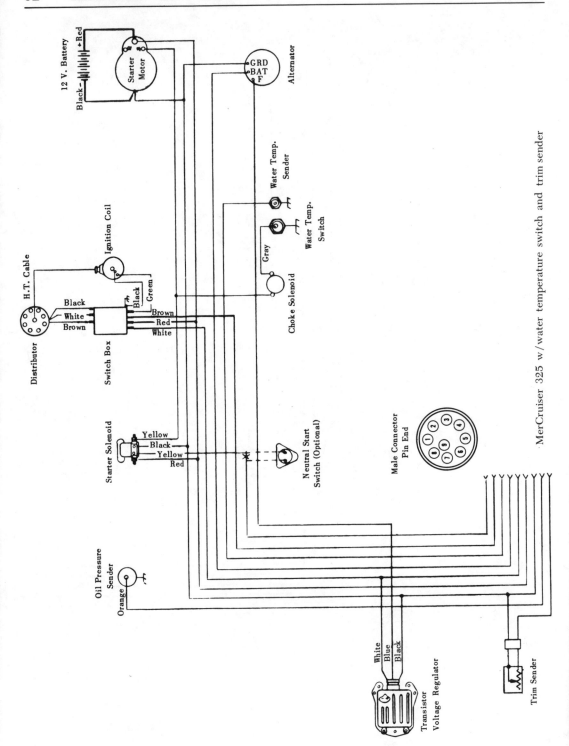

MerCruiser 325 w/water temperature switch and trim sender

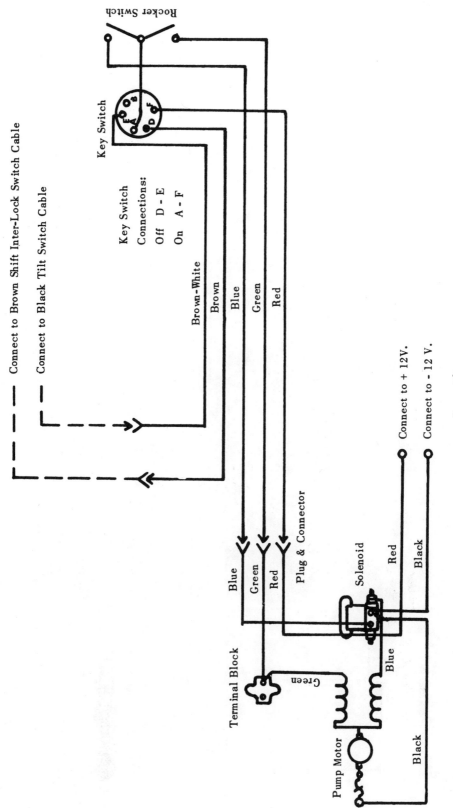

Rocker Switch

Key Switch

Connect to Brown Shift Inter-Lock Switch Cable

Connect to Black Tilt Switch Cable

Key Switch
Connections:
Off D - E
On   A - F

Brown-White

Brown

Blue

Green

Red

Connect to + 12V.

Connect to - 12 V.

Power tilt

Blue

Green

Red

Plug & Connector

Solenoid

Red

Black

Terminal Block

Green

Blue

Pump Motor

Black

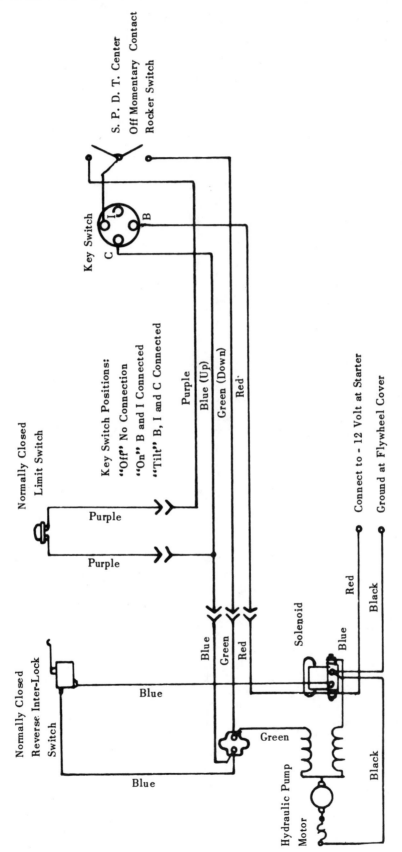

S. P. D. T. Center
Off Momentary Contact
Rocker Switch

Key Switch

Normally Closed
Limit Switch

Key Switch Positions:
"Off" No Connection
"On" B and I Connected
"Tilt" B, I and C Connected

Purple
Blue (Up)
Green (Down)
Red·

Purple

Purple

Normally Closed
Reverse Inter-Lock
Switch

Blue
Green
Red

Blue

Blue

Green

Blue

Solenoid

Blue
Red
Black

Connect to - 12 Volt at Starter
Ground at Flywheel Cover

Power trim with rocker switch

Black

Hydraulic Pump
Motor

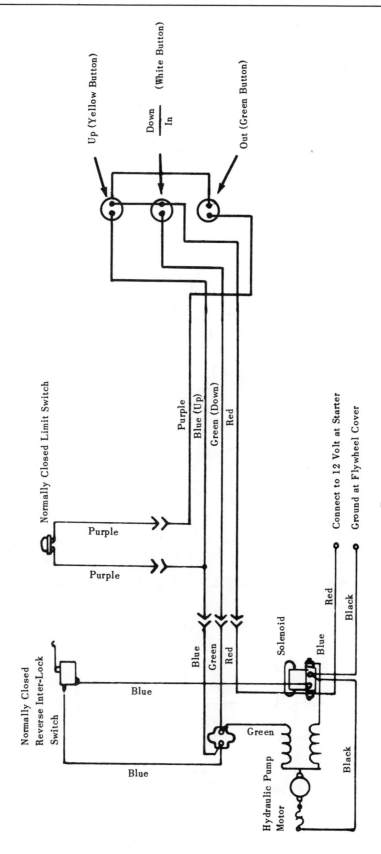

Up (Yellow Button)

Down — In (White Button)

Out (Green Button)

Normally Closed Limit Switch

Purple
Blue (Up)
Green (Down)
Red

Purple

Purple

Normally Closed
Reverse Inter-Lock
Switch

Blue

Blue

Blue
Green
Red

Blue

Green

Solenoid

Blue

Red

Black

Connect to 12 Volt at Starter

Ground at Flywheel Cover

Power trim with early push button

Hydraulic Pump
Motor

Black

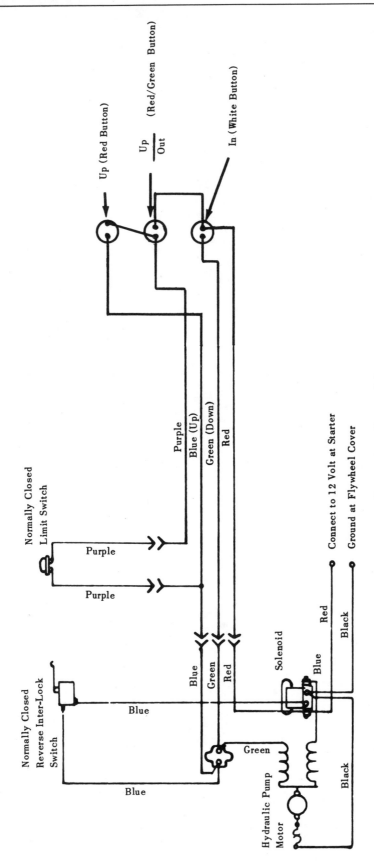

Power trim w/late push button

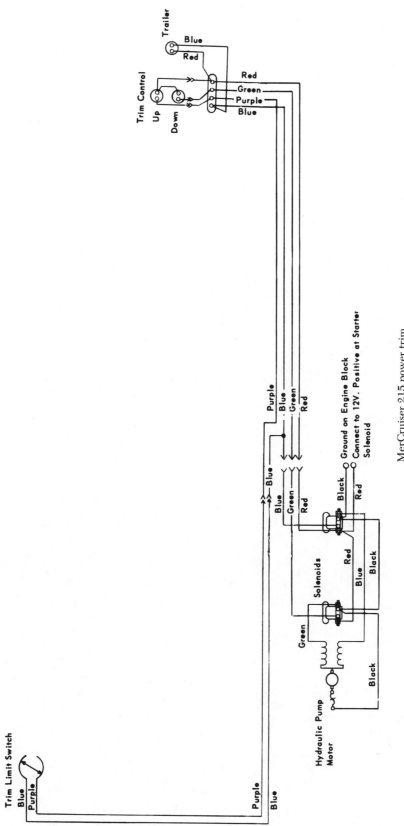

MerCruiser 215 power trim

Propeller Recommendations

Model (Engine hp)	Stern Drive	Aluminum Propellers Part Numbers		Dia (in.)	Pitch (in.)	No. of Blades	Approx Boat Length (ft)	Speed Range (mph)
		RH Rotation	LH Rotation					
		*C-48-31448A3	——	13½	25	2	§	41–49
		*C-48-31450A3	——	13¾	23	2	§	47–55
		C-48-32386A3	——	13¾	23	2	§	47–55
		*C-48-32744A3	——	13	21	3	15–16½	41–49
		C-48-32746A3	——	13	21	3	15–16½	41–49
		*C-48-32748A3	——	13	19	3	16–18	35–43
		C-48-32750A3	——	13	19	3	16–18	35–43
		*C-48-31458A3	——	13	17	3	17–19	29–37
110	I	C-48-32264A3	——	13	17	3	17–19	29–37
		*C-48-31460A3	——	13½	15	3	18½–21	23–31
		C-48-32390A3	——	13½	15	3	18½–21	23–31
		*C-48-30394A3	——	13½	13	3	21–25	17–25
		C-48-32392A3	——	13½	13	3	21–25	17–25
		*C-48-30396A3	——	14	11	3	23–27	13–21
		C-48-35936A3	——	14	11	3	23–27	13–21
		*C-48-30398A3	——	14	9½	3	27–Up+	8–18
rpm:		C-48-33242A3	——	14	9½	3	27–Up+	8–18
3700–4100		*C-48-30400A3	——	14	8½	3	Work Boat	1–8
		B-48-36008A1	——	14½	25	3	Dual, Fast	43–50
		B-48-36010A1	——	14½	23	3	Dual, Fast	38–45
		B-48-49634A1	——	15	21	3	16–18	33–40
110	IA	B-48-36014A1	——	15½	19	3	17–19	29–35
		B-48-36016A1	——	15¾	17	3	18½–21	24–31
		B-48-36018A1	——	16	15	3	20–25	19–26
		B-48-36020A1	——	16	13	3	23–27	15–21
rpm:		B-48-36022A1	——	16	11	3	Houseboat	8–17
3700–4100		B-48-36024A1	——	16	9	3	Work Boat	1–10
		B-48-36028A1	——	14½	27	3	Dual, Fast	42–48
		B-48-36008A1	——	14½	25	3	15–17	38–44
		B-48-36010A1	——	14½	23	3	16–18	35–42
120	IB	B-48-49634A1	——	15	21	3	17–19	33–40
		B-48-36014A1	——	15½	19	3	18–21	28–35
		B-48-36016A1	——	15¾	17	3	20–25	23–29
		B-48-36018A1	——	16	15	3	23–27	18–24
		B-48-36020A1	——	16	13	3	26–Plus	13–20
rpm:		B-48-36022A1	——	16	11	3	Houseboat	7–15
3900–4300		B-48-36024A1	——	16	9	3	Work Boat	1–9
		*C-48-31448A3	——	13½	25	2	§	50–60
		*C-48-31450A3	——	13¾	23	2	15–16½	45–53
		C-48-32386A3	——	13¾	23	2	15–16½	45–53
		*C-48-32744A3	——	13	21	3	16–18	39–47
		C-48-32746A3	——	13	21	3	16–18	39–47
		*C-48-32748A3	——	13	19	3	17–19	33–41
		C-48-32750A3	——	13	19	3	17–19	33–41
		*C-48-31458A3	——	13	17	3	18½–21	27–35
		C-48-32264A3	——	13	17	3	18½–21	27–35
140 (6 Cyl)	I	*C-48-31460A3	——	13½	15	3	21–25	21–29
		C-48-32390A3	——	13½	15	3	21–25	21–29
		*C-48-30394A3	——	13½	13	3	23–27+	16–24
		C-48-32392A3	——	13½	13	3	23–27+	16–24
		*C-48-30396A3	——	14	11	3	27–Up+	10–20
		C-48-35936A3	——	14	11	3	27–Up+	10–20
		*C-48-30398A3	——	14	9½	3	Work Boat	3–12
rpm:		C-48-33242A3	——	14	9½	3	Work Boat	3–12
3700–4100		*C-48-30400A3	——	14	8½	3	Hvy Wk Boat	1–3

Propeller Recommendations (cont.)

Model (Engine hp)	Stern Drive	Aluminum Propellers Part Numbers		Dia (in.)	Pitch (in.)	No. of Blades	Approx Boat Length (ft)	Speed Range (mph)
		RH Rotation	LH Rotation					
140 (6 Cyl) rpm: 3700–4100	IC	B-48-36030A1	——	16	25	2	Dual, Fast	45–50
		B-48-36008A1	——	14½	25	3	Dual, Fast	45–50
		B-48-36010A1	——	14½	23	3	Dual, Fast	41–47
		B-48-49634A1	——	15	21	3	16–18½	37–43
		B-48-36014A1	——	15½	19	3	17–19½	33–39
		B-48-36016A1	——	15¾	17	3	18½–21	27–35
		B-48-36018A1	——	16	15	3	20–25	22–29
		B-48-36020A1	——	16	13	3	23–27	16–24
		B-48-36022A1	——	16	11	3	Houseboat	10–18
		B-48-36024A1	——	16	9	3	Work Boat	1–11
140 (4 Cyl) rpm: 4200–4600	140	B-48-36028A4	——	14½	27	3	15–17 Dual	46–52
		B-48-36008A4	——	14½	25	3	15–17	43–49
		B-48-36010A4	——	14½	23	3	16–18	40–46
		B-48-49634A4	——	15	21	3	17–20	37–43
		B-48-36014A4	——	15½	19	3	18–21	34–40
		B-48-36016A4	——	15¾	17	3	20–25	29–35
		B-48-36018A4	——	16	15	3	23–27	25–31
		B-48-36020A4	——	16	13	3	26 Plus	21–27
		B-48-36022A4	——	16	11	3	Houseboat	17–23
		B-48-36024A4	——	16	9	3	Houseboat	Up to 17
888 rpm: 3800–4200	1.5:1	B-48-36008A4	——	14¼	25	3	Dual, Fast	49–59
		B-48-58426A4	——	15	23	3	Up to 17	45–54
		B-48-58424A4	——	15¼	21	3	17–19	41–49
		B-48-58422A4	——	15½	19	3	19–21	37–44
		B-48-36016A4	——	15¾	17	3	20–25	32–40
		B-48-36018A4	——	16	15	3	22–27	27–35
		B-48-36020A4	——	16	13	3	26–32	22–29
		B-48-36022A4	——	16	11	3	30–Plus	17–23
		B-48-36024A4	——	16	9	3	HB+ or WB+	1–18
160 165 rpm: 3900–4300	IC	B-48-36032A1	——	15½	27	2	Dual, Fast	55–61
		B-48-36028A1	——	14½	27	3	Dual, Fast	55–61
		B-48-36030A1	——	16	25	2	Dual, Fast	48–57
		B-48-36008A1	——	14½	25	3	Up to 17	48–57
		B-48-36010A1	——	14½	23	3	17–19	41–50
		B-48-49634A1	——	15	21	3	19–21	37–43
		B-48-36014A1	——	15½	19	3	20–25	33–39
		B-48-36016A1	——	15¾	17	3	23–27	27–35
		B-48-36018A1	——	16	15	3	26–Plus	22–29
		B-48-36020A1	——	16	13	3	30–Plus	16–24
		B-48-36022A1	——	16	11	3	Houseboat	10–18
		B-48-36024A1	——	16	9	3	Work Boat	1–11
190 225 310 rpm: 3700–4100	II 1.33:1	B-48-33238A1	B-48-33237A1	16¾	23	2	16–19	47–58
		●B-48-33880A1	●B-48-33879A1	16¾	21	3	——	——
		B-48-31680A1	B-48-31679A1	16¼	21	2	16–19	42–52
		●B-48-33882A1	●B-48-33881A1	16¾	19	3	——	——
		B-48-31678A1	B-48-31677A1	16¾	19	2	18–24	37–46
		●B-48-33884A1	●B-48-33883A1	16¾	17	3	——	——
		B-48-31676A1	B-48-31675A1	16¾	17	2	20–27	33–42
		B-48-31674A1	B-48-31673A1	15	17	3	20–27	31–40
		●B-48-33886A1	●B-48-33885A1	16¾	15	3	——	——
		B-48-31672A1	B-48-31671A1	16	15	3	24–33	26–37
		B-48-31670A1	B-48-31669A1	16¼	13	3	33 Plus	20–32
		B-48-31668A1	B-48-31667A1	16¾	11	3	35 Plus §	11–23
		B-48-35426A1	B-48-35425A1	16¾	9	3	Work Barges	

Propeller Recommendations (cont.)

Model (Engine hp)	Stern Drive	Aluminum Propellers Part Numbers		Dia (in.)	Pitch (in.)	No. of Blades	Approx Boat Length (ft)	Speed Range (mph)
		RH Rotation	LH Rotation					
Heavy-Duty rpm: 3700–4100	II 2:1	B-48-37780A1	——	20	29	3	N.A.	N.A.
		B-48-37778A1	B-48-37779A1	20	27	3	N.A.	N.A.
		B-48-37776A1	B-48-37777A1	20	25	3	N.A.	N.A.
		B-48-37774A1	B-48-37775A1	20	23	3	N.A.	N.A.
		B-48-37772A1	B-48-37773A1	20	21	3	N.A.	N.A.
		B-48-37770A1	B-48-37771A1	20	19	3	N.A.	N.A.
		B-48-37768A1	B-48-37769A1	20	17	3	N.A.	N.A.
		B-48-37766A1	B-48-37767A1	20	15	3	N.A.	N.A.
		B-48-37764A1	B-48-37765A1	20	13	3	N.A.	N.A.
200 rpm: 3700–4200	1.78:1	B-48-54352A1	B-48-54353A1	15½	31	3	Dual	50–58
		B-48-53496A1	B-48-53497A1	15½	29	3	Dual	47–55
		B-48-49978A1	B-48-49979A1	15¾	27	3	16–19	43–51
		B-48-49974A1	B-48-49973A1	16	25	3	16–19	39–47
		B-48-49972A1	B-48-49971A1	16⅜	23	3	17–21	35–42
		B-48-33880A1	B-48-33879A1	16¾	21	3	18–24	30–37
		B-48-33882A1	B-48-33881A1	16¾	19	3	23–28	25–32
		B-48-33884A1	B-48-33883A1	16¾	17	3	25–33	20–27
		B-48-33886A1	B-48-33885A1	16¾	15	3	Houseboat	15–22
215-H 215-E rpm: 3700–4200	2:1	B-48-57270A1	B-48-57271A1	18	29	3	17–19	42–49
		B-48-57268A1	B-48-57269A1	18¼	27	3	17–20	39–46
		B-48-57266A1	B-48-57267A1	18¾	25	3	18–21	36–43
		B-48-57264A1	B-48-57265A1	19¼	23	3	19–23	33–39
		B-48-57262A1	B-48-57263A1	19½	21	3	21–24	29–35
		B-48-54726A1	B-48-54725A1	19	19	3	22–26	24–31
		B-48-54724A1	B-48-54723A1	19¼	17	3	23–27	19–26
		B-48-54722A1	B-48-54721A1	19¾	15	3	24–29	14–21
		B-48-54720A1	B-48-54719A1	20	13	3	26–31	9–16
		B-48-54718A1	B-48-54717A1	20	11	3	WB+ or HB+	0–11
225 rpm: 3700–4200	1.78:1	B-48-54352A1	B-48-54353A1	15½	31	3	Dual	50–58
		B-48-53496A1	B-48-53497A1	15½	29	3	Dual, Fast	47–55
		B-48-49978A1	B-48-49979A1	15¾	27	3	16–20	43–51
		B-48-49974A1	B-48-49973A1	16	25	3	17–24	39–47
		B-48-49972A1	B-48-49971A1	16⅜	23	3	18–26	35–42
		B-48-33880A1	B-48-33879A1	16¾	21	3	23–28	30–37
		B-48-33882A1	B-48-33881A1	16¾	19	3	25–33	25–32
		B-48-33884A1	B-48-33883A1	16¾	17	3	Houseboat	20–27
		B-48-33886A1	B-48-33885A1	16¾	15	3	Houseboat	15–22
250 270 rpm: 3700–4200	III 2:1	B-48-47712A1	B-48-47711A1	18¾	29	3	18–20	42–49
		B-48-47710A1	B-48-47709A1	19	27	3	18–20	39–46
		B-48-47708A1	B-48-47707A1	19¼	25	3	18–21	36–43
		B-48-47706A1	B-48-47705A1	19¾	23	3	20–23	33–39
		B-48-47704A1	B-48-47703A1	20	21	3	22–25	29–35
		B-48-47702A1	B-48-47701A1	20	19	3	24–27	24–31
		B-48-47700A1	B-48-47699A1	20	17	3	24–30	19–26
		B-48-47698A1	B-48-47697A1	20	15	3	26–32	14–21
		B-48-47696A1	B-48-47695A1	20	13	3	28–34	9–16
		B-48-47694A1	B-48-47693A1	20	11	3	WB+ or HB+ and over 36	1–11
325	III 1.5:1	B-48-47708A1	B-48-47707A1	19¼	25	3	18–22	50–58
		B-48-47706A1	B-48-47705A1	19¾	23	3	21–24	46–53
		B-48-47704A1	B-48-47703A1	20	21	3	23–26	40–45
		B-48-47702A1	B-48-47701A1	20	19	3	25–28	35–42
		B-48-47700A1	B-48-47699A1	20	17	3	27–30	29–37

Propeller Recommendations (cont.)

Model (Engine hp)	Stern Drive	Aluminum Propellers Part Numbers		Dia (in.)	Pitch (in.)	No. of Blades	Approx Boat Length (ft)	Speed Range (mph)
		RH Rotation	LH Rotation					
		B-48-47698A1	B-48-47697A1	20	15	3	28–32	23–31
		B-48-47696A1	B-48-47695A1	20	13	3	30–34	18–25
		B-48-47694A1	B-48-47693A1	20	11	3	32–36	14–20
rpm: 3700–4200		B-48-47692A1	B-48-47691A1	20	9	3	WB+ or HB+ and over 36	1–16
		B-48-47712A1	B-48-47711A1	18¾	29	3	18–22	42–49
		B-48-47710A1	B-48-47709A1	19	27	3	18–22	39–46
		B-48-47708A1	B-48-47707A1	19¼	25	3	21–24	36–43
		B-48-47706A1	B-48-47705A1	19¾	23	3	23–26	33–39
325	III 2:1	B-48-47704A1	B-48-47703A1	20	21	3	25–28	29–35
		B-48-47702A1	B-48-47701A1	20	19	3	27–30	24–31
		B-48-47700A1	B-48-47699A1	20	17	3	28–32	19–26
		B-48-47698A1	B-48-47697A1	20	15	3	30–34	14–21
rpm:		B-48-47696A1	B-48-47695A1	20	13	3	32–36	9–16
3700–4200		B-48-47694A1	B-48-47693A1	20	11	3	WB+ or HB+ and over 36	1–11
		B-48-47712A1	B-48-47711A1	18¾	29	3	20–24	42–49
		B-48-47710A1	B-48-47709A1	19	27	3	20–24	39–46
		B-48-47708A1	B-48-47707A1	19¼	25	3	22–26	36–43
		B-48-47706A1	B-48-47705A1	19¾	23	3	24–29	33–39
390	III 2:1	B-48-47704A1	B-48-47703A1	20	21	3	26–31	29–35
		B-48-47702A1	B-48-47701A1	20	19	3	28–33	24–31
		B-48-47700A1	B-48-47699A1	20	17	3	32–36	19–26
		B-48-47698A1	B-48-47697A1	20	15	3	34–38	14–21
rpm:		B-48-47696A1	B-48-47695A1	20	13	3	36–40	9–16
3700–4200		B-48-47694A1	B-48-47693A1	20	11	3	WB+ or HB+ and over 40	0–11

N.A.—Not Available.
§—Dual motor installation or single installation on fast boats.
●—310 model only (others for 190 and 225 only).
WB+ —Work boat
HB+ —Houseboat
*—Bronze material

Periodic Maintenance and Lubrication

LUBRICATION
Fuel and Oil Recommendations
FUELS

All Mercruiser inboard/outdrive engines are capable of running on regular automotive gasoline, with the exception of the 390 hp, 482 cu in. V8. This engine is designed to run on premium fuel.

OIL RECOMMENDATIONS

Crankcase oil should be selected to give the best performance under the climatic and operating conditions prevalent in the area where the engine is operated. When the crankcase is drained, oil should be selected on the basis of the lowest temperature anticipated during the operating period, rather than on the temperature at the time of oil change.

Kiekhaefer Mercury recommends 4-CYCLE MARINE MOTOR OIL FORMULA 4R, for all of its four-cycle engines. If this is not available, use a good grade of oil of the correct viscosity which is classified "SE" (previously classified "MS").

The following chart shows the recommended viscosity for various temperature ranges and the intervals of oil change.

If the lowest anticipated temperature, during the interval in which the oil will remain in the crankcase, is	. . . the following Viscosity Oils are recommended.	When to Change Crankcase Oil Classification "SE"		
		Prevailing Daytime Temperature	Initial Oil Change Interval	Regular Oil Change Interval
90°F (32°C)	SAE 40 *	Above 90°F (32°C)	1st 60 days or 20 hours of operation, whichever occurs 1st.	Every 100 hrs of operation and at end of boating season.
32°F (0°C)	SAE 30 *	Above 32°F (0°C)	1st 60 days or 20 hours of operation, whichever occurs 1st.	Every 100 hrs of operation and at end of boating season.
0°F (−18°C)	SAE 20W *	Below 32°F (0°C) or during adverse operating conditions	First 30 days or 20 hours of operation, whichever occurs 1st.	Every 100 hrs of operation and at end of boating season.

ENGINE OIL CHANGE

1. Operate the engine until normal temperature is indicated. The crankcase should not be drained when cold or else suspended foreign material will cling to the sides of the oil pan.

2. Remove the dipstick and pump the oil out of the crankcase. An oil drain pump (part no. C-91-34429) is available from any Mercury dealer for this purpose, or an attachment for an ordinary hand drill can be purchased from an automotive parts store. The oil can be successfully pumped out of the crankcase via the dipstick tube.

Because of the effect of engine installation angle on oil level, the following steps should be followed when filling the crankcase.

NOTE: *A 1 pt can of Quicksilver 4-Cycle Engine Oil Supplement should be used with the initial oil fill. This is an additive which is required during the break-in period.*

3. Pour oil into the engine through the oil filler in the rocker arm cover until the oil level reaches the "full" mark on the dipstick.

4. Start the engine and run it at idle speed for five minutes.

5. Stop the engine and wait five minutes before checking the oil level.

6. Add enough oil to bring the level up to the "full" mark on the dipstick.

Oil Capacity Chart

Engine HP	Crankcase Capacity (qts) w/filter
120	4
140 (181 cu in.)	4
140 (191 cu in.)	5
160	5
165	5
215	7
225	①
250	7
270	7
325	8 (approx)
390	8 (approx)

①—Serial number 2278646 and below—5 qt
  Serial number 2278647 and above—7 qt

MAINTAINING OIL LEVEL

A proper oil level is an important factor in controlling oil consumption. An overly full crankcase allows oil to be splashed onto the cylinder walls by the reciprocating parts at a faster rate than the rings can control. The excess oil will be drawn into the combustion chamber and burned. A condition such as this should be investigated before assuming that the rings are bad.

Every internal combustion engine should use a certain amount of oil to act as a lubricant and cooling agent during break-in. The initial rate of consumption will decrease until it becomes stabilized after about 100 hours of operation.

When checking oil level, the following conditions must exist:

1. Engine must be warm;
2. Boat must be at rest in the water;
3. Dipstick must be pushed down to the stop; and,
4. Five minutes must be allowed for the oil to drain back into the pan.

If these steps are not followed, a false reading may result.

Additional oil may be added if the dipstick markings are not clear. The space between the "full" and "add" marks represents one quart. Add oil if the level is at or below the "add" mark.

OIL FILTER CHANGES

A full-flow oil filter filters all of the oil delivered by the oil pump. The interval of filter change is, consequently, very important. The filter should be changed after the first 20 hours of operation and every 100 hours of operation thereafter, and also at the end of each boating season. This corresponds to the frequency of engine oil change. Perform the following steps to change the oil filter.

1. Drain the oil from the crankcase.
2. Remove the filter from the cylinder block.
3. Coat the sealing ring on the new filter with engine oil and thread the filter onto the block.

NOTE: *The filter should be tightened securely, but only by hand.*

4. Fill the crankcase with the specified amount of oil. Be certain that the oil is of the correct viscosity.
5. Run the engine and carefully check for leaks.

Stern Drive Lubrication

CHECKING UPPER GEAR CHAMBER LUBRICANT LEVEL

CAUTION: *Do not check the lubricant level when the unit is hot from opera-*

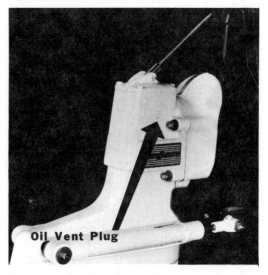
Upper gear chamber oil vent plug

tion. When adding or changing oil, use only Quicksilver Super-Duty Gear Lubricant. Do not use regular automotive grease.

MERCRUISER I

1. Remove the "oil fill" and "oil vent" plugs from the right and left sides of the upper driveshaft housing. The lubricant must be even with the edge of the threaded "oil vent" hole when the unit is level.
2. If the level is down, add Quicksilver Super-Duty Gear Lubricant.
3. Replace the "oil fill" and "oil vent" plugs and gaskets.

MerCruiser I oil fill plug in upper gear chamber

MerCruiser I oil vent plug in upper gear chamber

Oil fill plug—MerCruiser II

Sight glass on MerCruiser 215

MERCRUISER II

1. See Mercruiser I procedure above.

MERCRUISER 215

1. Check the oil level frequently and add oil if required. Check the oil level with the dipstick located on the inner transom plate.

2. If the oil level is below the mark on the dipstick, add oil. Use only Quicksilver Super-Duty Gear Lubricant.

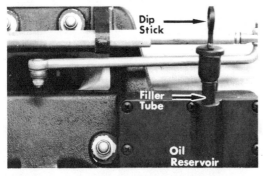

MerCruiser 215 outdrive oil level checking

MERCRUISER III

1. The oil level of the stern drive unit should be checked frequently; oil should be added if necessary.

2. Check the oil level in the sight glass located on the inner transom plate. If the oil level is not visible in the glass, remove the oil fill plug and add oil to bring the level to the line on the sight glass. Use only Quicksilver Super-Duty Gear Lubricant.

Draining and Filling the Drive Unit

MERCRUISER I (UPPER GEAR HOUSING)

The following procedure must be used to refill the gear housing when it has been completely drained.

Upper gear chamber oil fill plug—MerCruiser I

Upper gear chamber oil vent plug—MerCruiser I

1. Remove the "air vent" plug located on the left side of the gear housing, above the cavitation plate. Remove the "oil vent" plug, located on the right side of the drive-shaft housing and the filler plug located on the lower left side of the gear housing. Do not lose the washers.

2. Insert the lubricant tube into the filler plug hole and inject lubricant until excess fluid starts to run out of the "air vent" hole.

3. Replace the "air vent" plug and washer.

4. Continue filling through the gear housing filler plug until excess fluid begins to flow from the "oil vent" hole.

5. Replace the "oil vent" and gear housing filler plugs and washers.

MERCRUISER I (LOWER GEAR HOUSING)

The lower gear housing will automatically maintain a proper oil level if the upper gear chamber oil level is as specified. The two chambers are interconnected.

MERCRUISER II

NOTE: *The driveshaft housing gear chamber and lower unit gear chamber are connected.*

1. Drain the stern drive unit by removing the drain plug from the lower end of the gear housing on the left side. Remove the filler and vent plugs on the upper gear chamber.

2. Insert the lubricant tube into the drain plug hole in the lower unit and inject lubricant until excess lubricant begins to flow from the air vent or fill plug in the upper driveshaft housing.

3. Replace the air vent and filler and drain plugs with respective washers.

MERCRUISER 215 AND III

NOTE: *When draining and filling the stern drive, the unit must be installed in the bell housing.*

1. Remove the oil filler and vent plugs, and allow the oil to drain completely.

2. After draining the unit, reinstall the vent plug. The unit must be filled with a hand type lubricant pump through the filler hole.

3. The unit should be filled until the lu-

Oil fill and vent plug—MerCruiser III and 215

bricant level meets the sight line on the glass or the dipstick which is located on the inner transom plate reservoir.

4. After filling, thread the plug (with gasket) onto the gear housing and tighten securely.

Stern Drive Lubricant Capacities

Model	Capacity
MerCruiser "I" Driveshaft Housing ...	8 Fl Oz
MerCruiser "I" Gear Housing	18 Fl Oz
MerCruiser "IA-IB-IC" Driveshaft Housing	8 Fl Oz
MerCruiser "IA-IB-IC" Gear Housing .	23 Fl Oz
MerCruiser "120"–"140"–"160"–"165" .	28 Fl Oz
MerCruiser "II"–"200"–"225"	5¾ Qt *
MerCruiser "II" with Heavy-Duty Gear Housing	7 Qt *
MerCruiser "III"–"250"–"270"–"325"– "390"	4½ Qt +*
MerCruiser "215H" and "215E"	4 Qt *

* Approximately   + 4½ qt plus one qt in reservoir
NOTE: *After filling a stern drive unit, that had been drained of all lubricant, the lubricant level must be rechecked after a "run-in" period of about one minute. This procedure assures that any air pockets, which may have developed during filling, will be eliminated. Additional lubricant may have to be added after rechecking to "top-off" the unit.*

Component Lubrication

MERCRUISER I

1. Every 50 hours, or at least once a season, lubricate the following stern drive components:

 a. Ride-Guide steering cable end next to the hand nut

 b. Pivot socket of the steering arm

 c. The exposed shaft of the cable coming from the cable tube

 d. Gimbal housing upper and lower pivot pin

 e. Tilt pins on both sides of the gimbal ring.

NOTE: *On early models, the tapered end of the lubricant gun fits the counterbore. No grease fitting is used; however, if difficulty is encountered in forcing grease into the tilt pin, install fitting B-22-37668 in the tilt pin. The fitting must be removed after lubrication.*

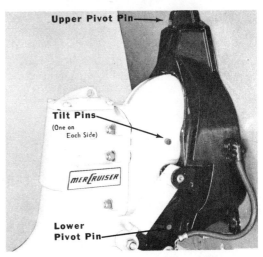

Late model lubrication points

 a. The Ride-Guide steering cable end next to the hand nut

 b. The inner transom mounting plate at the left side base of the crank unit and the top right side of the crank ring gear

 c. The gimbal housing upper and lower pivot pin

 d. The tilt pins on both sides of the gimbal housing

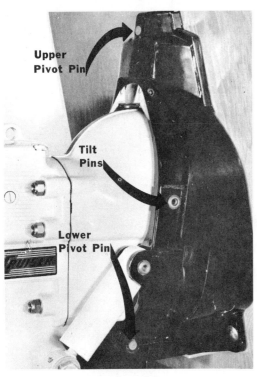

Lubrication points—early models

MERCRUISER II

Every 50 hours, or at least once a season, lubricate the following points with Quicksilver New Multipurpose lubricant.

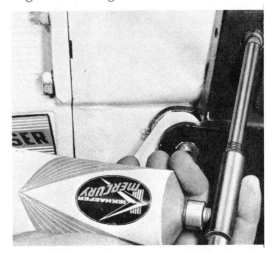

Tilt pin lubrication

MERCRUISER 215 AND III

1. Lubricate the drive unit upper and lower pivot pin with Quicksilver Anti-Corrosion Grease.

MANUAL STEERING

2. Lubricate the steering cable through the grease fitting.

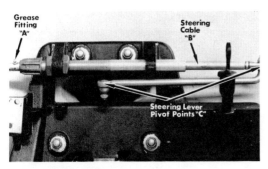

Steering cable lubrication

3. Apply a light coat of grease to the exposed portion of the steering cable and to the steering lever pivot points. Do not over-lubricate the cable.

POWER STEERING

4. Lubricate the steering cable through the grease fitting.

5. Apply a light coat of grease to the exposed portion of the power steering cable, to the steering lever pivot points and to the extension rod. Do not overlubricate.
   NOTE: *If a dual tie-bar is installed, lubricate its pivot points.*

ALTERNATOR

Under normal operating conditions, the alternator will not require lubrication.

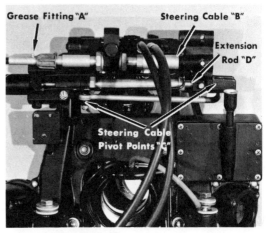

Power steering lubrication

STARTER

The starter motor end frames are equipped with oil-less bearings which do not require lubrication.

DISTRIBUTOR

The distributor cap should be removed every 100 hours. Apply a small amount (about the size of a match head) of high-melting-point, non-bleeding grease to the distributor cam surface. Add a drop of light engine oil to the breaker arm pivot point.

Periodic Maintenance and Lubrication

	After 1st 20 Hrs of Operation	Every 50 Hours of Operation	Every 100 Hours of Operation	Once Each Year
Starter motor and alternator		None Required		
Change engine oil	①		①	
Replace oil filter	●		●	
Clean oil filler cap			●	
Clean flame arrestor	●		●	
Change fuel filters				●
Change auxiliary fuel filter element				●
Check fuel system lines and connections for leaks	●	●		
Check battery electrolyte level	●	●		

Periodic Maintenance and Lubrication (cont.)

	After 1st 20 Hrs of Operation	Every 50 Hours of Operation	Every 100 Hours of Operation	Once Each Year
Check all electrical connections	●			●
Check water pump and alternator belts for tension	●	●		
Check cooling system hoses and connections for leaks	●		●	
Check power steering fluid level		③		
Check for loose, damaged or missing parts		●		●
Lubricate throttle and shift linkage pivot points				①
Lubricate breaker lever pivot *				①
Lubricate distributor cam *				②
Inspect breaker points *			●	
Check condition of spark plugs *				●
Tighten engine mount, drive, and trim cylinder fasteners	●		●	
Check engine alignment	●			●
Check transmission fluid level	③	③		
Clean transmission oil strainer screen				●
Check condition of oil cooler electrodes +		Every 6 Months		
Change transmission fluid				③
Check power tilt pump fluid level	§		§	
Check power trim pump oil level	①		①	
Check stern drive oil level	④	④		
Check hydraulic shift unit fluid level	⑤	⑤		
Lubricate drive unit upper and lower swivel pins and hinge pins +	②		②	
Lubricate steering cable and steering lever housing +	⑥		⑥	
Change stern drive unit oil				④
Check condition of trim tab and anodic plate +		Every 30 Days		

Periodic Maintenance and Lubrication (cont.)

	After 1st 20 Hrs of Operation	Every 50 Hours of Operation	Every 100 Hours of Operation	Once Each Year
Inspect propeller for possible damage			●	●
Lubricate propeller shaft splines +				②
Inspect bellows +		●		●
Inspect and clean exterior +				●
Lubricate U-joint coupling splines and check cross bearings		●		●

①—Use Formula 4 Quicksilver Oil (C-92-33157).
②—Use Quicksilver Anti-Corrosion Grease (C-92-45134).
③—Use Automatic Transmission Fluid (Type "A", Suffix "A").
④—Use Quicksilver SUPER-DUTY Lubricant (C-92-52650).
⑤—Use Non-Mineral Hydraulic Fluid SAE 70R1 or 70R3 (Brake Fluid).
⑥—Use New Multipurpose Lubricant (C-92-49588).
*—Does not apply to "Thunderbolt Ignition."
+—If unit is operated in salt water, require more frequent attention.
§—Refer to "3", above, for white high pressure pump; to "1" for black large reservoir pump; or use SAE 20W M.S. motor oil in white low pressure pump with booster valve.
NOTE: *Complete list of maintenance is not applicable to all models. The chart, above, is based on average operating conditions in utility service. Under severe operating conditions, continuous heavy duty or high speed operation, the inspection and maintenance intervals should be shortened.*

Where To Use Anti-Corrosion Grease		Where To Use Anti-Corrosion Oil	
Gear Housing Cover and Water Pump Cover Retainer Threads	X	Throttle Control Shaft Flexible Bushing OD to Steering	X
Water Pump Cartridge Between Insert and Housing	X	Throttle, Choke and Shift Linkage and Swivels	X
Propeller Shaft Splines, Nut, etc.	X	Reverse Lock Cam Surfaces	X
Shift Shaft Splines	X	Head Bolt Threads	X
Shift Shaft Coupler Splines	X	Manifold Screw Threads	X
Engine Water Pump Seal	X	Reverse Lock Pivot Shaft	X
Hinge Pins	X	Exterior Nut, Bolt, and Screw Threads	X
Swivel Pins	X	Reverse Lock Mechanism	X
Anchor Pins and Bushings	X		

Tilt Pin Adjustment

MERCRUISER I AND II

The gimbal ring is provided with holes to permit adjustment of the tilt lockpin for proper adjustment of tilt angle. The angle of the stern drive unit should be set so that the cavitation plate is about parallel with the bottom of the boat. The speed of a boat with the center of gravity located forward will sometimes be improved by tilting the unit out one pin hole. If the unit is tilted in this will allow more wetted surface and reduce speed, but will generally improve operation in rough water.

MERCRUISER 215 AND III

CAUTION: *Operation of the stern drive in extreme "in" or "out" position will increase steering torque. The stern drive unit should be trimmed to a safe operating angle to provide easy steering.*

1. The power trim is actuated by a button in the control lever (215) or in the trim control panel (III), and should be operated in neutral or Forward gear only.
2. To trim out: press the "up" button (215) or the "up/out" button (III).
3. To trim in: press the "in" button until the drive unit moves to proper trim.

TRIM TAB ADJUSTMENT

MerCruiser stern drives are equipped with an adjustable trim tab to balance steering torque, so that the steering will operate with equal ease to the left and right.

1. Operate the boat at the best throttle setting, and trim the boat as outlined in the preceding section.
2. Turn the steering wheel in both directions and note in which direction the boat turns more easily.
3. With the boat at rest, remove the plug from the driveshaft housing and loosen the allen head screw.
4. If the wheel turns more easily to the left, position the trailing edge of the trim tab to the left.
5. If the boat turns more easily to the right, position the trailing edge of the trim tab to the right.
6. Tighten the allen screw securely and reinstall the plug.
7. Operate the boat to check the setting and readjust the trim tab if necessary.

Tune-Up

To assure lasting results, it is advisable to follow a definite procedure of analysis and correction of all items which affect power, performance, and economy. The extent of a tune-up depends on the interval since the last engine service, although specific items should be serviced at regular intervals. When corrective action is necessary, refer to the appropriate sections of this book for detailed service information.

COMPRESSION TEST

1. Remove and inspect each spark plug for broken porcelain or badly worn electrodes. Also see the "Spark Plug Diagnosis Chart" for further information concerning spark plugs. All plugs should be of the same make and heat range listed in the specifications.
2. Remove the flame arrestor and block the choke in the wide open position.
3. Insert the compression gauge in the spark plug port and crank the engine through at least four compression strokes to obtain the highest possible reading.

Checking compression

4. Check and record the compression of each cylinder. Variation should not be more than 20 percent between the highest and lowest cylinders.
5. If one or more cylinders read low or uneven, inject a tablespoon of oil into the cylinders, crank the engine several times, and recheck the compression.

   a. If compression increases but does not reach normal, the rings are worn.

b. If compression does not improve, the valves are sticking or seating poorly.

c. If two adjacent cylinders indicate low compression, and injecting oil does not improve compression, suspect a head gasket leak between cylinders.

SPARK PLUGS

1. Perform step 1 of the preceding procedure.

2. For conventional plugs, perform the following steps.

a. If the plugs are in good condition, file the center electrode flat and adjust the gap to specifications.

b. Wipe the plug seats in the head clean, install new gaskets on used plugs, and install the plugs. Tighten them to the specified torque.

Checking spark plug gap—side electrode type

3. For surface gap spark plugs, perform the following steps.

a. Check the condition of the external insulator. If cracked, replace the plug.

Checking spark plug electrode depth—surface gap type

b. Check the depth of the center electrode as illustrated. If worn more than $\frac{1}{32}$ in. replace the plug with a new one.

c. Cracks around the internal insulator will not harm the plug and it may be used.

d. Clean the plug seats in the head, install new gaskets, and torque the plugs to the specified torque.

IGNITION SYSTEM

1. Check the spark plug leads for cracks and abrasions. Replace all leads that are not serviceable. Remove the distributor cap and inspect for cracks or carbon tracks. Replace the cap if damage is found.

2. Check the distributor centrifugal advance mechanism by turning the rotor clockwise by hand. Release the rotor and be sure that the rotor returns easily to the retarded position. If it does not return readily, disassemble the distributor to find the cause.

3. Clean the rotor and inspect for cracks or a badly worn electrode. Replace the rotor if damage is found.

Breaker Points and Condenser

NOTE: *The following does not pertain to the Thunderbolt (breakerless) ignition.*

1. Remove the distributor cap and rotor.

2. Remove the breaker points and condenser.

3. Examine the points and clean or replace as necessary.

4. Always replace the condenser when the points are replaced.

5. Dirty contacts should be cleaned with an ignition point file. Do not use emery cloth or sandpaper, since particles embedded in the points will cause arcing.

NOTE: *Where burned or badly pitted points are found, the cause should be determined and corrected before installing new points. Otherwise, new points will offer no better service than the old ones.*

6. Clean the distributor and breaker plate.

7. Install the points and condenser in position and tighten the screws securing them.

8. Tighten all connections.

9. Lubricate the distributor cam with a thin film of high-melting-point, non-bleeding grease, or replace the lubricating wick.

Breaker Point Alignment

1. Check the alignment of the distributor points with the points closed. Align new points where necessary, but do not attempt to align old points. Replace used points where serious misalignment is observed.

2. Align the points by bending the fixed contacts. Do not bend the breaker arm.

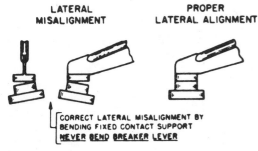

LATERAL MISALIGNMENT

PROPER LATERAL ALIGNMENT

CORRECT LATERAL MISALIGNMENT BY BENDING FIXED CONTACT SUPPORT
NEVER BEND BREAKER LEVER

Alignment of breaker points

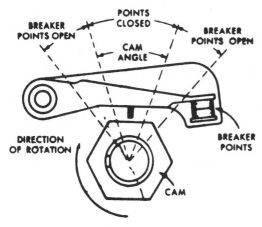

BREAKER POINTS OPEN
POINTS CLOSED
BREAKER POINTS OPEN
CAM ANGLE
DIRECTION OF ROTATION
BREAKER POINTS
CAM

Schematic diagram of breaker cam angle

Dwell Adjustment

MerCruiser 120, 140, 160, 165, and 200

1. Remove the distributor cap.
2. Remove the rotor and connect a dwell meter.
3. Slightly loosen the points lockscrew.
4. Crank the engine and adjust the dwell with a screwdriver, according to the listed specifications.
5. Install the rotor and cap and recheck the dwell with the engine running.

MerCruiser 215

1. If necessary, align the points by bending the stationary bracket.

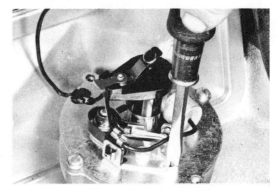

Breaker point adjustment on 4 and 6 cylinder models

2. Rotate the distributor until the rubbing block rests on the peak of the cam lobe, which will provide maximum breaker point opening.
3. Using a feeler gauge of specified thickness, adjust the points to the correct gap by loosening the lockscrew.
4. Tighten the lockscrew and check the adjustment with a dwell meter.

MerCruiser 225

1. Run the engine at idle and raise the window in the distributor cap.
2. Connect a dwell meter to the distributor.
3. Insert an allen wrench of the proper size into the head of the adjusting screw.
4. Turn the adjusting screw until the specified dwell is obtained.

NOTE: *In an emergency, when a dwell meter is not available, turn the adjusting screw in until the engine begins to miss,*

Setting dwell angle—MerCruiser 225

then turn the screw ½ turn in the opposite direction. As soon as possible thereafter, check the dwell and set it with a dwell meter.

IGNITION TIMING

All Engines

NOTE: *The timing marks are shown in the accompanying illustrations.*

1. Connect a timing light to no. 1 spark plug. Connect the power supply leads from the light to an appropriate power source.
2. Connect a tachometer to the engine.
3. Start the engine and run it at 500 rpm.
4. Shine the light at the timing tab.
5. Adjust the timing by loosening the distributor hold-down clamp and rotating the distributor as required until the timing mark on the balancer or pulley aligns with the mark on the tab which corresponds to the specifications.
6. Stop the engine and remove the timing light and tachometer.

MerCruiser 110 timing marks (early)

Timing marks on 4 and 6 cylinder models (late)

CARBURETOR IDLE SPEED ADJUSTMENT—ALL MODELS

The following carburetor adjustment(s) should be performed:

V8 engine timing marks (GM engines)

MerCruiser 215 engine timing marks

1. Clean or replace the carburetor intake fuel filter.
2. Be sure that the flame arrestor is installed.
3. Start the engine and allow it to reach normal operating temperature. Be sure that the choke is fully open.
4. Disconnect the throttle cable from the engine.
5. Adjust the idle speed screw to obtain the idle speed specified.
6. Adjust the idle mixture screw(s) until peak rpm is indicated on a tachometer.

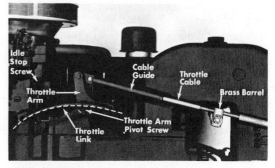

MerCruiser 120 idle adjustment

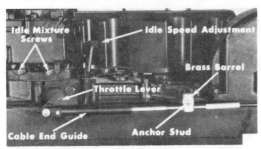

MerCruiser 140–200 idle adjustment

MerCruiser 225 (w/4GC carburetor) idle adjustment

MerCruiser 225, 250, 325 idle adjustment

NOTE: *Do not turn the idle mixture screw(s) tightly against the stop or else the needle and seat will be damaged.*

7. Shift the unit into forward gear.

8. Readjust the idle speed screw(s) to obtain the specified rpm.

9. Stop the engine and shift the unit into Neutral.

10. Connect the throttle cable. (See the "Throttle Cable Adjustment" which follows.)

THROTTLE CABLE ADJUSTMENT

1. Place the unit in neutral at idle.

2. Fasten the cable to the throttle lever.

3. Fully contract the throttle cable by grasping it behind the brass barrel and pushing it toward the throttle lever.

4. Adjust the brass barrel to align with the anchor stud.

NOTE: *On the MerCruiser 120 only, position the throttle arm so that the centerline of the link rod is over the center of the throttle arm pivot screw head prior to adjusting the brass barrel.*

5. Fasten the brass barrel on the stud.

6. Check to make sure that the primary throttle valves are fully open when the control handle is fully forward.

7. Return the throttle handle to neutral and check to be sure that the carburetor throttle lever is against the idle stopscrew.

AUTOMATIC CHOKE ADJUSTMENTS

MerCruiser 120, 140, 160, 165, 888, 215 (with Holley 4160), and 225 (with Rochester 4GC)

1. Remove the flame arrestor.

2. Check the choke valve for binding or sticking.

3. Loosen the three retaining screws.

4. Rotate the choke cover against coil tension until the index mark is aligned as follows:

MerCruiser 120, 140, 160, 165, 888, and 215: align the choke plate mark with the index mark on the housing.

MerCruiser 225: Set the choke plate mark three notches lean of the index point on the housing.

NOTE: *Rotate clockwise for lean.*

5. Before operation, the choke should be lightly closed at room temperature.

6. At normal operating temperature, the choke should move to full open.

7. After adjustment, tighten the retaining screws and replace the flame arrestor.

MerCruiser 200, 225, and 250 (with Quadrajet)

NOTE: *No adjustment is required on the MerCruiser 200 or on carburetors with electric chokes.*

1. Remove the flame arrestor.

2. Disconnect the choke coil rod from the lever.

3. Hold the choke valve in the carburetor shut and position the choke rod at the bottom of the choke lever hole.

4. Push the choke coil rod down to the bottom of its travel.

5. The top of the choke coil rod should now be even with the bottom of the hole in the choke lever.

6. Bend the choke coil rod until the position described in step 5 is reached.

7. Connect the choke coil rod and replace the flame arrestor.

MerCruiser 325

1. Remove the flame arrestor.

2. Disconnect the choke coil rod from the choke lever.

3. Hold the carburetor choke valve shut and position the choke coil rod at the top of the choke lever hole.

4. Pull the choke coil rod up to the end of its travel.

5. The top of the hole should be even with the bottom of the rod.

6. Bend the rod until the position described in step 5 is reached.

7. Connect the choke coil rod and reinstall the flame arrestor.

BATTERY AND BATTERY CABLES

1. Inspect the battery and cables for wear, cracking, or signs of corrosion.

2. Fill the cells to the proper level with distilled water.

3. When cleaning the battery, wash it first with a dilute ammonia or soda solution to neutralize the acid, then flush with clean water.

4. Clean the battery posts and cable connectors with a small inexpensive tool designed for this purpose. Apply a thin coating of petroleum jelly to the terminals and reinstall the cables.

5. If the battery has remained undercharged, check for a loose alternator drive belt, faulty alternator, or voltage regulator.

6. If the battery is using too much water, the voltage regulator may be too high.

ALTERNATOR—NON-INTEGRAL TYPE

1. Inspect the alternator slip rings and brushes for wear or dirt. Brushes should be replaced if worn down to less than half their original length.

2. Replace frayed or broken alternator wires and tighten all connections.

3. Adjust the alternator belt tension to ½ in. deflection at the middle of its longest span.

ALTERNATOR—INTEGRAL TYPE

1. Inspect terminals for corrosion and loose connections.

2. Check all wiring for frayed or loose insulation.

3. Check mounting bolts for tightness.

4. Adjust the alternator belt tension to ½ in. deflection at the middle of its longest span.

Cooling System

Inspect the cooling system for leaks, weak hoses, or loose clamps. Service as required.

ENGINE LUBRICATION

1. Check the crankcase oil level.

2. Fill as required.

3. Inspect the engine for oil (or fuel) leaks.

4. Replace the filter after the first 20 hours of operation and every 100 hours thereafter and at the end of each boating season.

STERN DRIVE LUBRICATION

1. Check the lubricant level in the stern drive and fill as required.

2. Lubricate the steering linkage, pivot pins, tilt pins, and lower pivot pins. Refer to the "Lubrication" section of this chapter.

VALVE ADJUSTMENT

All MerCruiser engines covered in this book use hydraulic type lifters. NO ADJUSTMENT SHOULD BE ATTEMPTED, EXCEPT BY AN AUTHORIZED DEALER.

CRANKCASE VENTILATION

1. Remove the hose(s) between the rocker arm covers and the carburetors.

2. Clean the hoses and fittings and reinstall them.

Engine Electrical

WARNING: *When testing or servicing the electrical or ignition system, the following precautions should be observed.*

1. Do not touch or disconnect any ignition system component while the engine is running, the key switch is on, or the battery cables are connected.

2. Do not reverse battery cable connections at the battery.

3. Do not spark the battery cables at the battery to check polarity.

4. Do not disconnect battery cables while the engine is running.

5. Use only test equipment as specified. Follow service procedures in the order listed.

Ignition Troubleshooting Chart

Symptom	Probable Cause
Starter turns engine but hard to start or won't start.	A. Faulty coil or condenser. B. Moisture on ignition wires or distributor cap. C. Fouled spark plugs or improper plug gap. D. Improper ignition timing. E. Ignition points improperly gapped, burned or dirty. F. Cracked distributor cap or rotor. G. Poor connections or damaged ignition wiring.
Poor idling.	A. Loose distributor base plate bearing. B. Corroded wire ends or distributor towers. C. Incorrect distributor point gap. D. Fouled spark plugs or improper plug gap. E. Incorrect ignition timing. F. Overheated spark plugs.
Engine misses while idling.	A. Dirty or incorrectly gapped spark plugs; cracked porcelain. B. Broken or loose ignition wires. C. Burned or pitted contact points. D. Faulty coil or condenser. E. Weak battery. F. Distributor cap or rotor cracked or burned. G. Incorrect distributor advance or point dwell. H. Moisture on ignition wires, distributor cap or spark plugs. I. Excessive play in distributor shaft.

Ignition Troubleshooting Chart

Symptom	Probable Cause
Engine has loss of power.	A. Incorrect ignition timing. B. Defective coil or condenser. C. Distributor rotor burned or cracked. D. Excessive play in distributor shaft. E. Worn distributor cam. F. Dirty or incorrectly gapped spark plugs.
Engine misses on acceleration.	A. Distributor contact points dirty or improperly gapped. B. Coil or condenser defective. C. Spark plugs dirty or gap too great. D. Incorrect ignition timing.
Engine misses at high speed.	A. Defective coil or condenser. B. Incorrect ignition timing. C. Distributor contact points dirty or incorrectly gapped. D. Distributor rotor burned or cracked. E. Excessive play in distributor shaft. F. Spark plugs dirty or gap set too wide. G. Distributor shaft cam worn. H. Faulty ignition wiring.
Engine backfires.	A. Spark plug cables improperly installed. B. Improper distributor timing.
Engine knocks or pings (most noticeable on quick acceleration or at full throttle).	A. Incorrect spark plugs. B. Ignition timing advanced too far.
Excessive fuel consumption.	A. Incorrect ignition timing. B. Faulty distributor advance. C. Fouled spark plugs.
Poor acceleration.	A. Faulty coil. B. Loose distributor base plate bearing. C. Distributor not advancing properly. D. Incorrect ignition timing. E. Incorrect spark plug gap.

Ignition Troubleshooting Chart (cont.)

Symptom	Probable Cause
Poor acceleration.	F. Fouled spark plugs. G. Overheated spark plugs.
Fouled spark plugs.	A. Improper plug gap adjustment.
Burned spark plugs.	A. Improper plug heat range. B. Improper ignition timing.

Autolite starter mounting bolts

STARTER (DELCO-REMY)

Removal

1. Disconnect the yellow wire from the solenoid (S) terminal and the red wires from the solenoid battery terminals. On V8 engines, also remove the lead from the R terminal.
2. Remove the two starter mounting bolts and flat washer.
3. Remove the cap screw from the top front of the starter motor.
4. Pull the starter forward and remove it. Do not lose the special plate between the starter and mounting pad.

Installation

1. Place the starter motor and solenoid assembly in position and install the two mounting bolts and the flat washer.
2. Install the cap screw which holds the starter motor to the mounting bracket.
3. Connect the yellow lead to the solenoid (S) terminal and the red wires to the solenoid battery terminal. On V8 engines, connect the pink lead to the R terminal.
4. Coat all connections with Liquid Neoprene to inhibit corrosion.

STARTER (AUTOLITE)

Removal

1. Disconnect the red starter cable at the starter terminal.
2. Remove the starter mounting bolts.
3. Pull the starter forward and remove it from the engine.

STARTER DRIVE REPLACEMENT

1. Loosen and remove the brush cover band and the starter drive plunger lever.
2. Loosen the thru-bolts and remove the drive end housing and return spring for the starter drive plunger lever.
3. If the drive end housing and needle bearings are not being replaced, insert a dummy shaft to retain the needles.
4. Remove the pivot pin (which retains the starter drive plunger lever) and remove the lever.
5. Remove the drive gear stop-ring retainer and the stop-ring from the end of the armature shaft and remove the drive gear.
6. Lubricate the armature shaft splines and install a new drive gear.
7. Install a new stop-ring.
8. Place the starter gear plunger lever on the starter frame and install the pivot pin. Be sure that the plunger lever engages the starter drive.
9. Install a new stop-ring retainer. Position the starter drive plunger lever return spring and drive end housing on the starter frame and tighten the thru-bolts to 55–75 in. lbs.
10. Install the starter drive plunger lever cover and brush cover band with the gasket on the starter and install the retaining screw.

Installation

1. Place the starter assembly on the flywheel housing and snug the bolts so that the starter seats squarely.
2. Torque the mounting bolts to specifications.
3. Connect all wires as they were removed.

STARTER SOLENOID

Removal

ALL MODELS (EXCEPT AUTOLITE)

NOTE: *The Autolite positive engagement starter is integral with the starter.*

1. Remove the starter motor.

2. Remove the outer screw and washer from the engine connector strap terminal.

3. Remove the two screws retaining the solenoid housing to the starter drive housing.

4. Twist the solenoid clockwise to remove the flange key from the keyway slot in the housing and remove the solenoid assembly.

Installation

1. Place the solenoid in position in the starter motor and twist the solenoid counterclockwise to engage the key in the keyway.

2. Apply a thin coat of sealer to the flange and field frame slot.

3. Install the two solenoid retaining screws into the drive housing.

4. Install the starter motor and test the operation of the solenoid and starter.

ALTERNATOR

There are two basic types of alternator systems used on MerCruisers, with individual variations of each.

The first type is the Alternator Regulator system. Two types of standard alternators are used: a 32 ampere and a 42 ampere. The 42 amp alternator can be identified by no. 1100619-42A, which is stamped on the drive end frame and the 32 amp alternator by no. 1100721-32A, which is stamped on the drive end frame. The alternators are identical except for the rotors. A 32 amp alternator uses rotor no. B-38022, while the 42 amp alternator uses rotor no. B-33331. These two alternators use three different regulator circuits: (1) Relay regulator with indicator light; (2) relay regulator with ammeter; and (3) transistor regulator with ammeter. Regulators can be identified as follows.

1. Regulators used with indicator lights have no. 506 on the regulator base.

2. Regulators used with ammeter systems have no. 507 stamped on the regulator base.

3. Transistor regulator (B-37707) can be used only on MerCruiser engines with an ammeter in the instrument panel.

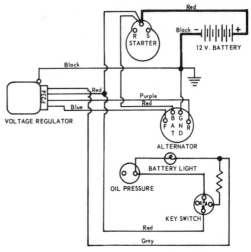

Relay voltage regulator with indication light schematic diagram

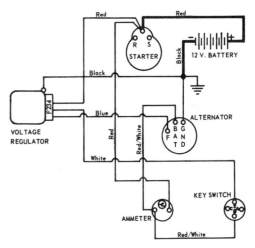

Relay voltage regulator and ammeter schematic diagram

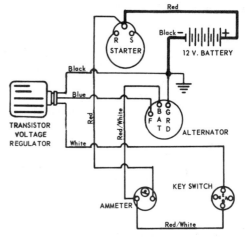

Transistor voltage regulator and ammeter schematic diagram

The second type is the integral charging type, which features an explosion-resistant frame at each end and a solid-state regulator mounted inside the slip-ring frame. All regulator components in this system are enclosed and there is no provision for adjustment.

ALTERNATOR PRECAUTIONS

1. When installing a battery, always be sure that the polarities are the same.

2. When connecting a booster battery, be sure to connect the negative terminals together and the positive terminals together.

3. When connecting a charger to the battery, connect the positive lead to the battery first, then the negative lead.

4. Never operate the alternator on an open circuit. Be sure that all connections in the circuit are tight.

5. Do not short or ground any of the terminals on the alternator or regulator.

6. Do not attempt to polarize the alternator.

Alternator Troubleshooting

1. If the light does not come on when the key is ON, before the engine is started, check the following:
   a. Burned-out bulb
   b. Defective socket
   c. Defective wiring
   d. Defective regulator

2. If the light stays on after the engine starts, check the following:
   a. Socket defects
   b. Defective wiring
   c. Diode failure
   d. Defective regulator
   e. Loose drive belt

3. Noise from the alternator can be caused by:
   a. Worn or dirty bearings
   b. Loose mounting bolts
   c. Loose drive pulley
   d. Defective diodes
   e. Defective stator
   f. Worn belt

Removal—All Types

CAUTION: *Disconnect the black ground cable from the negative battery terminal to prevent accidental shorting when the leads are removed from the alternator.*

1. Disconnect and tag the leads from the back of the alternator.

2. Remove the alternator mounting brace bolt and remove the belt from the pulley.

3. Remove the attaching hardware which holds the alternator to the support brackets and remove the alternator. Do not lose the spacer on the bolt.

Installation—All Types

NOTE: *This procedure can also be used for replacement alternator installation. When installing a replacement alternator, be sure that the unit is mounted so that the slip-ring end frame and brush holder are in the same position as in the replaced unit. This may require rotating the slip-ring end frame. To do this,*

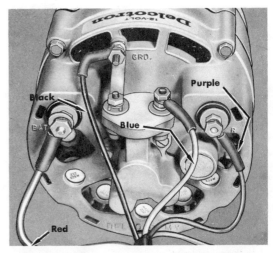

Alternator wiring connections indicator light in the system

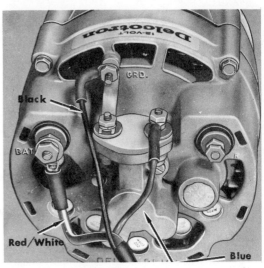

Alternator wiring connections—ammeter in the system

loosen the thru-bolts and rotate the slip-ring end frame either 90° or 180° in the appropriate direction.

1. Install the bolt, spacer, and nut which hold the alternator to the support bracket.

2. Swing the alternator toward the engine and install the drive belt.

3. Install the mounting brace bolt and washer, but do not tighten the belt.

4. Adjust the belt tension to ½ in. deflection at the middle of its longest span.

5. Connect the ends of the wiring harness to the alternator.

6. Run the engine and be sure that everything is functioning properly.

REGULATOR

Kiekhaefer recommends that the regulator be replaced with a new unit if it is defective. Before replacing the regulator, be sure that the base of the regulator is properly grounded and that the connector strip is not loose.

Replacement—Relay Type

1. Lift the hatch which secures the wiring harness connector to the regulator and pull the connector away.

2. Remove the screws which fasten the regulator to the mounting bracket.

3. The voltage regulator must be mounted on a vibration-dampening bracket. The bracket was not supplied with early MerCruiser engines. When installing voltage regulators for these engines, use B-33614A1 voltage regulator mount.

4. Plug the wiring harness connector

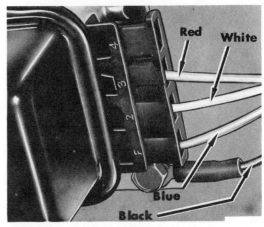

Voltage regulator connections—ammeter in the system

Voltage regulator mounting bracket installed on the transom

Regulator in position on the mounting bracket

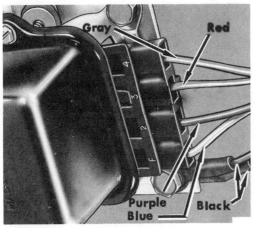

Voltage regulator connections—indicator in the system

into the new regulator while matching terminals on both regulators.

5. Position the regulator and vibration mount on the transom so that the regulator leads are NOT drawn tight.

6. Mark the location of the regulator mounting bracket.

7. Remove the regulator mounting screws and detach the regulator from the mounting bracket.

8. Remove the two wood screws which pass through the rubber grommets and install them with their points toward the wood.

9. Fasten the mounting bracket to the transom, with the mounting screws in a vertical position.

10. Install the terminal of the black harness lead under one regulator mounting screw and fasten the regulator to the bracket with three screws.

11. Secure the wiring harness to the transom with a clip so that the wire between the clip and regulator is not drawn tight.

Replacement—Transistor Type

This regulator can only be used with engines using an ammeter in the instrument panel. To adapt the engine wiring harness for use with a transistor voltage regulator, refer to the instructions that accompany the kit.

DISTRIBUTOR

Removal

ALL MODELS

1. Disconnect the distributor primary lead from the coil.

2. Match-mark the distributor body in line with the rotor.

3. Remove the distributor hold-down bolt and clamp. Remove the distributor from the engine, noting the relative position of the distributor in the block.

NOTE: *Do not rotate the engine with the distributor removed, since this will disturb ignition timing.*

INSTALLATION— ENGINE NOT DISTURBED

1. Turn the rotor approximately ⅛ turn clockwise past the match mark on the distributor housing.

2. Work the distributor down into the block with the distributor positioned as noted during removal.

NOTE: *It may be necessary to move the rotor slightly to engage the distributor drive gear with the camshaft gear, but the rotor and match mark should be aligned when the distributor is installed.*

3. Replace the hold-down bolt and clamp and then tighten the bolt.

4. Connect the coil primary lead.

5. If removed, install the spark plug leads.

6. Time the ignition as outlined under "Tune-Up."

INSTALLATION—ENGINE DISTURBED

1. Locate no. 1 piston in the firing position by either of these methods:

    a. Remove no. 1 plug and hold your finger over the spark plug hole until compression is felt when the engine is cranked. Continue cranking until the pointer aligns with the mark on the crankshaft pulley.

    b. Remove the rocker cover and crank the engine until no. 1 intake valve closes. Continue cranking until the pointer aligns with the mark on the crankshaft pulley.

2. Install the distributor in the block in its normal installed position.

3. Press down firmly on the distributor housing and crank the engine in short bursts to make sure that the oil pump shaft is engaged. Install the clamp and the bolt.

4. Turn the distributor body slightly until the points just open. Tighten the clamp bolt.

5. Place the cap in position and make sure that the rotor aligns with no. 1 spark plug terminal.

6. Install the cap, primary lead, and spark plug wires.

7. Start the engine and set the ignition timing.

BREAKER POINT REPLACEMENT

Four and Six Cylinder Distributor

1. Remove the distributor cap and place it out of the way.

2. Remove the rotor.

3. Remove the primary and condenser lead wires from the terminal.

4. Remove the contact set attaching screw and remove the breaker set.

5. Clean all oil and dirt from the breaker plate.

6. Place the new point assembly in position on the breaker plate and install the attaching screw.

7. Carefully wipe the protective film from the breaker point assembly.

8. Be sure to engage the pilot on the point set with the hole in the plate.

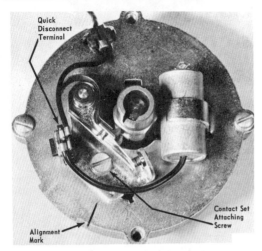

Breaker plate on 4 and 6 cylinder distributor

9. Connect the primary and condenser leads to the terminal.

10. Check and adjust the points for proper alignment, bending the stationary contact if necessary.

11. Set the contact point opening with a dwell meter. Feeler gauges may be used, but it should be checked on a dwell meter.

12. Install the rotor and cap.

13. Set the ignition timing.

V8 Distributor

1. The point set is replaced as a unit, and the spring tension and alignment are set at the factory.

2. Remove the distributor cap.

3. Remove the two screws holding the point set to the breaker plate.

4. Remove the primary and condenser leads from the insulated connection.

5. Reverse steps three and four to install the point set.

V8 distributor (except 888 and 215) showing wire positions

6. Install the primary and condenser leads as shown in the illustration.

7. If the engine has 250 hours on it, replace the cam wick. Squeeze the assembly together at the base and lift it out. Remove all the old lubricant from the cam surface and install a new lubricator wick. Adjust the lubricator wick so that it just touches the cam lobes.

THUNDERBOLT IGNITION

The Thunderbolt Ignition System is a capacitance discharge breakerless system using a rotating metal disc instead of the conventional breaker points. The system consists of a trigger assembly, an ignition coil, and a switch box.

WARNING: *This system is capable of producing 40,000 volts at the spark plugs. When testing or servicing the system, do not touch or disconnect any ignition components while the engine is running, the key switch is on, or while the battery cables are connected. Also, see the precautions listed at the beginning of the engine electrical system.*

Checking the Thunderbolt System

The following parts are required to check the system:

    a. Trigger assembly;
    b. Ignition coil;
    c. Switch box assembly;
    d. Voltmeter (0–15 or more);
    e. Short jumper lead and an ohmmeter.

Checking the Spark Plugs

See "Tune-Up."

Checking Spark at the Plug Leads

1. Remove one spark plug lead from the plug.

2. Remove the ground electrode from a standard type spark plug, connect it to the spark plug lead, and ground it on the engine.

3. DO NOT HOLD THE SPARK PLUG IN YOUR HAND WHILE MAKING THIS CHECK.

4. Turn the engine over with the starter and watch for spark at the plug. If no spark is observed, make the following check.

NOTE: *If one or more cylinders are missing, perform the preceding check on all plug leads.*

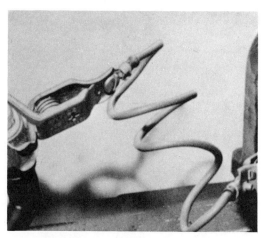

Checking for spark at the plugs

Checking Coil for Spark

1. Remove the secondary coil lead from the distributor and place the end of the lead ½ in. from a ground.

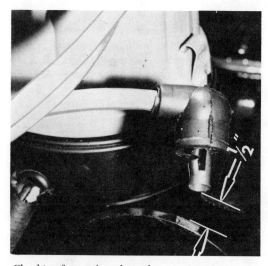

Checking for spark at the coil

WARNING: *Do not hold the wire in your hand while making this check.*

2. Turn the engine over and watch for spark.

   a. If spark is observed, the cause of no spark in the spark plug test is in the secondary section of the distributor. Remove the distributor cap and check the rotor, inside the cap, and spark plug lead wires.

   b. If no spark is observed, proceed with the following check.

Wiring and Connections

1. Connect a voltmeter to the red wire terminal on the switch box. Connect the negative voltmeter lead to the ground on the engine.

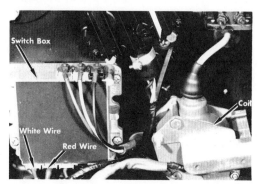

Voltmeter connections

2. With the key in the "off" position, observe the voltmeter.

   a. The meter should indicate battery voltage. If the meter reads below battery voltage, or no voltage is indicated, check the red wire with an ohmmeter for an open circuit. If the meter indicates battery voltage, proceed with the next step.

3. Remove the positive voltmeter lead from the red wire terminal and connect it to the white wire terminal.

4. With the key switch in the "on" position, observe the voltmeter.

   a. The voltmeter should indicate battery voltage. If the meter reads below

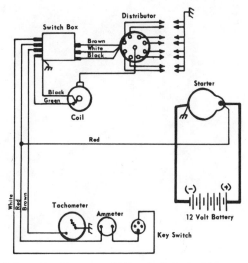

Schematic diagram of Thunderbolt ignition systems

battery voltage, or no voltage is present, check the white wire, key switch, and key switch wiring with an ohmmeter for an open circuit or high resistance.

b. If the meter indicates battery voltage, turn the key off and make the following check.

Distributor Trigger, Switch Box, and Coil

1. Remove the brown, white, and black trigger leads from the switch box and connect the brown, white, and black trigger leads from a new trigger to the switch box. Connect a jumper from the trigger housing to ground.

2. Place the coil secondary lead as outlined under "Checking Coil for Spark," step 1.

3. Turn the key switch on and pass a metal object (e.g., feeler blade, nail file) back and forth between the trigger inductance coils and observe the spark between the coil lead and ground.

a. If spark is observed, the original trigger is not functioning and should be replaced.

b. If no spark is observed, and a clicking noise is heard from the coil, the coil is shorted and should be replaced.

c. If no spark is observed and no click is heard, proceed as follows.

4. Remove the wires from the switch box and install a new switch box.

5. Connect all wires and repeat the "Checking Spark at the Plug Leads" test.

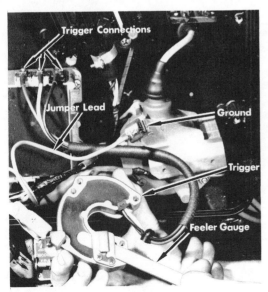

Checking the trigger switch

Fuel System

PRECAUTIONS

1. Before servicing the fuel system, disconnect the negative battery terminal to prevent accidental shorting which may ignite fuel that may be spilled when the fuel lines are disconnected.

FUEL LINE CHECK VALVE

110, 120, and 150 Only

A check valve and fuel line can be installed on these engines in the form of a kit available from the dealer. If the engine is not equipped with a fuel line check valve, install one as follows.

1. Remove the tee fitting from the carburetor and install the fitting on the discharge side of the fuel pump.

2. Remove the present restrictor and install the check valve (B-22-45122) into the tee fitting on the intake side of the fuel filter.

3. Connect the hose (B-32-45121) between the check valve and tee fitting.

4. Reverse the fuel line and install.

5. Remove the clip and install clip (B-54-28938).

Fuel line check valve installed

FUEL PUMPS

All fuel pumps used on MerCruiser engines are of the diaphragm type. The fuel pump is operated by an eccentric on the camshaft which directly actuates the pump rocker arm (four-cylinder and six-cylinder models) or by an eccentric on the camshaft which actuates the pump rocker arm through a pushrod (V8 models). The eight-cylinder pump delivers a larger volume of fuel and is mounted inverted (relative to the six-cylinder pump) with the pushrod pointing down.

Fuel Pump Volume Test

1. Disconnect the fuel line at the carburetor and direct the line into a container graduated in points.

2. Start the engine and run it at idle speed, using the fuel in the carburetor and lines.

3. Measure the time required to deliver one pint of fuel. At idle the pump should deliver one pint of fuel in 30–45 seconds.

4. If no fuel, or only a small amount, flows from the pump, the fuel line is clogged or the pump is inoperative. Remove the fuel tank filler cap and disconnect both intake and outlet lines from the pump and blow through the lines to clear them.

5. Reconnect the lines and repeat the test.

REMOVAL

1. Disconnect the intake and outlet lines from the fuel pump and pump cover.

2. Remove the fuel pump mounting bolts and lockwashers.

3. Remove the fuel pump and gasket.

4. On V8 models with a pushrod, remove the two adaptor mounting bolts and lockwashers and remove the adaptor and gasket from the block.

5. Remove the pushrod from the block.

DISASSEMBLY

Fuel pumps may be disassembled for cleaning or repairs by using the accompanying illustrations. The only exception to this is the dual-diaphragm type fuel pump which is not repairable and must be replaced. On pumps of this type, inspect the sight glass for fuel. If fuel is present, remove the pump and replace it with a new one.

On disassembly, if either of the pump castings is damaged, replacement of the pump is advisable. Diaphragm repair kits are available for servicing fuel pumps.

When assembling the fuel pump, assemble in reverse order of disassembly. Be sure that the diaphragm is flexed to its full stroke while tightening the cover screws or else the diaphragm protector will not be properly centered. This will cause premature wear of the diaphragm due to rubbing on the fuel pump casting.

INSTALLATION

1. If removed, install the pushrod and adaptor on the block. Use new gaskets.

2. Install the fuel pump, using a new gasket.

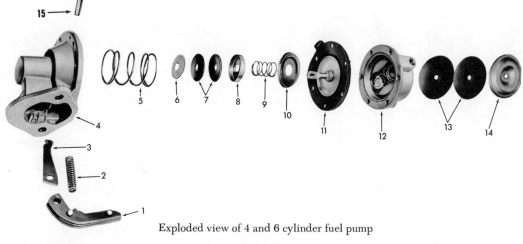

Exploded view of 4 and 6 cylinder fuel pump

1. Rocker arm	6. Lower seal retainer	11. Diaphragm
2. Rocker arm return spring	7. Oil seal	12. Fuel cover and valves
3. Actuating lever	8. Upper seal retainer	13. Pulsator diaphragm
4. Pump body	9. Seal spring	14. Pulsator cover
5. Diaphragm spring	10. Diaphragm spring upper seat	15. Rocker arm pin

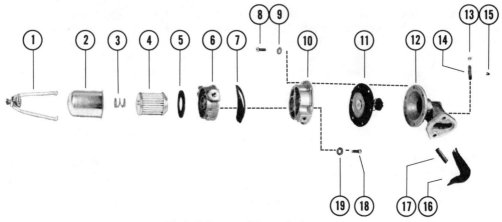

Exploded view of Carter fuel pump

1. Filter cover retainer	6. Pulsator housing	11. Diaphragm	16. Rocker arm
2. Filter cover	7. Pulsator	12. Pump body	17. Rocker arm spring
3. Filter spring	8. Screw	13. Rocker arm pin plug	18. Screw
4. Filter	9. Lockwasher	14. Rocker arm pin	19. Lockwasher
5. Filter gasket	10. Valve body	15. Rocker arm retainer	

3. Connect the fuel lines to the fuel pump.

4. Start the engine and check for leaks and proper operation.

CARBURETORS

Various carburetors are used on Mer-Cruiser engines to meet the particular demands of the engine and stern drive, depending on the size of the engine, horsepower, and application.

CAUTION: *Before making any carburetor adjustments, be sure that the carburetor-to-manifold bolts and the manifold-to-cylinder head bolts are tight and preventing air leaks. The engine must be warmed to operating temperature (at least 15 minutes running time) or carburetor misalignment will occur.*

Carburetor Troubleshooting Chart

Flooding	Rough Idle	Economy	Hesitation	Acceleration Flatness	Surge	Low Top Speed or Power	Cold Operation	Stalling	Hard Hot-Starting	Check Points ▲	What to Look For
1	★		★				★	1	★	Idle adjustment	Correct speed and mixture
2	3		★	3	3			3	★	Float adjustment	Use correct gauge
		1	★				★			Pump rod adjustment	Use correct dimension, throttle valves closed
	★						1a	★	1	Automatic choke adjustment	Set to latest specification
							1b	★		Choke rod adjustment	Use correct gauge
							1c		2	Unloader adjustment	Use correct gauge, throttle valves wide open; check to see that throttle linkage allows wide open position

Carburetor Troubleshooting Chart (cont.)

Complaint										Check Points ▲	What to Look For
Flooding	Rough Idle	Economy	Hesitation	Acceleration Flatness	Surge	Low Top Speed or Power	Cold Operation	Stalling	Hard Hot-Starting		
							1d	★		Secondary lockout adjustment	Proper clearance so cam is free to move with throttle valves closed
							1e	★		Secondary contour adjustment	Proper clearance so throttle valves are free to move with choke open
		2a		1	4a		1	★		Power piston	Dirty, distorted, sticking, incorrect part
		2b		2	4b		2	★		Power valve	Dirty, sticking, incorrect part
		4		3	1		4	★		Metering jets	Loose, plugged, incorrect part
1	★	★						2	3	Needle and seat	Worn, damaged, dirty incorrect part
	★	★	3	4	2	★				Venturi cluster	Dirty, loose screws, incorrect part
3	★				★			★	★	Float	Bent, leaky
	3							★		Idle needles	Worn, damaged
4			★	★		★	★	★		Throttle valves	Sticking, open or closed, damaged
4	★	★	★	★	★	★	★	★	★	Gaskets	Improper seal, hard or brittle material, loose screws
	2							★	★	Idle passages	Dirty
	★	★				★	★			Power piston vacuum passage	Plugged or vacuum leaks
	★	★					3		★	Choke vacuum passage	Plugged or vacuum leaks
	★	★		★			★			Throttle body heat passage	Plugged with carbon
	★	★								Pump body	Crack or loose fit on plunger shaft
			3				★			Pump plunger	Hard or worn leather, distorted spring, stuck vent ball check
★										Fuel filter	Clogged or dirty filter

Carburetor Troubleshooting Chart (cont.)

Flooding	Rough Idle	Economy	Hesitation	Acceleration Flatness	Surge	Low Top Speed or Power	Cold Operation	Stalling	Hard Hot-Starting	Check Points ▲	What to Look For
			4				★			Pump inlet check	Out-of-round, damaged seat, stuck
★		★					★	★	★	Pump discharge check	Out-of-round, damaged seat, stuck, distorted spring
			★	★			2	★	★	Choke piston	Dirty, damaged, sticking
		1					4		4	Operator	Operating habits, correct procedures
			2							Pump discharge jets	Dirt, must be open

▲—Numbers under each complaint indicate order of probability of causes listed.
★—Indicates other possible troubles.

Removal

ROCHESTER B AND BC

The Rochester model B carburetor is a single-barrel downdraft type with a manual choke. The BC model is identical to the model B except that the BC uses an automatic choke.

1. Remove the flame arrestor.
2. Remove the fuel line from the carburetor and the fuel filter.
3. Remove the intake fuel filter nut from the intake fuel filter.
4. Remove the filter element, spring, and two gaskets.
5. Clean the element by washing it in solvent and allowing it to air-dry.
6. Disconnect the fuel and choke heat lines (BC only) from the carburetor.
7. Disconnect the throttle rod from the throttle lever.
8. Remove the carburetor attaching nuts and remove the carburetor from the manifold.

ROCHESTER 2GC

This is a two-barrel carburetor equipped with an automatic choke. The major portion of the calibrated metering components are located in the venturi cluster and can be serviced readily by removing the air horn assembly.

1. Remove the flame arrestor.
2. Disconnect the fuel lines, choke heater connection, and the crankcase ventilation connection.
3. Detach the throttle rod from the throttle.
4. Remove the four mounting nuts and remove the carburetor from the manifold.

HOLLEY 2300-C

The Holley 2300-C is a two-barrel, downdraft carburetor, using four metering systems: an idle system; a main metering system; a power enrichment system; and an accelerator pump system.

1. Remove the flame arrestor assembly.
2. Disconnect the fuel intake line, making sure that no fuel is spilled that could cause a fire. Disconnect the choke heat wires.
3. Remove the four carburetor retaining nuts.
4. Remove the carburetor from the manifold.

ROCHESTER 4GC

The model 4GC is a four-barrel carburetor. It provides the advantage of two carburetors in one housing by dividing the carburetor into a primary and secondary side. The primary side controls fuel metering throughout idle and part-throttle speeds. The secondary side feeds extra air and fuel to the engine in response to increased power demands.

1. Remove the flame arrestor.
2. Disconnect the fuel line and choke heat tube.
3. Disconnect the throttle rod at the carburetor and remove the throttle return spring.
4. Remove the four attaching nuts and washers.
5. Remove the carburetor from the manifold.
6. Remove and discard the carburetor gasket.

HOLLEY 4160

This is a four-barrel downdraft type carburetor which functions as two carburetors. The primary stage supplies fuel and air throughout the entire operating range, while the secondary stage supplies a greater quantity of air and fuel upon engine demand.

1. Remove the flame arrestor and gasket.
2. Disconnect the fuel intake hose at the carburetor and discard the retaining clamp.
3. Be careful not to spill fuel which could cause a fire.
4. Remove the four carburetor mounting nuts.
5. Remove the carburetor from the manifold and remove the gasket.

ROCHESTER 4MV QUADRAJET

This is a four-barrel downdraft carburetor which uses two stages of operation. The primary side has small bores with a triple venturi set-up which provides more stable and finer fuel control in idle and economy ranges of operation. The secondary side has extremely large bores with greatly increased air capacity for power operation.

1. Remove the flame arrestor.
2. Disconnect the fuel line.
3. Detach the throttle linkage.
4. Disconnect the choke coil rod (applies to thermostatic choke carburetors only).
5. Remove the choke solenoid and linkage (carburetors with electric choke only).
6. Remove the four carburetor attaching nuts.

7. Remove the carburetor from the manifold and discard the gasket.

DISASSEMBLY AND INSPECTION

Carburetor repair kits are recommended for each overhaul operation. They are available from your dealer or from any reputable automotive supply house. These kits, which are usually packaged with instructions, contain all the necessary parts for a complete carburetor overhaul.

Disassemble the carburetor referring to the accompanying illustration for each particular carburetor.

Dirt, gum, and varnish on the exterior moving parts of the carburetor are often responsible for poor performance and operation. For this reason, all parts, except those noted, should be cleaned in carburetor solvent.

WARNING: *Rubber parts, plastic parts, diaphragms, and pump plungers should not be immersed in carburetor cleaner or they will be destroyed. Do not soak parts in carburetor cleaner for any longer than is necessary, or the finish on certain parts will be removed by the corrosive action of the solvent.*

Inspect all parts as follows:

1. Inspect all castings for signs of corrosion or cracking.
2. Blow out all passages in the castings with compressed air and allow the parts to air dry. Do not attempt to clean small passages with a piece of wire.
3. Carefully inspect all parts for wear and replace those that are worn.
4. Remove carbon from the throttle shafts with sandpaper. Never use emery cloth.
5. Inspect the float needles and seats for wear. If either is worn, replace both the needles and seats.
6. Inspect the float pins for excessive wear.
7. Inspect the floats for dents or holes. Check the inside of the floats for liquid by shaking the float.
8. Inspect the throttle shafts for excessive wear (looseness or rattle in the body flange casting). Replace the flange assembly if it is excessively worn.
9. Inspect the idle mixture screws for burrs and replace if any are found.
10. Examine the fast idle cam for wear or damage.

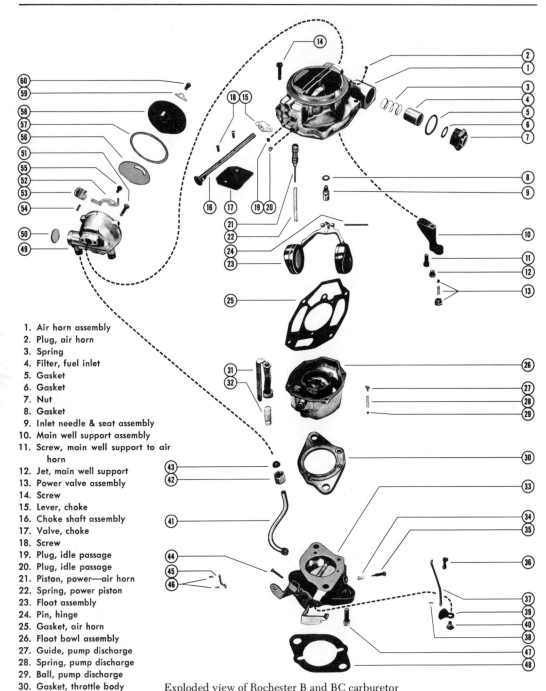

1. Air horn assembly
2. Plug, air horn
3. Spring
4. Filter, fuel inlet
5. Gasket
6. Gasket
7. Nut
8. Gasket
9. Inlet needle & seat assembly
10. Main well support assembly
11. Screw, main well support to air horn
12. Jet, main well support
13. Power valve assembly
14. Screw
15. Lever, choke
16. Choke shaft assembly
17. Valve, choke
18. Screw
19. Plug, idle passage
20. Plug, idle passage
21. Piston, power—air horn
22. Spring, power piston
23. Float assembly
24. Pin, hinge
25. Gasket, air horn
26. Float bowl assembly
27. Guide, pump discharge
28. Spring, pump discharge
29. Ball, pump discharge
30. Gasket, throttle body
31. Pump assembly
32. Spring
33. Throttle body assembly
34. Spring
35. Idle adjusting needle
36. Clip, choke rod—upper
37. Rod, choke
38. Clip, choke rod—lower
39. Cam, fast idle
40. Screw
41. Choke tube assembly
42. Nut

Exploded view of Rochester B and BC carburetor

43. Packing, choke tube nut
44. Idle stop screw
45. Link
46. Pin, hair
47. Screw
48. Gasket, carb. flange
49. Choke housing assembly
50. Welch plug
51. Screw

52. Lever assembly
53. Choke piston
54. Pin
55. Screw
56. Plate, baffle
57. Gasket
58. Stat cover & coil assembly
59. Retainer
60. Screw

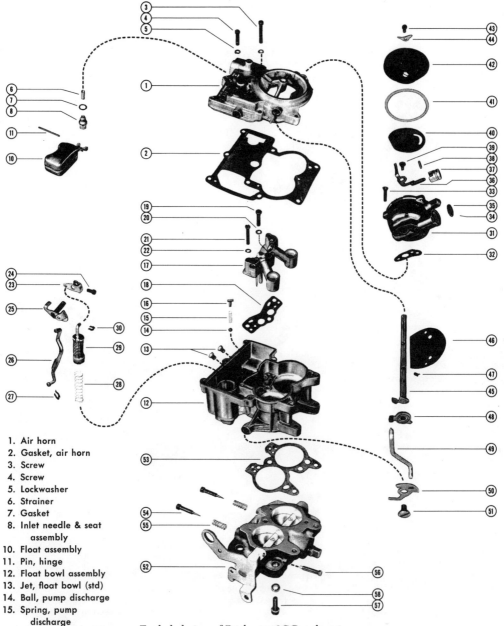

Exploded view of Rochester 2GC carburetor

1. Air horn
2. Gasket, air horn
3. Screw
4. Screw
5. Lockwasher
6. Strainer
7. Gasket
8. Inlet needle & seat assembly
10. Float assembly
11. Pin, hinge
12. Float bowl assembly
13. Jet, float bowl (std)
14. Ball, pump discharge
15. Spring, pump discharge
16. Guide, pump discharge
17. Venturi cluster assembly
18. Gasket, venturi cluster
19. Screw
20. Gasket
21. Screw
22. Lockwasher
23. Lever, pump—air horn
24. Screw, air horn pump lever
25. Pump shaft & lever assembly
26. Rod, pump
27. Clip, retainer—pump rod
28. Spring
29. Pump assembly
30. Clip, retainer
31. Choke housing assembly
32. Gasket, choke housing
33. Screw
34. Plug, ball—choke housing
35. Welch plug, choke housing
36. Lever assembly
37. Choke piston, choke housing
38. Pin
39. Screw
40. Plate, baffle
41. Gasket, stat cover and coil
42. Stat cover & coil assembly
43. Screw
44. Retainer
45. Choke shaft assembly
46. Valve, choke
47. Screw
48. Choke lever & collar assembly
49. Rod, choke
50. Cam, fast idle—float bowl
51. Screw
52. Throttle body assembly
53. Gasket, throttle body
54. Idle adjusting needle
55. Spring
56. Idle stop screw
57. Screw
58. Lockwasher

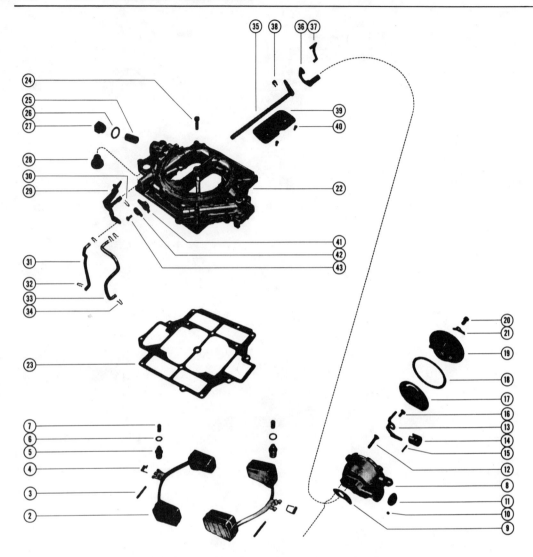

Exploded view of Rochester 4GC carburetor bowl cover

2. Float assembly
3. Pin, hinge—float to air horn
4. Spring, torsion—float
5. Inlet needle and seat assembly
6. Gasket, inlet needle and seat
7. Strainer, inlet needle and seat
8. Choke housing assembly
9. Gasket, choke housing
10. Plug, ball—choke housing
11. Welch plug, choke housing
12. Screw
13. Lever assembly, choke piston
14. Choke piston, choke housing
15. Pin
16. Screw

17. Plate baffle—choking housing
18. Gasket, stat cover and coil
19. Stat cover and coil assembly
20. Screw
21. Retainer
22. Air horn assembly
23. Gasket, air horn
24. Screw, air horn to float bowl
25. Filter, air horn nut
26. Gasket, air horn filter nut
27. Nut, filter—air horn
28. Boot, float bowl pump
29. Pump shaft and lever assembly
30. Clip, pump shaft and lever
31. Rod, pump

32. Clip, retainer—pump rod
33. Rod, choke
34. Pin hair—choke rod
35. Choke shaft assembly
36. Choke shaft assembly,
      intermediate
37. Rod, choke shaft
38. Clip, choke shaft rod
39. Valve, choke—choke shaft
40. Screw
41. Choke lever and collar assembly
42. Lever, trip—choke shaft
43. Screw, trip lever to choke shaft

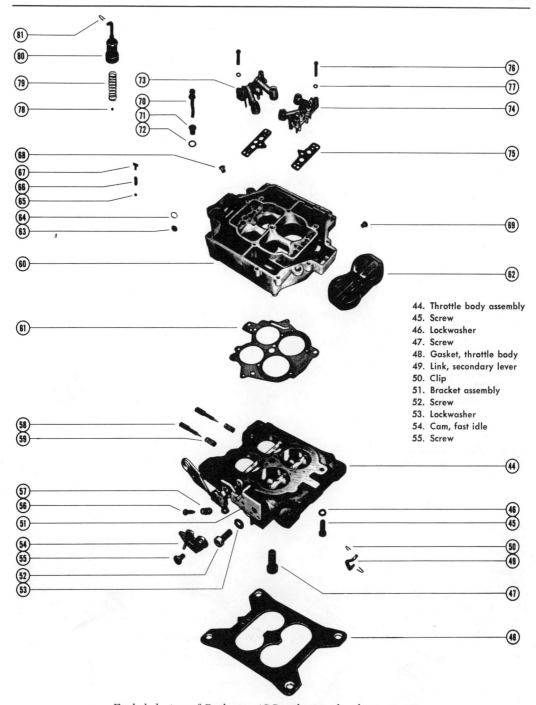

44. Throttle body assembly
45. Screw
46. Lockwasher
47. Screw
48. Gasket, throttle body
49. Link, secondary lever
50. Clip
51. Bracket assembly
52. Screw
53. Lockwasher
54. Cam, fast idle
55. Screw

Exploded view of Rochester 4GC carburetor bowl components

56. Idle stop screw	65. Ball, pump discharge	74. Venturi cluster assembly
57. Spring, idle stop screw	66. Spring, pump discharge	75. Gasket, venturi cluster
58. Idle adjusting needle	67. Guide, pump discharge	76. Screw
59. Spring	68. Jet, primary—float bowl	77. Lockwasher
60. Float bowl assembly	69. Jet, secondary—float bowl	78. Ball
61. Gasket, carburetor flange	70. Power piston assembly	79. Spring
62. Throttle valve assembly	71. Power valve assembly	80. Pump assembly, float bowl
63. Strainer, inlet	72. Gasket, power valve	81. Pin, hair—float bowl pump
64. Retainer	73. Venturi cluster assembly	

1. Screw
2. Choke plate
3. Gasket
4. Accelerating pump discharge nozzle
5. Gasket
6. Choke shaft
7. Accelerating pump discharge needle

8. Screw
9. Screw
10. Accelerating pump operating lever
11. Retainer
12. Spring
13. Sleeve nut
14. Secondary throttle shaft
15. Secondary throttle plate
16. Screw

17. Throttle connecting rod
18. Retainer
19. Choke housing
20. Choke rod
21. Gasket
22. Fast idle cam assembly
23. Choke rod seal
24. Choke housing shaft and lever
25. Retainer

26. Main body
27. Throttle body to main body gasket
28. Screw
29. Screw
30. Diaphragm lever assembly
31. Fast idle cam lever
32. Throttle Body

33. Screw
34. Spring
35. Screw
36. Screw
37. Primary throttle shaft assembly
38. Primary throttle plate

39. Screw
40. Screw
41. Accelerating pump cam
42. Gasket
43. Screw
44. Choke thermostat housing clamp
45. Choke thermostat housing and spring

46. Choke thermostat housing gasket
47. Nut
48. Lockwasher
49. Spacer
50. Choke thermostat lever
51. Choke thermostat link and piston assembly
52. Screw and washer

53. Screw and washer
54. Cover
55. Diaphragm spring
56. Diaphragm assembly
57. Screw and washer
58. Secondary housing
59. Retainer
60. Gasket

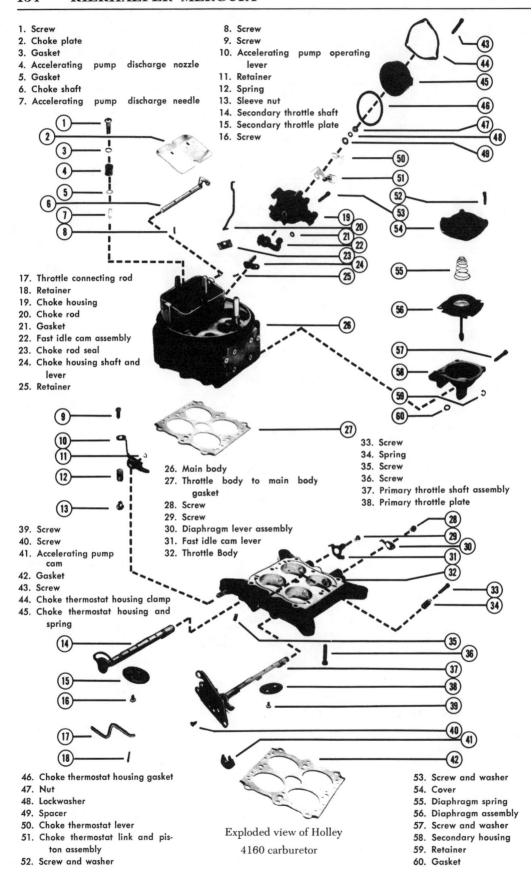

Exploded view of Holley
4160 carburetor

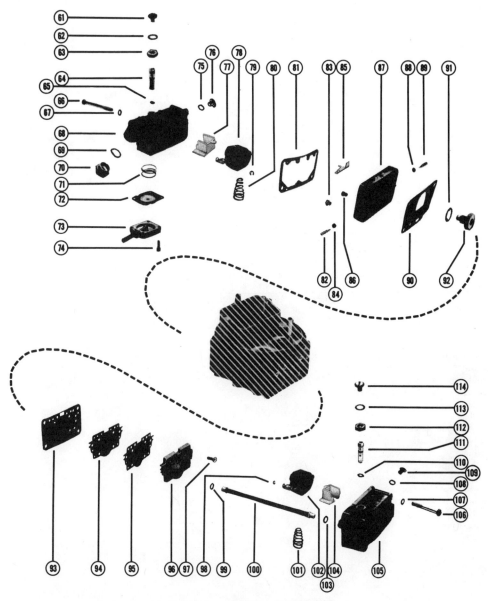

Exploded view of Holley 4160 carburetor

61. Lock screw
62. Gasket
63. Fuel level adjusting nut
64. Fuel inlet needle and seat
65. O ring seal
66. Screw
67. Gasket
68. Primary fuel bowl
69. Gasket
70. Fuel inlet fitting
71. Diaphragm spring
72. Diaphragm assembly
73. Accelerating pump cover
74. Retaining screw and lockwasher
75. Gasket
76. Fuel level sight plug
77. Baffle plate
78. Float

79. Retainer
80. Float spring
81. Primary fuel bowl gasket
82. Idle adjusting needle
83. Main jet
84. Seal
85. Baffle plate
86. Main jet
87. Primary metering block
88. Seal
89. Idle adjusting needle
90. Primary metering block gasket
91. Power valve gasket
92. Power valve
93. Gasket
94. Secondary plate
95. Metering body gasket
96. Secondary metering body

97. Screw, clutch
98. Retainer
99. O ring seal
100. Fuel line
101. Spring
102. Float
103. O ring seal
104. Baffle plate
105. Secondary fuel bowl
106. Screw
107. Gasket
108. Gasket
109. Fuel level sight plug
110. O ring seal
111. Fuel inlet needle and seat
112. Fuel level adjusting nut
113. Gasket
114. Lock screw

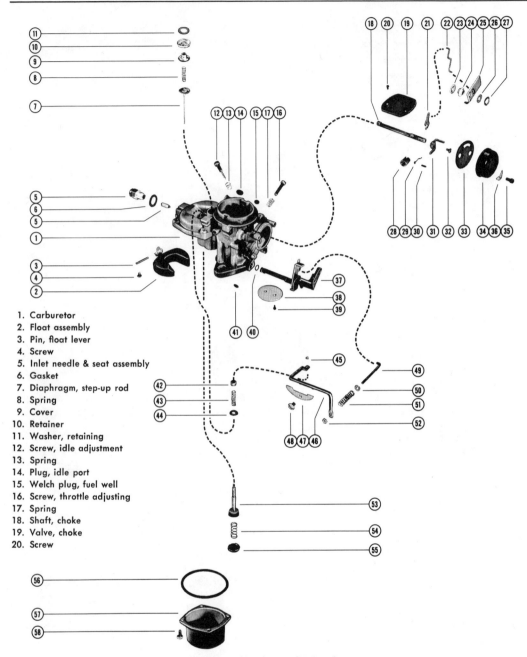

1. Carburetor
2. Float assembly
3. Pin, float lever
4. Screw
5. Inlet needle & seat assembly
6. Gasket
7. Diaphragm, step-up rod
8. Spring
9. Cover
10. Retainer
11. Washer, retaining
12. Screw, idle adjustment
13. Spring
14. Plug, idle port
15. Welch plug, fuel well
16. Screw, throttle adjusting
17. Spring
18. Shaft, choke
19. Valve, choke
20. Screw

Exploded view of Rochester RBS carburetor

21. Lever, choke	34. Coil housing assembly	47. Retainer, pump arm
22. Rod, fast idle connector	35. Screw	48. Screw
23. Washer	36. Retainer	49. Link, pump arm connector
24. Collar, fast idle cam	37. Shaft and lever assembly	50. Retainer
25. Cam, fast idle	38. Valve, throttle	51. Spring
26. Washer, fast idle cam	39. Screw	52. Nut
27. Retainer	40. O ring	53. Pump assembly
28. Piston, choke	41. Welch plug	54. Spring, pump—lower
29. Link, choke piston to lever	42. Bushing, pump	55. Retainer, pump—lower
30. Pin, link to choke piston	43. Spring, pump—upper	56. Gasket, float bowl
31. Lever, choke piston	44. Washer, pump (upper)	57. Bowl, float—carburetor
32. Screw	45. Retainer	58. Screw
33. Gasket, coil housing	46. Arm, pump	

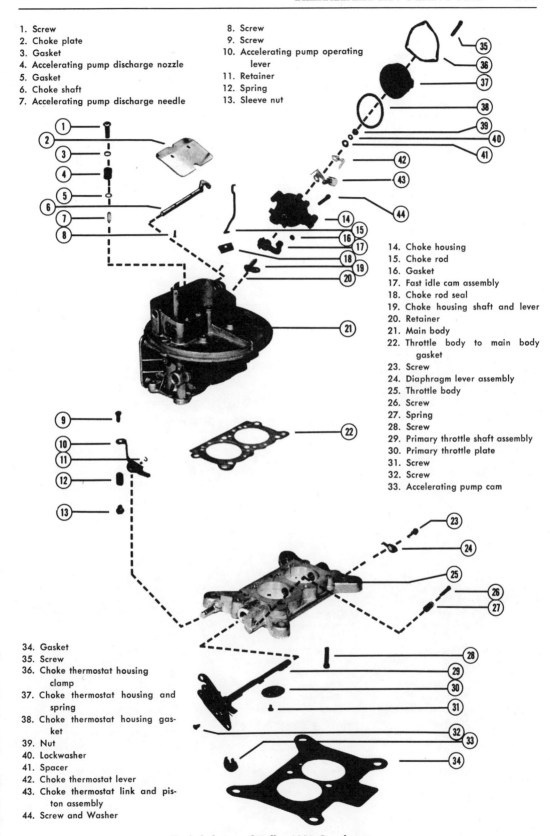

1. Screw
2. Choke plate
3. Gasket
4. Accelerating pump discharge nozzle
5. Gasket
6. Choke shaft
7. Accelerating pump discharge needle
8. Screw
9. Screw
10. Accelerating pump operating lever
11. Retainer
12. Spring
13. Sleeve nut

14. Choke housing
15. Choke rod
16. Gasket
17. Fast idle cam assembly
18. Choke rod seal
19. Choke housing shaft and lever
20. Retainer
21. Main body
22. Throttle body to main body gasket
23. Screw
24. Diaphragm lever assembly
25. Throttle body
26. Screw
27. Spring
28. Screw
29. Primary throttle shaft assembly
30. Primary throttle plate
31. Screw
32. Screw
33. Accelerating pump cam

34. Gasket
35. Screw
36. Choke thermostat housing clamp
37. Choke thermostat housing and spring
38. Choke thermostat housing gasket
39. Nut
40. Lockwasher
41. Spacer
42. Choke thermostat lever
43. Choke thermostat link and piston assembly
44. Screw and Washer

Exploded view of Holley 2300-C carburetor

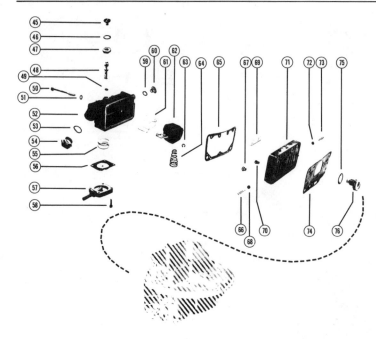

Exploded view of Holley 2300-C carburetor

45. Lockscrew
46. Gasket
47. Fuel level adjusting nut
48. Fuel inlet needle and seat
49. O ring seal
50. Screw
51. Gasket
52. Primary fuel bowl
53. Gasket
54. Fuel inlet fitting
55. Diaphragm spring
56. Diaphragm assembly
57. Accelerating pump cover
58. Retaining screw and lockwasher
59. Gasket
60. Fuel level sight plug
61. Baffle plate
62. Float
63. Retainer
64. Float spring
65. Primary fuel bowl gasket
66. Idle adjusting needle
67. Main jet
68. Seal
69. Baffle plate
70. Main jet
71. Primary metering block
72. Seal
73. Idle adjusting needle
74. Primary metering block gasket
75. Power valve gasket
76. Power valve

1. Air horn assembly
2. Lever, air valve lockout
3. Roll pin, lockout lever
4. Holder kit, secondary metering rod
5. Metering rod, secondary
6. Screw
7. Screw
8. Screw
9. Lever, actuating—pump
10. Roll pin, hinge—pump lever
11. Pump assembly
12. Spring, pump return
13. Needle and seat assembly
14. Gasket, needle and seat
15. Pull clip, float needle
16. Gasket, air horn
17. Metering rod, primary
18. Jet, primary
19. Choke shaft and lever assembly
20. Screw, choke lever attaching
21. Lockwasher, choke lever screw

22. Nut, choke lever screw
23. Valve, choke—choke shaft
24. Screw, choke valve to choke shaft
25. Float assembly
26. Pin, hinge—float
27. Lever, intermediate choke
28. Baffle, float bowl
29. Rod, choke
30. Clip, choke rod
31. Cam, fast idle
32. Rod, vacuum control
33. Clip, vacuum control rod
34. Bracket assembly, vacuum control
35. Screw, vacuum control bracket to float bowl
36. Control assembly, vacuum
37. Hose, vacuum
38. Power piston assembly
39. Spring, metering rod—primary
40. Retainer, power piston
41. Retainer, pump discharge ball
42. Ball, pump discharge

43. Spring, power piston
44. Insert, float bowl
45. Float bowl assembly
46. Screw, idle stop
47. Spring, idle stop screw
48. Spring, filter nut
49. Filter, fuel inlet
50. Nut, filter—fuel inlet
51. Gasket, filter nut
52. Gasket, throttle body
53. Rod, pump
54. Clip, pump rod
55. Throttle body assembly
56. Idle needle, throttle body
57. Spring, idle needle
58. Screw, throttle body to float bowl
59. Lever, cam
60. Lever, fast idle
61. Screw, lever and cam to throttle body

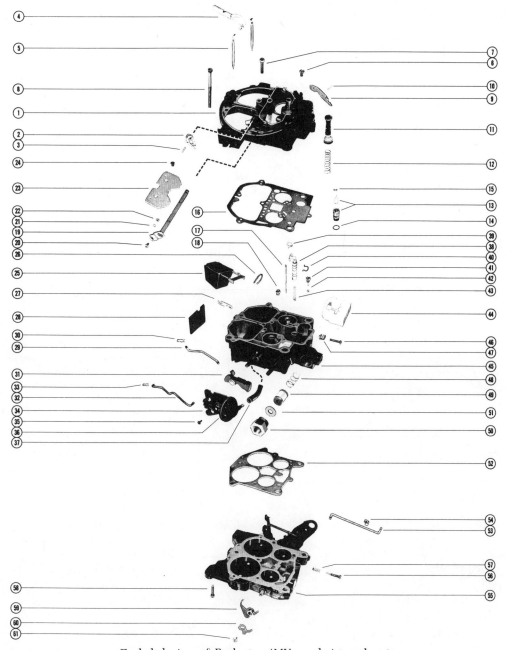

Exploded view of Rochester 4MV quadrajet carburetor

11. Check all throttle levers or valves for binding or other damage.

12. Check all filters for dirt or clogging and replace as necessary.

Assemble the carburetor, referring to the accompanying illustrations for each particular carburetor. Use all of the parts contained in the rebuilding kit, especially the gaskets. Install and adjust the carburetor.

Installation

ROCHESTER B AND BC

1. Install the carburetor on the mounting studs using a new gasket. Tighten the retaining nuts securely and evenly.

2. Connect the fuel line to the carburetor.

3. Connect the throttle rod to the throttle shaft lever.

4. On the BC carburetor only, connect the choke keat tube to the choke housing.

5. Adjust the idle speed and mixture.

ROCHESTER 2GC AND 4GC

1. Be sure that the throttle flange body and intake manifold mounting surfaces are clean.

2. Install the carburetor on the studs using a new gasket.

3. Install the four attaching nuts and tighten them evenly and securely.

4. Install the choke heat tube and fuel lines.

5. Install the throttle rod and return spring.

6. Install the flame arrestor.

7. Adjust the idle speed and mixture.

HOLLEY 2300-C

1. Be sure that the old gasket material is removed from the carburetor and intake manifold mounting flanges.

2. Place a new carburetor gasket on the manifold.

3. Install the carburetor on the spacer block. Install the retaining nuts and tighten them evenly.

4. Connect the choke heat wires to the carburetor.

5. Connect the fuel line to the float bowl.

6. Adjust the idle speed and idle fuel mixture.

7. Install the flame arrestor.

HOLLEY 4160

1. Be sure that all mounting faces are clean and free of all old gasket material.

2. Install the carburetor on the studs using a new gasket and tighten the retaining nuts evenly and securely.

3. Connect the choke heat wires to the carburetor.

4. Tighten the choke heat tube at the carburetor.

5. Install a new retaining clamp on the fuel intake hose.

6. Install the hose on the fuel intake fitting.

7. Tighten the clamp.

8. Adjust the idle speed and mixture.

9. Install the flame arrestor and mounting gaskets.

ROCHESTER 4MV QUADRAJET

1. Install the baffle plate and new base gasket on the intake manifold.

2. Install the carburetor on the manifold and tighten the attaching nuts securely and evenly.

3. Connect the throttle linkage.

4. Connect the fuel line.

5. Adjust the choke.

6. Install the flame arrestor.

7. Adjust the idle speed and mixture.

CARBURETOR ADJUSTMENTS

Most of the following carburetor adjustments can be made with the carburetor installed on the engine. These should be done after the carburetor has been overhauled and installed on the engine.

Rochester Model B

IDLE SPEED AND MIXTURE

1. This adjustment should be performed with the flame arrestor installed.

2. Connect a tachometer to the coil primary terminal and to ground.

3. With the engine operating and the choke valve open, adjust the idle and mixture as follows.

   a. Adjust the idle speed screw to give an idle speed of 500 rpm.

   b. Adjust the mixture screw to give the highest steady rpm at idle speed.

   c. Repeat the adjustment for a fine tune.

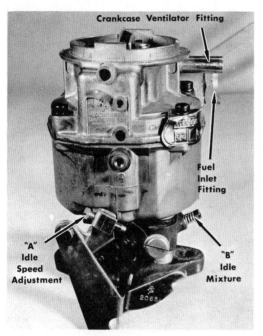

Rochester Model B idle and mixture adjusting screws

FLOAT LEVEL

1. Remove the flame arrestor from the air horn.

2. Disconnect the fuel line at the carburetor.

3. Remove the four cover attaching screws.

4. Lift the cover straight up to prevent damaging the floats.

5. Place the cover and float assembly on a flat surface.

6. Carefully bend the float arms horizontally so that each float is centered in the gasket.

7. Check the level adjustment. The distance from the top of the gasket to the top of each float should be $1\frac{9}{32}$ in.

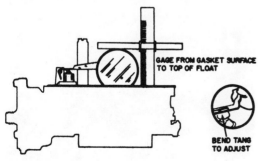

Rochester Model B float level adjustment

FLOAT DROP

1. Hold the cover assembly upright, allowing the floats to hang freely.

2. Carefully bend the float tang so that the float is $1\frac{3}{4}$ in. below the gasket surface.

3. Install the air horn by reversing the removal procedure.

4. If necessary, adjust the idle speed and mixture.

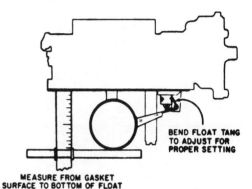

Rochester Model B float drop adjustment

FUEL FILTER REPLACEMENT

1. Remove the fuel line connection from the fuel filter.

2. Remove the fuel filter nut from the carburetor body.

3. Remove the filter element, spring, and two gaskets.

4. Reverse the procedure to replace the filter. Install the filter element with the small end of the cone facing the filter nut.

Rochester Model BC

IDLE SPEED AND MIXTURE

1. See this procedure under "Rochester Model B."

AUTOMATIC CHOKE

1. Adjust the automatic choke by loosening the three screws securing the bakelite choke cover.

2. Remove the cover, insert a screwdriver, and set the scribe mark on the cover in line with the index mark on the choke housing.

3. Tighten the cover screws.

CHOKE ROD SETTING

1. No adjustment is necessary except to be sure that the idle screw contacts the

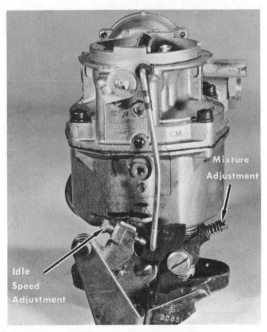

Rochester Model BC idle and mixture adjusting screws

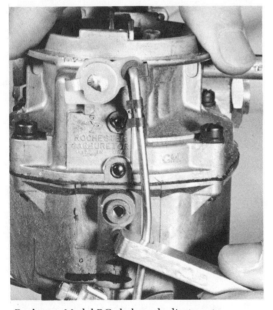

Rochester Model BC choke rod adjustment

cam when the choke valve is completely open or closed.

2. If the screw drops off the idle cam in either position, bend the choke rod to position the cam correctly.

FLOAT LEVEL

1. Remove the carburetor flame arrestor.

2. Disconnect the fuel line at the carburetor.

3. Unscrew the fitting at the choke vacuum tube at the cover.

4. Disconnect the choke heat tube.

5. Disconnect the tube from the carburetor air intake tube.

6. Disconnect the choke rod from the choke lever by removing the spring clip.

7. Remove the four carburetor cover screws.

8. Lift the cover assembly straight up to prevent damaging the floats.

9. Adjust the float level in the same manner and to the same specification as the Rochester model B.

FLOAT DROP

1. See this procedure under "Rochester Model B."

2. Install the carburetor cover in the reverse order from removal.

3. If necessary, adjust the idle speed and mixture.

Rochester 2GC

IDLE SPEED AND MIXTURE

1. Connect a tachometer and vacuum gauge to the engine.

2. With a thoroughly warmed engine, be sure that the choke is fully open.

3. Start the engine and run it at idle. Adjust the idle speed screw to 475 rpm.

4. Adjust each idle mixture screw separately to give peak vacuum and rpm readings. Approximate idle mixture adjustments can be made by setting the idle mixture screws lean, to a moderate rough

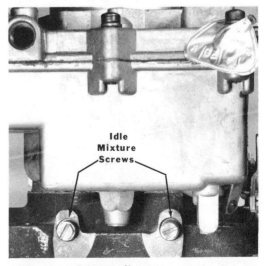

Rochester Model 2GC idle mixture screws

idle, which will produce a slight vacuum and rpm loss. Back out (enrichen) the idle mixture screws ¼ turn.

NOTE: *Do not turn the mixture screws against the seats or the needles will be damaged.*

5. Stop the engine and remove the vacuum gauge and tachometer.

6. Test the operation of the engine with the boat under operating conditions.

Float Level and Drop

1. Remove the bowl cover and gasket from the carburetor.

2. Invert the cover on a flat surface.

3. The distance from the air horn gasket to the toe of the float at the sharp-edged seam should be ⅝ in. Carefully bend the float hinge arm as required to obtain this distance.

4. Hold the cover in an upright position and measure the distance from the gasket to the bottom of the float, which should be 1²⁹⁄₃₂ in. Bend the tang at the end of the float hinge to achieve this distance.

5. Recheck both settings after the adjustment in step 4.

6. Install the bowl cover.

7. Recheck the idle and mixture settings, and adjust if necessary.

Pump Rod Adjustment

1. Back off the idle screw until the throttle valves are completely closed.

2. While holding the throttle valves closed, check the distance from the top of the air horn to the top of the pump rod, which should be 1⁵⁄₃₂ in.

3. Bend the accelerator pump rod carefully to obtain this (1⁵⁄₃₂ in.) dimension.

Automatic Choke

1. Normal setting of the automatic choke is with the scribe mark on the cover aligned with the long case mark on the choke housing.

Choke Rod

No adjustment is provided.

Unloader Adjustment

1. Place the throttle in the wide open position.

2. Using a 0.160 in. gauge or drill, be sure that the gauge just slides freely be-

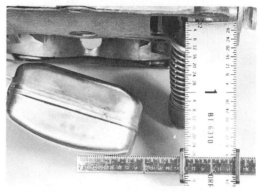

Rochester Model 2GC float adjustment

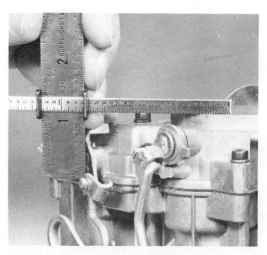

Rochester Model 2GC pump rod alignment

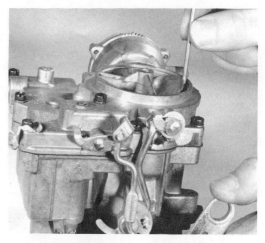

Rochester Model 2GC unloader adjustment

tween the upper edge of the choke valve and the bore of the carburetor.

3. Carefully bend the throttle lever tang to obtain this clearance.

Rochester 4GC

Complete the following adjustments with the carburetor on the engine and in the order listed.

IDLE SPEED AND MIXTURE

1. Make the idle mixture adjustment with the flame arrestor installed.
2. Connect a tachometer to the engine.
3. With the engine thoroughly warmed, be sure that the choke is fully open.
4. Start the engine and run it at idle. Adjust the idle speed screw to 500 rpm.
5. Adjust each idle mixture screw separately to give peak rpm.
6. Approximate settings can be made as detailed in step 4 of the "Idle Speed and Mixture" adjustment for the Rochester 2GC.
7. Shut off the engine and remove the tachometer.

FLOAT LEVEL AND FLOAT DROP

1. Remove the bowl cover, with its gasket, from the carburetor.
2. Invert the air horn with the gasket in place. The distance from the gasket surface to the top heels of the primary floats should be $1\frac{3}{8}$ in. The distance from the gasket surface to the top heels of the secondary floats should be $1\frac{11}{32}$ in. Bend the float arm to adjust this distance.
3. With the air horn still inverted, the distance from the gasket to the center of the dimple on the primary float should be $\frac{11}{16}$ in. Distance from the gasket to the center of the dimple at the toe of the secondary float should be $\frac{9}{16}$ in. Bend the toe of the float while holding the float arm to adjust this dimension. Recheck the adjustment in step 2.
4. Hold the air horn upright and measure the distance from the gasket to the center of the dimples on both primary and secondary floats. This should be $1\frac{3}{8}$ in.

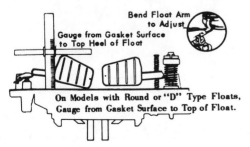

Rochester 4GC float level adjustment

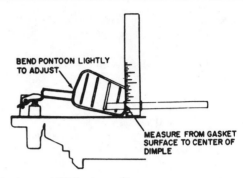

Rochester 4GC float toe adjustment

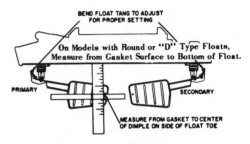

Rochester 4GC float drop adjustment

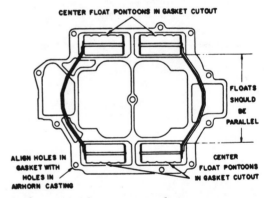

Rochester 4GC float centering adjustment

Bend the float tang to adjust this dimension.

NOTE: *Round pontoon or D type floats are measured to the lowest point.*

5. Center the floats in the cut-out sections of the gasket. The sides of the floats must be parallel to the adjacent sides of the gasket. Bend the float arms to adjust.
6. Install the bowl cover.

PUMP ROD ADJUSTMENT

1. Back off the idle screw and allow the primary valves to close.
2. The distance from the top of the air horn next to the pump plunger to the bottom plunger shaft should be $1\frac{1}{32}$ in.

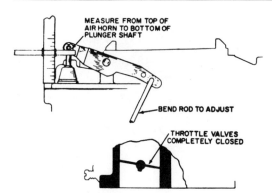

Rochester 4GC pump rod adjustment

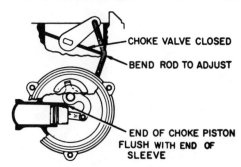

Rochester 4GC intermediate choke rod adjustment

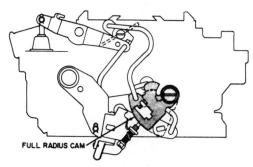

Rochester 4GC choke rod adjustment

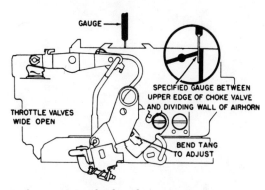

Rochester 4GC unloader adjustment

3. Bend the pump rod to adjust this setting.

4. Readjust the idle to 500 rpm.

AUTOMATIC CHOKE

1. The normal setting of the choke is when the scribed mark on the cover is aligned with the long cast mark on the choke housing.

INTERMEDIATE CHOKE ROD

1. With the coke cover and baffle removed, hold the choke valve closed. Push lightly on the end of the choke piston to remove all lash from the linkage and check to see that the choke piston is flush with the end of the sleeve.

2. Bend the intermediate choke rod if necessary to correctly position the choke piston.

3. Install the baffle and cover.

CHOKE ROD

1. No adjustment is necessary, except to make sure that the idle screw contacts the cam when the choke valve is completely open or closed.

2. If the screw drops off the cam in either choke position, bend the choke rod to position the cam correctly.

CHOKE UNLOADER

1. With the choke trip lever contacting the choke counterweight lever, hold the throttle valve in the wide open position.

2. A clearance of 0.120 in. should exist between the top of the choke valve and the dividing wall of the air horn.

3. Bend the tang on the fast idle cam to correct this adjustment.

SECONDARY THROTTLE LOCKOUT

1. With the choke valve closed so that the secondary lockout tang is in the fast

idle cam slot, check the clearance between the fast idle cam and tang; it should be 0.015 in.

2. Bend the tang horizontally to achieve this distance.

SECONDARY THROTTLE CONTOUR CLEARANCE

1. Hold the choke valve wide open and position the secondary lockout lever as illustrated. Clearance between the cam and tang should be 0.110 in.

2. Bend the tang vertically to adjust.

SECONDARY THROTTLE VALVE LOCK SPRING

1. Adjust the carburetor idle speed and mixture. Be sure that the secondary throttle valves are closed.

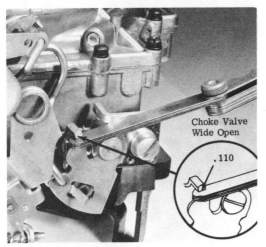

Choke Valve
Wide Open

.110

Rochester 4GC secondary throttle valve lock spring adjustment

Adjust Float
Parallel to
Bowl Floor

Holley 4160 dry float level adjustment

Secondary Throttle Stop
Screw Location

Holley 4160 secondary throttle stop screw location

2. Shut off the engine and insert a 0.050 in. feeler gauge between the idle screw and the idle cam.

3. Measure the clearance between the secondary lock spring and the secondary throttle operating lever; it should be 0.025 in.

4. Bend the lock spring to adjust this distance.

Holley 4160

FLOAT LEVEL (DRY)

1. This adjustment is made only as a bench adjustment, with the carburetor disassembled.

2. With the float bowl upside down, adjust the float parallel to the floor of the bowl by loosening the lockscrew and turning the adjusting nut.

SECONDARY THROTTLE STOP SCREW ADJUSTMENT

1. Back out the secondary throttle stop-screw until the secondary throttle plates are closed in the base.

2. Turn the screw in until it touches the stop on the lever, then add ½ turn.

ACCELERATOR PUMP LEVER CLEARANCE

1. With the throttle valves wide open, and the pump lever held down, insert a 0.015 in. minimum feeler gauge between the adjusting nut and the operating lever.

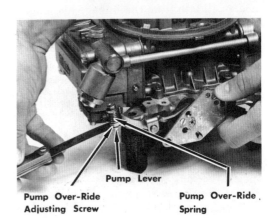

Pump Lever

Pump Over-Ride
Adjusting Screw

Pump Over-Ride
Spring

Holley 4160 accelerator pump lever clearance

Holley 2300-C

FLOAT LEVEL ADJUSTMENT (WET)

1. With the flame arrestor removed and the ignition off, remove the sight plug. Remove the lower bowl attaching screw (farthest from the fuel intake).

2. Drain off the fuel into a container to prevent spillage.

3. Reinstall the fuel bowl screw.

4. With the engine running, the fuel

level should be in line with the threads of the bottom of the sight plug hole. A tolerance of ±1/32 in. is allowed.

5. To correct the fuel level, loosen the lockscrew and turn the adjusting nut clockwise to lower the fuel level or counterclockwise to raise the fuel level. A 1/6 turn of the locknut equals approximately 1/16 in. in fuel level.

6. After the adjustment, tighten the lockscrew.

7. Operate the engine until the fuel level is stabilized, then recheck the level at the sight plug.

Removing the sight plug on Holley 2300-C

Removing the fuel bowl lever screw on Holley 2300-C

8. If necessary, repeat the adjustment until the proper fuel level is attained.

9. Replace the sight plug.

ACCELERATOR PUMP LEVER CLEARANCE

1. With the throttle valves at wide open throttle, insert a 0.015 in. minimum gauge between the adjusting nut and the operating lever. Be sure to hold the pump lever down.

2. Adjust the pump over-ride screw until the correct clearance is attained.

NOTE: *There must be no free movement of the pump lever at idle.*

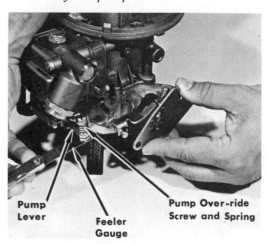

Accelerator pump lever clearance—Holley 2300-C

CHOKE UNLOADER ADJUSTMENT

1. Hold the throttle valves in the wide open position and insert a 5/32 in. drill between the upper edge of the choke valve and the inner wall of the air horn.

2. Press a finger lightly against the choke control lever. A slight drag should be felt as the drill is pulled out.

3. To adjust this clearance, bend the tab on the kick-down lever, until the correct clearance is obtained.

AUTOMATIC CHOKE ADJUSTMENT

1. See "Automatic Choke Adjustment" under the Holley 4160 carburetor section.

IDLE SPEED AND MIXTURE

1. See this procedure under "Holley 4160."

2. Adjust the pump over-ride screw until the correct clearance is obtained.

3. There must be no free-play of the pump leverage when the throttle is at idle.

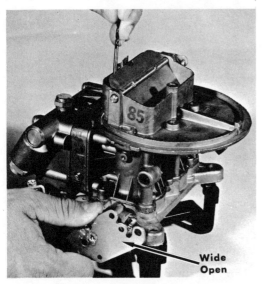

Holley 2300-C choke unloader adjustment

Choke Unloader

1. Hold the throttle valves in the wide open position and insert a 5/32 in. drill between the upper edge of the choke valve and the inner wall of the air horn.

2. Press a finger lightly against the choke control lever. A slight drag should be felt when the drill is pulled out.

3. To adjust this clearance, bend the tab on the kick-down lever until the correct opening is obtained.

Holley 4160 choke unloader adjustment

Float Level (Wet)

1. With the flame arrestor removed and the ignition off, remove the sight plug. Re-

Removing the sight plug for wet float level adjustment on Holley 4160

move the lower bowl attaching screw farthest from the fuel intake.

2. Drain the fuel into a shallow pan, being careful not to create a fire hazard.

3. Reinstall the fuel bowl screw.

4. With the engine running, the fuel level should be on a level with the threads at the bottom of the sight plug port ($\pm$1/32 in.).

5. To correct the fuel level, loosen the lockscrew and turn the adjusting nut clockwise to lower the fuel level or counterclockwise to raise the fuel level.

6. Each 1/6 turn of the adjusting nut equals approximately 1/16 in. in fuel level.

7. Tighten the lockscrew.

8. Operate the engine until the fuel level is stabilized and recheck the level at the sight plug.

9. If necessary, repeat the adjustment until the fuel level is correct.

10. Replace the sight plug.

11. Use this procedure on primary and secondary bowls.

Idle Speed and Mixture

1. This adjustment should be made with the boat as level as possible.

2. Seat the idle adjusting needles lightly and back each off one (1) full turn.

NOTE: *Do not seat the needles tightly or they will be damaged.*

3. Start the engine and allow it to reach operating temperature.

Idle Fuel Adjusting Needle

Idle adjusting needle on Holley 4160

4. Adjust the idle speed screw to the rpm specified. (See "Specifications.")

5. First, set one of the two idle adjusting needles for the highest steady vacuum reading. If a vacuum gauge is not available, obtain the smoothest running maximum idle speed by turning the idle adjusting needle in until the rpms begin to drop off. Back off the needle over the "high spot" until the rpms begin to fall off again. Set the idle adjusting needle halfway between the two points for satisfactory idle mixture setting. Repeat the procedure with the other needle. If these adjustments show an increase in idle speed, reset the idle speed screw to the specified rpm and repeat the adjustment on the idle adjusting needles.

Automatic Choke

1. The automatic choke is set at the factory for the best all-around operation.

2. If, for some reason, a richer or leaner mixture during warm-up is desired, it can be obtained by rotating the thermostat cover. Never set the index mark on the cover more than two graduations from the factory setting.

Rochester 4MV Quadrajet

NOTE: *The fast idle cam lever adjusting screw has not been removed from some Quadrajet carburetors installed on 225, 250, and 325 cu in. engines, serial no. 2404127 and below. These engines will automatically run at fast idle following a cold start and will continue to run at fast idle until the automatic choke has opened sufficiently to allow normal idle. This condition is abnormal and is not* required on marine applications. This spring and screw should be removed and discarded. It may be necessary to readjust the throttle cable and idle stop-screw to obtain correct idle. If the fuel intake filter on engines serial no. 2314316 and below does not allow sufficient fuel flow, replace it with a new filter, part no. B-35-53386. MerCruiser engines between serial nos. 2314317 and 2494935 do not have an intake filter installed in the Quadrajet carburetor. When these engines are serviced, install a new filter (B-35-53386) and spring (B-24-48143). Engines with serial no. 2494936 or above have the new filter and spring installed.

The following adjustments can be made with the carburetor on the engine. Make the adjustments in the order given.

Float Level

1. Remove the flame arrestor.

2. Remove the air horn from the float bowl.

3. Measure from the top of the float bowl gasket surface (gasket removed) to the top of the float at the toe $\frac{1}{16}$ in. back. Do not gauge at the numbers on the float. The float level should be $\frac{1}{4}$ in. Bend the arm up or down to obtain the required float level. Be sure that the retaining pin is firmly seated and the float tang is seated on the float needle.

4. Reinstall the air horn.

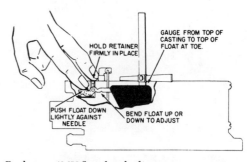

Rochester 4MV float level adjustment

Pump Adjustment

1. Disconnect the secondary actuating link.

2. With the throttle valves closed and the pump rod in the specified hole in the lever (see "Specifications"), measure from the top of the choke valve wall to the top of the pump stem. Bend the pump lever to

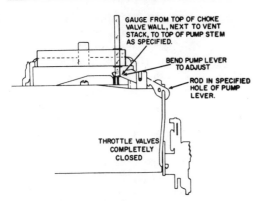

Rochester 4MV pump adjustment

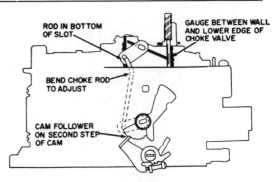

Rochester 4MV choke rod adjustment

obtain the distance stated in the specifications.

3. Connect the actuating link.

CHOKE ROD

1. Place the cam follower on the second step of the fast idle cam and against the high step. Rotate the choke valve toward the closed position by lightly pushing down on the vacuum break lever.

2. The dimension between the lower edge of the choke valve and the air horn wall should be as specified. (See "Specifications.") Bend the choke rod to adjust.

AIR VALVE DASHPOT

1. Push in the vacuum break stem until the diaphragm is seated. The clearance (see "Specifications"), must exist between the dashpot rod and the end of the slot in the air valve lever. Bend the rod at the air valve end to adjust the clearance.

VACUUM BREAK ADJUSTMENT

1. Push in the vacuum break stem until the diaphragm is seated, then hold the choke valve toward the closed position.

2. The dimension between the lower edge of the air horn wall and the choke valve should be as specified (see "Specifications").

3. Bend the vacuum break tang to adjust.

UNLOADER ADJUSTMENT

1. Hold the choke valve closed with a rubber band on the vacuum break lever and open the primary throttle valves to the wide open position.

2. The dimension between the edge of the choke valve and the air horn wall should be as specified. Bend the fast idle lever tang to adjust.

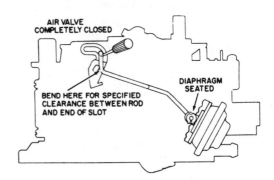

Rochester 4MV air valve lockout adjustment

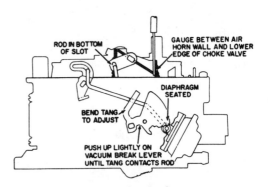

Rochester 4MV vacuum break adjustment

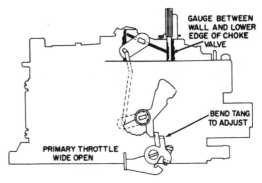

Rochester 4MV unloader adjustment

Air Valve Lockout

1. Open the choke valve wide by rotating the vacuum break lever. The choke rod must be to the top of the slot in the choke lever.

2. The dimension between the edge of the air valve and the lockout lever tang must be as specified. Bend the upper end of the lockout lever tang to adjust.

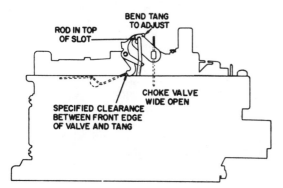

Rochester 4MV air valve lockout adjustment

Choke Adjustment

1. Carburetors equipped with electric choke do not require adjustment.

Choke Coil Rod

1. With the choke valve completely closed, and the choke rod at the bottom of the choke lever slot, push the choke coil rod down to the end of its travel.

2. The rod should be positioned as illustrated. Bend the choke coil rod to adjust.

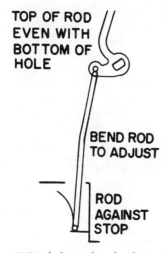

Rochester 4MV choke coil rod adjustment (225 and 250 engines)

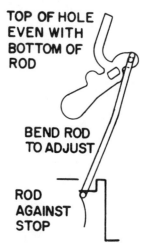

Rochester 4MV choke coil rod adjustment (325 engines)

Idle Speed and Mixture

1. The flame arrestor must be installed.
2. Connect a tachometer to the engine.
3. Start the engine and allow it to reach operating temperature with the choke fully open.
4. Disconnect the throttle cable.
5. Adjust the idle speed screw to obtain 550–600 rpm.
6. Adjust each idle mixture screw separately to give peak rpm.
7. Readjust the idle speed screw to give 550–600 rpm with the unit in gear.
8. Stop the engine and remove the tachometer.
9. Reconnect the throttle cable.

Engine Mechanical

Mercury engines covered in this book are of four-cylinder, six-cylinder or V8 design. All engines are not necessarily used in any model year.

IN-HULL SERVICE

NOTE: *The operations listed in this section can be accomplished with the engine mounted in the hull. Since "Engine Removal" and the operations which can only be done with the engine removed from the hull are dependent upon "Outdrive Removal", these operations are not included in this book. "Outdrive Removal" is a very complex operation re-*

quiring a great many special tools which would normally only be found in a well-equipped repair facility, such as a dealership.

INTAKE MANIFOLD

Removal and Installation

4 AND 6 CYLINDER

The four-cylinder and six-cylinder intake and exhaust manifolds are removed as a unit.

1. Disconnect the exhaust pipe flange and remove all connections to the carburetor.

2. Take off all the vacuum lines at the manifold and carburetor.

3. Remove the carburetor.

4. Remove the retaining bolts from the side of the cylinder head.

5. To separate the intake and exhaust manifolds, remove the one retaining bolt and two nuts at the center.

6. Install the manifold in the reverse order of the removal procedure.

V8 (EXCEPT 302 CU IN.)

1. Remove the air cleaner.

2. Drain the coolant.

3. Disconnect the:

  a. Battery cables at the battery;

  b. Coolant hoses at the manifold;

  c. Crankcase ventilation hoses as required;

  d. Fuel line at the carburetor;

  e. Accelerator linkage;

  f. Vacuum hose at the distributor;

  g. Ignition coil and temperature sending switch wire.

4. Remove the distributor cap and scribe the rotor position relative to the distributor body.

5. Remove the distributor.

6. If applicable, remove the Delcotron upper bracket.

7. Remove the manifold-to-head attaching bolts, then remove the manifold and carburetor as an assembly.

8. If the manifold is to be replaced, transfer the carburetor (and mounting studs), water outlet, and thermostat (use a new gasket), heater hose adaptor, and, if applicable, the choke coil.

9. Before installing the manifold, thoroughly clean the gasket and seal surfaces of the cylinder heads and manifold.

10. Install the manifold end seals, fold-ing the tabs if applicable, and the manifold/head gaskets, using a sealing compound around the water passages.

11. When installing the manifold, care should be taken not to dislocate the end seals. It is helpful to use a pilot in the distributor opening. Tighten the manifold bolts to 30 ft lbs.

12. Install the ignition coil.

13. Install the distributor with the rotor in its original location as indicated by the scribe line. If the engine has been disturbed, refer to the distributor R & R procedures above.

14. If applicable, install the Delcotron upper bracket and adjust the belt tension.

15. Connect all components disconnected in step 3 above.

16. Fill the cooling system, start the engine, check for leaks, and adjust the ignition timing and carburetor idle speed and mixture.

V8 (302 CU IN.)

1. Drain the cooling system.

2. Disconnect the upper radiator hose from the thermostat housing and the bypass hose from the manifold.

3. Remove the flame arrestor.

4. Remove the distributor cap and wires from the engine. Mark the position of the distributor rotor in relationship to the intake manifold, remove the primary wire from the coil, then remove the distributor hold-down bolt and the distributor.

5. Remove all vacuum lines from the intake manifold and remove the temperature sending-unit wire.

6. Disconnect the fuel line and any vacuum lines from the carburetor.

7. Remove all carburetor linkage and kick-down linkage that attaches to the intake manifold.

8. Remove the manifold attaching bolts and the manifold. If it is necessary to pry the manifold to loosen it from the engine, use care not to damage any gasket sealing surfaces.

9. Clean all gasket surfaces and firmly cement new gaskets in place. The gaskets should be securely locked in place before attempting to install the manifold.

10. Reverse the above procedure to reinstall.

11. Torque the intake manifold bolts, in sequence, to the specifications listed in the "Torque Specifications" chart.

EXHAUST MANIFOLD

Removal and Installation

4 AND 6 CYLINDER

See the "Removal and Installation" procedures listed for the intake manifold of four-cylinder and six-cylinder engines because the manifolds are removed as a unit.

V8 (EXCEPT 302 CU IN.)

1. If equipped with A.I.R., remove the air injector manifold assembly. The ¼ in. pipe threads in the manifold are straight threads. Do not use a ¼ in. tapered pipe tap.
2. Disconnect the battery.
3. If applicable, remove the air cleaner preheater shroud.
4. Remove the exhaust pipe flange nuts, then hang the pipe with wire.
5. Remove the manifold mounting bolts (end bolts first), then remove the manifold.
6. To install, clean the mating surfaces, then install the manifold with the center bolts first. Install the end bolts, then tighten all bolts to 20 ft lbs.
7. To complete installation, reverse steps 1 through 3.

V8 (302 CU IN.)

1. Remove the cooling hose from the manifold.
2. Remove the dipstick housing bracket and the fuel filter mount from the port manifold.
3. Disconnect the exhaust hoses.
4. Remove the attaching bolts and washers and remove the manifolds.
5. Installation is the reverse of removal.

CYLINDER HEAD

Removal and Installation

4 AND 6 CYLINDER

1. Drain the cooling system and remove the flame arrestor. Disconnect the PCV hose.
2. Disconnect the accelerator rod at the bellcrank on the manifold and the fuel and vacuum lines at the carburetor.
3. Disconnect the exhaust pipe at the manifold flange, then remove the manifold bolts and clamps and remove the manifolds and carburetor as an assembly.
4. Remove the fuel and vacuum line retaining clip from the water outlet. Disconnect the wire harness from the heat

sending unit and coil, leaving the harness clear of the clips on the rocker arm cover.
5. Disconnect the radiator hose at the water outlet housing and the battery ground strap at the cylinder head.
6. Disconnect the wires and remove the spark plugs. On the six-cylinder engine, disconnect the coil-to-distributor primary wire lead at the coil and remove the coil.
7. Remove the rocker arm cover. Back off the rocker arm nuts, pivot the rocker arms to clear the pushrods, and remove the pushrods.
8. Remove the cylinder head bolts, the cylinder head, and the gasket.

To install:
1. Place a new cylinder head gasket over the dowel pins in the cylinder block.
2. Guide and lower the cylinder head into place over the dowels and gasket.
3. Oil the cylinder head bolts, install them, and run them down snug.
4. Tighten the cylinder head bolts a little at a time with a torque wrench in the correct sequence. Final torque should be as specified.
5. Install valve pushrods down through the cylinder head openings and seat them in their lifter sockets.
6. Install the rocker arms, balls, and nuts and tighten the rocker arm nuts until all pushrod play is taken up.
7. Install the thermostat, thermostat housing, and water outlet, using new gaskets. Connect the coolant hose.
8. Install the heat sending switch and torque it to 15–20 ft lbs.
9. Clean the old spark plugs or install new ones. Set the gaps to 0.035 in.
10. Use new plug gaskets and torque to 20–25 ft lbs.
11. Install the coil (on six-cylinder engines) and then connect the heat sending unit and coil primary wires, and connect the battery ground cable at the cylinder head.
12. Clean the surfaces and install a new gasket over the manifold studs. Install the manifold. Install the bolts and clamps and torque them as specified.
13. Connect the throttle linkage.
14. Connect the PCV, fuel, and vacuum lines and secure the lines in a clip at the water outlet.
15. Fill the cooling system and check for leaks.
16. Adjust the valves if necessary.

17. Install the rocker arm cover and position the wiring harness in the clips.
18. Clean and install the flame arrestor.

V8 (EXCEPT 302 CU IN.)

1. Remove the intake manifold as previously outlined.
2. Remove the exhaust manifolds as previously outlined and tie them out of the way.
3. Back off the rocker arm nuts and pivot the rocker arms out of the way so the pushrods can be removed. Identify the pushrods so they can be installed in their original positions.
4. Remove the cylinder head bolts and remove the heads.
5. Install the cylinder heads using new gaskets. Install the gaskets with the bead up.

NOTE: *Coat a steel gasket with sealer on both sides. If a composition gasket is used, do not use sealer.*

6. Clean the bolts, apply sealer to the threads, and install them hand tight.
7. Tighten the head bolts a little at a time in the sequence shown. Head bolt torque is listed in the specifications.
8. Install the intake and exhaust manifolds.
9. Adjust the valves as previously described.

V8 (302 CU IN.)

1. Drain the cooling system.
2. Remove the intake manifold and the carburetor as an assembly, following the "Removal" procedures under "Intake Manifold."
3. Disconnect the spark plug wires, marking them as to placement. Position them out of the way of the cylinder head. Remove the spark plugs.
4. Disconnect the exhaust pipe(s) at the exhaust manifold(s).
5. Disconnect the battery ground cable at the cylinder head (if applicable).
6. Remove the rocker arm covers.
7. In order to remove the right head, it may be necessary to remove the alternator mounting bracket bolt and spacer, the ignition coil, and the air cleaner inlet duct from the right cylinder head.
8. Loosen the rocker arm stud nuts enough to rotate the rocker arms to the side, in order to facilitate the removal of the pushrods. Remove the pushrods in sequence, so they may be installed in their original positions.
9. Remove the cylinder head retaining bolts, noting their positions. On the 351 W engine, it is first necessary to remove the exhaust manifold from the cylinder head. Lift the cylinder head off the block.
10. Remove and discard the old cylinder head gasket.

To install:

1. Clean all surfaces where gaskets are to be installed. These include the cylinder head, intake manifold, valve rocker arm cover, and cylinder block surfaces. On 351 W engines—which have had the exhaust manifold removed to remove the head from the block—the cylinder head exhaust manifold should also be cleaned.
2. If the head was removed for replacement of the head gasket, check the flatness of the cylinder head and engine block gasket surfaces. The method for this checking is explained in the "Engine Rebuilding" section under "Cylinder Head Reconditioning."
3. On 351 W engines where the exhaust manifold has been removed, coat the cylinder head and the exhaust manifold gasket areas with a film of graphite grease.
4. Position the new cylinder head gasket over the cylinder dowels on the block. Coat the head bolts with water-resistant sealer.
5. Position a new gasket(s) on the muffler inlet pipe(s).
6. Position the cylinder head to the block, and install the retaining bolts, each in its original position. On all engines except the 351 W, on which the exhaust manifold has been removed to facilitate the removal of the head, it is important to determine whether the exhaust manifold studs are guided properly into position on the exhaust pipe when positioning the head for installation.
7. Step-torque all the cylinder head retaining bolts in their proper sequence. The bolts should be torqued first to 50 ft lbs, then to 60 ft lbs, and finally to the torque specification found in the "Torque Specifications Chart."
8. On 351 W engines, install a new exhaust manifold gasket and position the exhaust manifold(s), making sure that the exhaust manifold studs are fitted properly into the exhaust pipe connection(s). Torque the exhaust manifold bolts to specifications.

9. Tighten the nuts on exhaust manifold studs, and torque them to 18 ft lbs.

10. Clean and inspect the pushrods one at a time. Clean the oil passage within each pushrod with a suitable solvent and blow the passage out with compressed air. Check the ends of the pushrods for nicks, grooves, roughness, or excessive wear. Visually inspect the pushrods for straightness and replace any bent ones. Do not attempt to straighten the pushrods.

11. Install the pushrods in their original positions. Apply Lubriplate or a similar product to the valve stem tips and to the pushrod guides in the cylinder head.

12. Apply Lubriplate or a similar product to the fulcrum seats and sockets. Turn the rocker arms to their proper position and tighten the stud nuts enough to hold the rocker arms in position. Make sure that the lower ends of the pushrods have remained properly seated in the valve lifters.

13. Perform a preliminary valve adjustment.

14. Apply a coat of oil-resistant sealer to the upper side of a new valve cover gasket. Position the gasket on the valve cover with the cemented side of the gasket facing the valve cover.

15. Install the valve cover(s). Tighten and torque the bolts.

16. Install the intake manifold and carburetor, following the procedure under "Intake Manifold Installation."

17. Refer to the "Belt Tension Adjustment" procedure at the end of the "Engine Electrical" section, and adjust all drive belts which were removed.

18. Refill the cooling system.

19. Connect the battery ground cable at the cylinder head (if applicable).

20. Install the spark plugs and connect the spark plug wires.

21. Start the engine and check for leaks.

22. With the engine running, check and adjust the carburetor idle speed and mixture.

23. With the engine running, listen for abnormal valve noises or irregular idle and correct them.

CYLINDER HEAD OVERHAUL

See the procedures listed in the "Engine Rebuilding Section."

ROCKER ARMS AND PUSHRODS

Removal and Installation

ALL ENGINES EXCEPT 302 CU IN.

1. Remove the valve covers.
2. Remove the rocker arm nuts, rocker arm balls, and rocker arms.
3. Remove the pushrods.
4. Segregate the rocker arms, balls, and pushrods so that they can be installed in their original locations.
5. Install the pushrods. Be sure that the pushrods seat in the lifter sockets.
6. Install the rocker arms, rocker arm balls, and rocker arm nuts. Tighten the rocker arms until all lash is removed. When installing new rocker arms, coat the rocker arms and balls with Molykote or its equivalent.
7. Adjust the valves as outlined later.
8. Install the rocker arm cover.
9. Adjust the carburetor idle speed and mixture.

V8 (302 CU IN.)

1. Remove the rocker arm covers.
2. Remove the rocker arm stud nut, ball unit, and rocker arm.
3. Remove the pushrods.
4. Segregate the rocker arms, balls, and pushrods so they may be installed in their original locations.
5. Apply Molykote to the top of the valve stem and ball units.
6. Install the rocker arm ball unit and rocker arm. Install the stud nuts.
7. Tighten the stud nuts until all lash is removed.
8. Check the valves as detailed later.
9. Install the rocker arm covers.
10. Adjust the carburetor idle speed and mixture.

VALVE ADJUSTMENT

NOTE: *This procedure is not a normal running adjustment. Under normal operating conditions the valves should not require adjustment. This procedure should only be used in the event that the valve train is removed or disturbed.*

HYDRAULIC VALVE ADJUSTMENT

4 and 6 Cylinder

1. Perform the following adjustment with the engine stopped.
2. Remove the valve cover.

3. Adjust the valves when the lifter is on the base circle of the camshaft lobe.

4. Mark the distributor housing with chalk at no. 1 and 6 firing positions (plug wires).

5. Remove the plug wires at the spark plugs and remove the coil wire.

6. Remove the distributor cap and plug wires.

7. Crank the engine until the distributor rotor points to no. 1 firing position and the breaker points are open. In this position the following valves can be adjusted:

No. 1 Cylinder—Exhaust and Intake
No. 2 Cylinder—Intake
No. 3 Cylinder—Exhaust
No. 4 Cylinder—Intake
No. 5 Cylinder—Exhaust
No. 6 Cylinder—Exhaust

Back out the adjusting nut until lash is felt at the pushrod. This can be determined by checking the pushrod side-play while moving the nut. Turn the nut down until all lash is removed. When play is removed, turn the nut down an additional ¾ turn.

8. Crank the engine until the distributor rotor points to no. 6 firing position and the breaker points are open. In this position, the following valves can be adjusted:

No. 2 Cylinder—Exhaust
No. 3 Cylinder—Intake
No. 4 Cylinder—Exhaust
No. 5 Cylinder—Intake
No. 6 Cylinder—Intake and Exhaust

Adjust the valves as outlined in the preceding step.

9. Install the distributor cap and connect the plug wires and coil wire.

10. Install the rocker arm cover and adjust the carburetor.

V8 (EXCEPT 302 CU IN.)

1. Remove the valve cover and adjust the valves with the lifter on the base circle of the camshaft lobe.

2. Crank the engine with the starter or by hand (spark plugs removed) until the mark on the damper aligns with the "0" mark on the timing tab. This can be determined by placing your fingers on no. 1 spark plug port until compression is felt. This is no. 1 firing position.

3. With the engine in no. 1 firing position, the following valves can be adjusted:

Left-Hand Rotation Engines—
    Exhaust: 1-3-4-8
    Intake: 1-2-5-7
Right-Hand Rotation Engines—
    Exhaust: 1-2-5-7
    Intake: 1-3-4-8

Back off the adjusting nut until lash is felt. This can be determined by checking the pushrod side-play as the nut is turned. Turn the adjusting nut down until all play is removed. Tighten the nut an additional ¾ turn. No other adjustment is required.

4. Crank the engine ONE more revolution until the "0" mark and the pointer align again. This is no. 6 firing position. In this position, the following valves can be adjusted:

Adjusting hydraulic valve lifters on 4 and 6 cylinder engines

Hydraulic valve lifter adjustment (V8 except 302 cu in.)

Left-Hand Rotation Engines—
 Exhaust: 2-5-6-7
 Intake: 3-4-6-8
Right-Hand Rotation Engines—
 Exhaust: 3-4-6-8
 Intake: 2-5-6-7
5. Install the rocker arm covers.
6. Adjust the carburetor idle speed and mixture.

V8 (302 CU IN.)

1. Valve clearance adjustment is not necessary. If a noise is present in the valve train (which is not caused by a collapsed lifter) use the following procedure to check for worn valve train components.
2. Position the piston of a given cylinder on TDC after the compression stroke.
3. Apply pressure to slowly bleed down the valve lifter until the plunger is completely bottomed.
4. While holding the lifter in the fully collapsed position, check the clearance between the rocker arm and valve stem tip. The feeler gauge width must not exceed 3/8 in., and the clearance must be 0.083–0.183 in. Replace worn parts as necessary.
5. Perform the above check on each suspected cylinder.

Hydraulic valve lifter adjustment—302 cu in. engine

ENGINE COOLING

Standard Cooling

MerCruisers with over 90 hp have dual-pump cooling. One pump is used to pull water up to the engine and the other is used to circulate the water. Thermostatic heat control provides fast and controlled warm-up and controlled water temperature at all times.

Closed Cooling System

Engines which are equipped with a closed cooling system are cooled with fresh water circulated through a heat exchanger. Fresh water in the system is cooled by sea water which flows through the heat exchanger and is discharged overboard. The fresh water system of the cooling system is pressurized and the coolant temperature is thermostatically controlled.

Precautions

1. Do not operate the engine without cooling water flowing through the sea water pump, or else the pump will be damaged.
2. Do not remove the heat exchanger cap while the engine is hot. This has the same effect as removing the radiator cap from a car radiator while the engine is hot. Serious injury could result.

MERCRUISER STERN DRIVE - 120, 140, 160 & 165 STANDARD COOLING SYSTEM

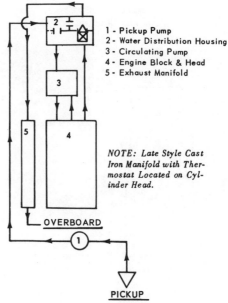

1 - Pickup Pump
2 - Water Distribution Housing
3 - Circulating Pump
4 - Engine Block & Head
5 - Exhaust Manifold

NOTE: Late Style Cast Iron Manifold with Thermostat Located on Cylinder Head.

MerCruiser 120 thru 165 standard cooling system

MERCRUISER STERN DRIVE - 215, 250 & 270
STANDARD COOLING SYSTEM

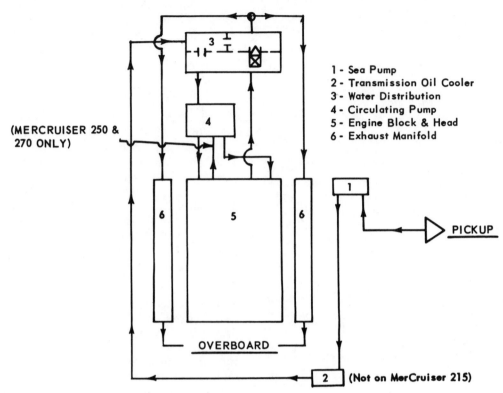

1 - Sea Pump
2 - Transmission Oil Cooler
3 - Water Distribution
4 - Circulating Pump
5 - Engine Block & Head
6 - Exhaust Manifold

MerCruiser 215, 250, and 270 standard cooling system

MERCRUISER 325
STANDARD COOLING SYSTEM

1 - Sea Pump
2 - Transmission Oil Cooler
3 - Engine Oil Cooler
4 - Water Distribution
5 - Circulating Pump
6 - Engine Block and Head
7 - Exhaust Manifolds

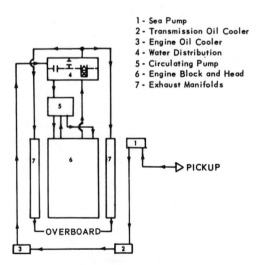

MerCruiser 325 standard cooling system

HEATED MANIFOLD COOLING SYSTEM

1 - Sea Pump
2 - Transmission Oil Cooler*
3 - Engine Oil Cooler▲
4 - Water Distribution Hsg.
5 - Engine Circulating Pmp.
6 - Engine Block & Heads
7 - Manifold
8 - Exhaust Elbows

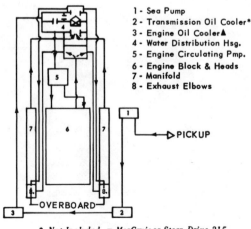

* *Not Included on MerCruiser Stern Drive 215*
▲ *Not Included on 215-270 MerCruiser Stern Drive and Inboard*

MerCruiser 215 thru 325 heated manifold cooling system

MERCRUISER STERN DRIVE 120-140-160 AND 165 FRESH WATER COOLING SYSTEM

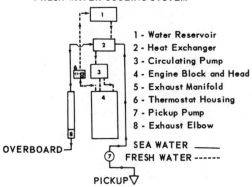

1 - Water Reservoir
2 - Heat Exchanger
3 - Circulating Pump
4 - Engine Block and Head
5 - Exhaust Manifold
6 - Thermostat Housing
7 - Pickup Pump
8 - Exhaust Elbow

SEA WATER _____
FRESH WATER ------

OVERBOARD

PICKUP ▽

MerCruiser 120 thru 165 fresh water cooling system

MERCRUISER STERN DRIVE and INBOARD ENGINE 215 and 270 FRESH WATER COOLING SYSTEM (SQUARE RESERVOIR)

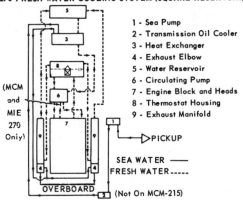

1 - Sea Pump
2 - Transmission Oil Cooler
3 - Heat Exchanger
4 - Exhaust Elbow
5 - Water Reservoir
6 - Circulating Pump
7 - Engine Block and Heads
8 - Thermostat Housing
9 - Exhaust Manifold

(MCM and MIE 270 Only)

▷PICKUP

SEA WATER _____
FRESH WATER -----

(Not On MCM-215)

MerCruiser 215 and 270 fresh water cooling system

MERCRUISER STERN DRIVE and INBOARD ENGINE 225-250-270-325 FRESH WATER COOLING SYSTEM (ROUND RESERVOIR)

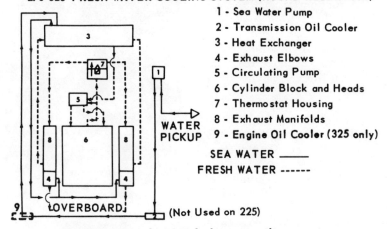

1 - Sea Water Pump
2 - Transmission Oil Cooler
3 - Heat Exchanger
4 - Exhaust Elbows
5 - Circulating Pump
6 - Cylinder Block and Heads
7 - Thermostat Housing
8 - Exhaust Manifolds
9 - Engine Oil Cooler (325 only)

SEA WATER _____
FRESH WATER ------

WATER PICKUP

OVERBOARD

(Not Used on 225)

MerCruiser 225 thru 325 fresh water cooling system

MERCRUISER STERN DRIVE and INBOARD ENGINE 325 and 390 FRESH WATER COOLING SYSTEM (SQUARE RESERVOIR)

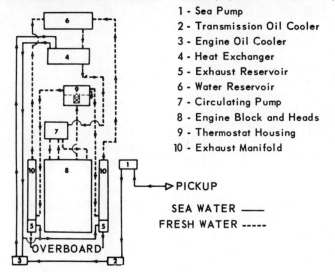

1 - Sea Pump
2 - Transmission Oil Cooler
3 - Engine Oil Cooler
4 - Heat Exchanger
5 - Exhaust Reservoir
6 - Water Reservoir
7 - Circulating Pump
8 - Engine Block and Heads
9 - Thermostat Housing
10 - Exhaust Manifold

▷PICKUP

SEA WATER _____
FRESH WATER -----

OVERBOARD

MerCruiser 325 and 390 fresh water cooling system

INSPECTION

1. Inspect all hoses and connections for cracks and deterioration.

2. Check for loose hose connections and defective hoses or gaskets.

Heat Exchanger Pressure Cap

1. The heat exchanger pressure cap should be checked and washed with clean water at regular tune-up intervals.

2. Check the rubber seal on the cap for tears or cracks.

4 and 6 cylinder water pump location

REPLACEMENT

1. Remove the water hose(s) from the thermostat housing.

2. Remove the thermostat housing bolts, housing, and gasket.

3. Remove the thermostat and inspect the valve to be sure that it is in good condition.

4. Place the thermostat in water which has been heated to 25° F above the temperature stamped on the valve. The valve should open completely.

5. Remove the thermostat and place it in water that has been cooled to 10° F below the temperature stamped on the valve. The thermostat valve should close completely.

6. If the thermostat is in good condition, as indicated by the tests in steps 4 and 5, reinstall it using a new gasket.

7. If it is defective, replace it with a new one, using a new gasket.

Circulating Water Pump

4, 6, AND 8 CYLINDER ENGINES

Removal

1. Drain the cooling system.

2. Remove the pulley bolts.

3. Loosen the alternator upper brace and swivel bolt and remove the drive belt.

4. Remove the pulley.

5. Remove the pump-to-cylinder block bolts and remove the pump and old gasket.

Inspection

1. Check the pump for cracks and wear.

2. Clean and inspect the sealing surface.

3. If the pump is serviceable, install it with a new gasket. If not, replace the pump with a new one.

V8 water pump location

Installation

1. Install the pump assembly with a new gasket coated with sealer. Tighten the bolts to specifications.

2. Install the pump pulley and tighten the bolts to specifications.

3. Connect the hoses and fill the cooling system.

4. Install the drive belt and tighten the upper brace and swivel bolt.

5. Adjust the drive belt as specified at the beginning of this chapter.

6. Start the engine and check for leaks.

Fresh Water Cooling System Maintenance

4, 6, AND 8 CYLINDER ENGINES

The fresh water section of the cooling system should be drained and refilled with new coolant at least once a year. Use the following instructions for draining and refilling.

1. The coolant level should be checked periodically and coolant added as necessary.

2. If the coolant level is excessively low, the cooling system should be checked for leaks and repaired as necessary.

3. Normal coolant level is ½ in. below the top of the exchanger. If the exchanger is overfilled, excess coolant will flow out the overflow pipe when the engine reaches operating temperature.

DRAINING INSTRUCTIONS

4 and 6 Cylinder Engines with Fresh Water Cooling

1. Remove the cap from the heat exchanger.

CAUTION: *The heat exchanger is equipped with a 14 lb pressure cap. To remove the cap, turn a quarter of a turn to allow the pressure in the cooling system to escape, and then turn the cap all the way off.*

2. Remove the drain plug from the cylinder block, and the drain plug near the bottom of the heat exchanger.

3. Place a container under the drains to prevent water from draining into the boat.

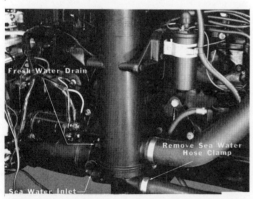

Fresh water cooling system drain plugs

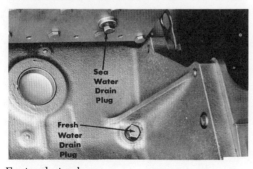

Engine drain plugs

4. When the fresh water section of the system has drained thoroughly, apply sealant to the threads of the plugs and reinstall the plugs securely.

Draining the Fresh Water Cooling System

1. Remove the drain plugs from the bottom of the manifold and heat exchanger.

2. Remove the hose from the heat exchanger.

3. Remove the water intake hose from the intake side of the heat exchanger and plug the end of the hose to prevent water from entering the boat.

4. Place a container under the drains to prevent water from draining into the boat.

5. When the fresh water cooling system has drained thoroughly, coat the plugs with sealer and install the plugs securely.

6. Reinstall the hose and clamps.

Cleaning the Sea Water Section of the Exchanger

1. If necessary, remove the heat exchanger from the engine.

2. Remove the end plates from the exchanger.

3. Clean the water passages by inserting a suitably sized brush.

4. Coat both sides of a new end plate gasket with sealant and install the gasket.

5. Install the end plates on the exchanger.

6. Install the screws and tighten them securely.

7. If removed, install the heat exchanger on the engine.

8. Fill the system and operate the engine, checking for leaks.

V8 Engines with Fresh Water Cooling

DRAINING THE FRESH WATER COOLING SECTION

1. Remove the cap from the heat exchanger.

2. Remove the drain plug (A) from the bottom of the exchanger.

3. Remove the drain plugs from the manifolds and cylinder block. One plug is located in the bottom of each manifold and one plug is located on each side of the cylinder block.

4. Drain the system into containers.

5. Coat the plugs with sealant and reinstall securely.

Heat exchanger drain locations (190 thru 225)

Engine drain plug location (190 thru 225)

Heat exchanger end plate (starboard side)

Heat exchanger end plate (port side)

DRAINING THE SEA WATER COOLING SECTION

1. Remove drain plug (B) from the bottom of the exchanger.

2. Loosen the hose clamp (C) and remove the hose from the exchanger.

3. Remove the water intake hose from the intake side of the sea water pump and plug the hose to prevent water from entering the boat.

4. Drain the water into a container and install the intake hose, after removing the plug.

5. Coat the plug with sealant and install it securely.

CLEANING THE SEA WATER SECTION OF THE EXCHANGER

1. Refer to the instructions under "Cleaning the Sea Water Section of the Exchanger" for four-cylinder and six-cylinder models.

NOTE: *The starboard and port end plates are not interchangeable. The alignment marks must be as illustrated. Be sure that the gaskets are positioned correctly.*

Filling the Cooling System

All Models

NOTE: *When filling the cooling system, it is best to use soft water. If soft water is not available, hard water may be used, although it may leave deposits of scale on the internal parts of the cooling system, due to the high mineral content of hard water.*

Engines Not Exposed To Freezing Temperatures

1. Fill the cooling system with a mixture of clean soft water and an automotive cooling system rust inhibitor, mixed to the proportions recommended by the inhibitor manufacturer.

2. Remove the cap and fill the heat exchanger with water, allowing room for the rust inhibitor.

3. Add the rust inhibitor.

4. Start the engine and run at idle.

5. While the engine is running, add enough water to the engine to bring the level of water to ½ in. below the top of the exchanger (1 in. on 225 models).

6. Check all hose connections and fittings for leaks.

7. Install the heat exchanger cap.

8. Check the engine temperature. It should not exceed 180° F.

Engines Exposed To Freezing Temperatures

1. Fill the engine to the proper level with a mixture of clean soft water and permanent type antifreeze mixed to the proportions recommended by the antifreeze manufacturer for the lowest temperature to which the engine will be exposed.

NOTE: *Alcohol-base or methanol-base coolants or plain water are not recommended for your engine at any time.*

If the engine is operated any time when the possibility of freezing temperatures no longer exists, the coolant should be drained and the engine refilled with a coolant mixture described under the preceding section.

2. Before filling the system, torque the cylinder head bolts and all manifold bolts to specifications.

3. Remove the exchanger cap and fill the system with clean soft water.

4. Start the engine and run it at idle. The level of the water should be ½ in. below the top of the reservoir (1 in. on 225 models).

5. Stop the engine and determine the quantity of antifreeze needed according to the antifreeze manufacturer's recommenda-

tion for the volume of the cooling system.

6. Remove the drain plug on the side of the engine and drain off enough water for the antifreeze to be added. Replace the plug and tighten it securely.

7. Add the antifreeze to the exchanger. If the level of the water is not as specified (step 4), add water as required.

8. Check all hose connections and fittings for leaks. Check the temperature gauge which should not exceed 180° F.

Water Pick-up Pump (V8 Engines)

REMOVAL

NOTE: *The following procedure applies to pumps designated B-46-32901A2 (V8 engines), B-46-47506A1, and B-46-58001A4.*

1. Loosen the adjustment bracket and remove the drive belt.

2. Before removing the water intake hose, make provisions to plug the hose to prevent water from entering the boat.

3. Remove the intake and outlet hoses and plug the intake hose.

4. Remove the screw(s) securing the pump to the mounting bracket.

INSTALLATION

1. Install the mounting screws and align the drive belt with washers if necessary.

2. Install the intake and outlet hoses after removing the plug from the intake hose.

3. Install the drive belt.

4. Install the adjustment bracket screw and adjust the belt tension.

5. Start the engine and check for leaks.

Outdrive Unit

Different outdrives are used with different groups of engines, according to the horsepower of the engine and the intended uses of the rig. When ordering parts for outdrives, always specify the engine horsepower and the outdrive serial number.

To assure correct and durable operation after assembly, all adjustments and torque values specified must be maintained.

NOTE: *Repair procedures in this section are limited to those that can be accomplished with an average number of hand tools. Keep in mind that an attempt to effect repairs without the specified factory tools is false economy, and will only lead to premature failure of parts, due to improper assembly. Any repair not listed here should be referred to an authorized service facility.*

PROPELLER

Removal

ALL MODELS

1. Place a block of wood between the propeller and the cavitation plate to prevent the propeller from turning while removing the propeller nut.
2. Remove the propeller nut.
3. Bend back the tabs on the tab washer and remove the tab washer, cupped thrust washer, propeller, and thrust hub and the washer assembly.

INSTALLATION

1. Installation is the reverse of removal.

GEAR HOUSING

All Models through 888

There are several types of gear housings in this range, classified according to the following chart:

MerCruiser Model	Gear Housing Type
1	Straight cut bevel gear
1–1A–1B–1C	Spiral cut bevel gear
1A–1B–1C–120 140–160–165	Spiral cut bevel gear with E–Z shift

REMOVAL

1. Drain the gear lubricant as detailed in the "General Information and Lubrication" section of this chapter.
2. Remove the propeller.
3. Remove the three locknuts from the leading edge of the gear housing assembly.
4. Remove the two locknuts located in the center bottom side of the cavitation plate.
5. Remove the trim tab.
6. Remove the allen head screw from inside the trim tab cavity.
7. Separate the gear housing from the driveshaft housing and place it in a vise with soft jaws.

WATER PUMP REPLACEMENT

1. Remove the O-ring from the upper end of the driveshaft.
2. Remove the centrifugal slinger from the driveshaft.
3. Remove the water pump body by removing the nuts and lockwashers and the cap screw and lockwasher.
4. Remove the impeller, impeller drive pin, gaskets, and face plate.
5. Check the impeller and water pump insert closely for wear or damage.
6. Remove the flushing screw seal and gasket and allow water to drain from the pump base assembly.

NOTE: *The flushing screw is not used on later gear housings.*

7. Remove the base assembly and remove the O-ring from the pump base.
8. Position the water pump base assembly and gasket in the gear housing.
9. Install the water pump base-to-face plate gasket and replace the stainless face plate.
10. If the water pump impeller drive pin and impeller hub are excessively worn, a new pin should be bonded to the driveshaft with type AV Loctite, using the following procedure. If this condition does not exist, proceed to step 11.

   a. Using fresh solvent, clean the driveshaft from the face plate to the drive splines. Clean the impeller insert and drive pin. Do not allow solvent to contact the pump base oil seal.

   b. Rotate the driveshaft so that the flat faces up. Smear AV Loctite on the

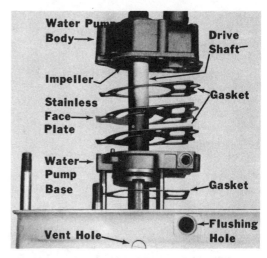

Water pump (outdrive) MerCruiser I thru 165

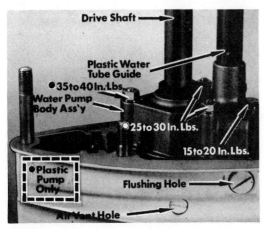

Installed water pump assembly (MerCruiser I thru 165)

shaft section on which the impeller will ride.

c. Roll the drive pin in this puddle and leave it centered on the flat.

d. Slide the impeller onto the shaft with the keyway aligned with the drive pin. Slowly push the impeller down to the face plate.

e. Rotate the impeller several times as far as the drive pin will allow to thoroughly coat the impeller insert with Loctite.

f. Wipe off any excess Loctite which appears above the impeller.

g. Proceed with step 13.

11. Place the drive pin on the driveshaft, holding it in position with a dab of New Multipurpose Lubricant.

12. Carefully check the condition of the impeller and set it in place over the driveshaft.

13. Insert the stainless water pump cartridge in the water pump and place the water pump body-to-face plate gasket in position.

14. Slide the water pump body over the driveshaft and impeller.

15. Turn the shaft clockwise and press the water pump body in place at the same time, seating the impeller. Be sure that the impeller drive pin is in the groove of the impeller.

16. Replace the lockwashers and tighten the nuts and cap screw.

NOTE: *Refer to the torque values listed in the "Specifications" for these attachings. Failure to respect the torque values will lead to leakage or cracking of the pump.*

17. Install the plastic water tube guide in the pump body recess.

18. Replace the O-ring and driveshaft slinger.

19. On gear housings with interconnected oil chambers, install the O-ring in the recess with adhesive.

CAUTION: *If Loctite is used during assembly, allow the gear housing to remain horizontal at room temperature (not more than 120° F) for at least 12 hours. The gear housing can then be reinstalled.*

INSTALLATION

1. If the water intake tube was removed when the gear housing was separated, coat the upper end of the tube with New Multipurpose Lubricant so that it will slip easily into the rubber seal in the driveshaft housing.

2. Place a light coat of New Multipurpose Lubricant on the end of the water tube.

3. Apply a heavy coat of New Multipurpose Lubricant to the driveshaft splines.

4. Be sure that the shift control lever and the gear housing are in Forward gear before installing the gear housing. Hold the unit in Forward gear by applying light pressure to the propeller shaft in a counterclockwise direction.

5. Insert the driveshaft into the driveshaft housing, aligning the water tube with the water tube guide and the driveshaft splines with the upper driveshaft.

6. Be sure that the water intake tube enters the plastic guide in the water pump body recess.

7. Rotate the propeller shaft to align the driveshaft splines. Be sure that the upper and lower shift shaft splines are aligned.

8. With the two housings joined, install and tighten the stopnuts to the proper torque.

9. Install the trim tab and tighten the screw to specifications. Replace the plastic plug.

10. Adjust the trim tab.

MerCruiser II and MerCruiser II Heavy-Duty

The MerCruiser II and MerCruiser II Heavy-Duty outdrives are almost identical except for application. There is, however, no water pump on the outdrives with smaller units.

REMOVAL

1. Remove the propeller and trim tab. On 1.33:1 units, rotate the drive 180°, release the reverse locks and drain the lubricant. On 1.78:1 units, use the Power Trim to tilt the unit, easing drainage of the lubricant.

2. Remove the hex head cap screws and allen head screws from the cavitation plate area.

3. Separate the gear housing from the driveshaft housing.

NOTE: *Reverse locks and 180° rotation are not incorporated into the 1:78:1 drive since it has the Power Trim hydraulic system.*

INSTALLATION

1. Place a new gasket on the driveshaft housing-to-gear housing mating surface. Before joining the housings, position the trim tab allen head screw and, on later models, install the oil tube in the driveshaft housing.

NOTE: *When replacing complete gear housing assemblies on units serial number 1602186, it is not necessary to install the oil tube in the gear housing, since the early style driveshaft housing is not machined to accept the oil tube. The oil tube seal must be removed from the ball bearing retainer. Also, it is not necessary to install the oil tube in the gear housing when a late style driveshaft housing is replaced on units serial no. 1602186.*

2. Join the gear housing and driveshaft housing by inserting the driveshaft through the sliding clutch. Install the nuts and screws and tighten them to specifications.

3. Refill the drive unit with approved lubricant.

MerCruiser 215 (E and H Models)

CAUTION: *Do not attempt to remove the gear housing from these models. Gear housing removal requires that the drive unit be removed from the transom (see NOTE on page 151).*

MerCruiser III

REMOVAL

1. Tilt up the drive unit with the hydraulic system.

2. Remove the propeller and trim tab.

3. Remove the allen head screw and elastic stopnuts which hold the gear housing to the driveshaft housing.

4. Support the gear housing while removing the attaching nuts. It should begin to separate from the driveshaft housing as the nuts are removed.

INSTALLATION

1. Align a new gasket on the driveshaft housing-to-gear housing mating surface. Before joining the gear housing, install the trim tab allen head screw.

2. Join the gear housing and driveshaft housing by inserting the driveshaft into the gear splines.

3. Install and tighten the elastic stopnuts.

4. Refill the drive unit with fresh lubricant of the approved type.

5. Check the reservoir level.

6. Install the trim tab.

7. Install the propeller.

3 · Outboard Marine Corporation

General Information and Specifications

INTRODUCTION

OMC Stern Drive, a division of Outboard Marine Corporation supplies inboard/outdrive installations to the makers of over 200 boats. Powerplants are available from 90 horsepower to 245 horsepower, with popular horsepower models in between.

OMC stern drives are constantly being tested and evaluated in Florida, Lake Michigan and various proving grounds in Europe. From this rigorous testing program have come such developments as Lyfanited aluminum parts (a process which protects the metal anodizing). All dissimilar metals are protected by a buffer to prevent electrolysis.

OMC stern drive engines are equipped with such features as water cooled exhaust manifolds which retain water after shutdown, to minimize corrosion, exhaust valve rotators to distribute heat and wear evenly, main and connecting rod bearings made especially for marine use and an oil-drain tube to permit easy oil changes. OMC outdrives are equipped with Selectrim, which permits a 90° port to starboard turning radius and a 75° tilt, even while underway.

General Engine Specifications

Year	Engine Cu. In. Displacement	No. of Cyls.	Advertised Horsepower	Bore and Stroke (in.)	Advertised Compression Ratio	Oil Pressure @ rpm (psi)
1967	153	L4	120	3.875 × 3.250	8.5:1	35 @ 2,000
	225	V-6	155	3.750 × 3.400	9.0:1	40 @ 2,400
	283	V-8	185	3.875 × 3.000	9.0:1	
	300	V-8	200	3.750 × 3.400	9.0:1	40 @ 2,400

General Engine Specifications (cont.)

Year	Engine Cu. In. Displacement	No. of Cyls.	Advertised Horsepower	Bore and Stroke (in.)	Advertised Compression Ratio	Oil Pressure @ rpm (psi)
1968	153	L4	120	3.875 × 3.250	8.5:1	35 @ 2,000
	225	V-6	155	3.750 × 3.400	9.0:1	40 @ 2,400
	283	V-8	185	3.875 × 3.000	9.0:1	30–45 @ 2,000
	283	V-8	210	3.875 × 3.000	9.0:1	30–45 @ 2,000
1969	153	L4	120	3.875 × 3.250	8.5:1	35 @ 2,000
	225	V-6	155	3.750 × 3.400	9.0:1	40 @ 2,400
	307	V-8	210	3.875 × 3.250	8.5:1	30–45 @ 2,000
1970	153	L4	120	3.875 × 3.250	8.5:1	35 @ 2,000
	225	V-6	155	3.750 × 3.400	9.0:1	40 @ 2,400
	307	V-8	210	3.875 × 3.250	8.5:1	30–45 @ 2,000
1971	153	L4	120	3.875 × 3.250	8.5:1	35 @ 2,000
	225	V-6	155	3.750 × 3.400	9.0:1	40 @ 2,400
	307	V-8	215	3.875 × 3.530	8.5:1	30–45 @ 2,000
	307	V-8	235	3.875 × 3.250	8.5:1	30–45 @ 2,000
1972	153	L4	120	3.875 × 3.250	8.5:1	35 @ 2,000
	225	V-6	155	3.750 × 3.400	9.0:1	40 @ 2,400
	250	L6	165	3.875 × 3.250	8.5:1	30–45 @ 2,000
	307	V-8	225	3.875 × 3.250	8.5:1	30–45 @ 2,000
	307	V-8	245	3.875 × 3.250	8.5:1	30–45 @ 2,000

Tune-Up Specifications

When analyzing compression test results, look for uniformity among cylinders rather than specific pressures.

Engine		Spark Plugs			Distributor		Ignition Timing (deg)	Compression Pressure (psi)	Fuel Pump Pressure (psi)	Idle Speed (rpm)
Year	(hp)	Type	Gap (in.)	Point Dwell (deg)	Point Gap (in.)					
1967	120	AC-C44N	0.035	31–34	0.019 *	4 BTDC	130	3.5–4.5	500	
	155	AC-43S	0.035	30	0.016	5 BTDC	①	4–5.75	550 (in gear)	
	185	AC-C43	0.035	26	0.020	8 BTDC	150	7–9	550	
	200	AC-43S	0.035	30	0.016	2½ BTDC	①	4–5	550 (in gear)	
1968	120	AC-C44N	0.035	31–34	0.019 *	4 BTDC	130	3.5–4.5	500	
	155	AC-43S	0.035	30	0.016	5 BTDC	①	4–5.75	550 (in gear)	
	185	AC-C43	0.035	30	0.018	8 BTDC	150	7–9	550	
	210	AC-C43	0.035	30	0.018	8 BTDC	150	7–9	550	
1969	120	AC-C44N	0.035	31–34	0.019 *	4 BTDC	130	3.5–4.5	500 (in gear)	
	155	AC-43S	0.035	30	0.016	5 BTDC	①	4–5.75	550 (in gear)	
	210	AC-C43	0.035	30	0.018	10 BTDC	165	7–9	550	
1970	120	AC-C44N	0.035	31–34	0.019 *	4 BTDC	130	3.5–4.5	500 (in gear)	
	155	AC-43S	0.035	30	0.016	5 BTDC	①	4–5.75	550 (in gear)	
	210	AC-CR43K	0.035	30	0.018	10 BTDC	165	7–9	550	
1971	120	AC-C44RN	0.035	31–34	0.019 *	4 BTDC	130	3.5–4.5	500 (in gear)	
	155	AC-M43S	0.035	30	0.016	5 BTDC	①	4–5.75	550 (in gear)	
	215	②	0.035	30	0.018	10 BTDC	165	7–9	550	
	235	②	0.035	30	0.018	3 BTDC	165	7–9	600	
1972	120	AC-CR44N	0.035	31–34	0.019 *	4 BTDC	130	3.5–4.5	500 (in gear)	
	155	AC-M43S	0.035	30	0.016	5 BTDC	①	4–5.75	550 (in gear)	
	165	AC-M43T	0.035	31–34	0.019 *	6 BTDC	130	3.5–4.5	500 (in gear)	
	225	AC-MR43T	0.035	30	0.018	10 BTDC	165	7–9	550	
	245	AC-MR43T	0.035	30	0.018	10 BTDC	165	7–9	600	

*—0.016 used points.
①—Lowest reading within 75% of highest reading.
②—Cyl. Heads w/ 14 mm. × $^{13}/_{16}$ Hex Plugs—AC-CR43K; Cyl. Heads w/ 14 mm. Taperseat Plugs—AC-R43T.

Firing Orders

FRONT

① ② ③ ④

1 – 3 – 4 – 2

120 HP

FRONT

① ②
③ ④
⑤ ⑥

1 – 6 – 5 – 4 – 3 – 2

155 HP

FRONT

① ② ③ ④ ⑤ ⑥

1-5-3-6-2-4

165 HP

FRONT

① ②
③ ④
⑤ ⑥
⑦ ⑧

1 – 8 – 4 – 3 – 6 – 5 – 7 – 2

185, 210, 215, 225, 235, and 245 HP

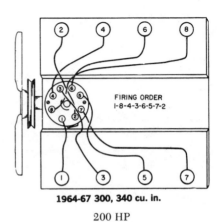

FIRING ORDER
I-8-4-3-6-5-7-2

1964-67 300, 340 cu. in.

200 HP

Crankshaft and Connecting Rod Specifications

All measurements are given in in.

| | | Crankshaft | | | | Connecting Rod | | |
Year	Engine (hp)	Main Brg. Journal Dia.	Main Brg. Oil Clearance	Shaft End-Play	Thrust on No.	Journal Diameter	Oil Clearance	Side Clearance
1967	120	2.2983–2.2993	0.0029–0.0003	0.002–0.006	Rear Main	1.999–2.000	0.0007–0.0027	0.0085–0.0135
	155	2.4995	0.0004–0.0015	0.004–0.008	2	2.000	0.0002–0.0023	0.006–0.014①
	185	②	③	0.003–0.011	Rear Main	1.999–2.000	0.0007–0.0027	0.009–0.013
	200	2.4995	0.0004–0.0015	0.004–0.008	3	2.000	0.0002–0.0023	0.006–0.014①
1968	120	2.2983–2.2993	0.0029–0.0003	0.002–0.006	Rear Main	1.999–2.000	0.0007–0.0027	0.0085–0.0135
	155	2.4995	0.0004–0.0015	0.004–0.008	2	2.000	0.0002–0.0023	0.006–0.014①

Crankshaft and Connecting Rod Specifications (cont.)

All measurements are given in in.

Year	Engine (hp)	Crankshaft				Connecting Rod		
		Main Brg. Journal Dia.	Main Brg. Oil Clearance	Shaft End-Play	Thrust on No.	Journal Diameter	Oil Clearance	Side Clearance
1968	185	②	③	0.003–0.011	Rear Main	1.999–2.000	0.0007–0.0027	0.009–0.013
	210	②	③	0.003–0.011	Rear Main	1.999–2.000	0.0007–0.0027	0.009–0.013
1969	120	2.2983–2.2993	0.0029–0.0003	0.002–0.006	Rear Main	1.999–2.000	0.0007–0.0027	0.0085–0.0135
	155	2.4995	0.0004–0.0015	0.004–0.008	2	2.000	0.0002–0.0023	0.006–0.014①
	210	②	③	0.003–0.011	Rear Main	1.999–2.000	0.0007–0.0027	0.009–0.013
1970	120	2.2983–2.2993	0.0029–0.0003	0.002–0.006	Rear Main	1.999–2.000	0.0007–0.0027	0.0085–0.0135
	155	2.4995	0.0004–0.0015	0.004–0.008	2	2.000	0.0002–0.0023	0.006–0.014①
	210	②	③	0.003–0.011	Rear Main	1.999–2.000	0.0007–0.0027	0.0085–0.0135
1971	120	2.2983–2.2993	0.0029–0.003	0.002–0.006	Rear Main	1.999–2.000	0.0007–0.0027	0.0085–0.0135
	155	2.4495	0.0004–0.0015	0.004–0.008	2	2.000	0.0002–0.0003	0.006–0.014①
	215	②	③	0.003–0.011	Rear Main	1.999–2.000	0.0007–0.0027	0.0085–0.0135
	235	②	③	0.003–0.011	Rear Main	1.999–2.000	0.0007–0.0027	0.0085–0.0135
1972	120	2.2983–2.2993	0.0029–0.0003	0.002–0.006	Rear Main	1.999–2.000	0.0007–0.0027	0.0085–0.0135
	155	2.4495	0.0004–0.0015	0.004–0.008	2	2.000	0.0002–0.0003	0.006–0.014①
	165	2.2983–2.2993	④	0.002–0.006	Rear Main	1.999–2.000	0.0007–0.0027	0.0009–0.0014
	225	②	③	0.003–0.011	Rear Main	1.999–2.000	0.0007–0.0027	0.0085–0.0135
	245	②	③	0.003–0.011	Rear Main	1.999–2.000	0.0007–0.0027	0.0085–0.0135

①—Total of both connecting rods.
②—No. 1—2.2984–2.2993; Nos. 2, 3, 4—2.2983–2.2993; No. 5—2.2978–2.2988.
③—No. 1—0.0008–0.0020; Nos. 2, 3, 4—0.0018–0.0020; No. 5—0.0010–0.0036.
④—No. 1—0.002; All others—0.0035 (max.).

Ring Gap Specifications (in.)

Year	Engine (hp)	Top Compression	Bottom Compression	Oil Control
1967	120	0.010–0.020	0.010–0.020	0.015–0.055
	155	0.010–0.020	0.010–0.020	0.015–0.035
	185	0.010–0.020	0.010–0.020	0.015–0.055
	200	0.010–0.020	0.010–0.020	0.015–0.035
1968	120	0.010–0.020	0.010–0.020	0.015–0.055
	155	0.010–0.020	0.010–0.020	0.015–0.035
	185	0.010–0.020	0.010–0.020	0.015–0.055
	210	0.010–0.020	0.010–0.020	0.015–0.055
1969	120	0.010–0.020	0.010–0.020	0.015–0.055
	155	0.010–0.020	0.010–0.020	0.015–0.035
	210	0.010–0.020	0.010–0.020	0.015–0.055
1970	120	0.010–0.020	0.010–0.020	0.015–0.055
	155	0.010–0.020	0.010–0.020	0.015–0.035
	210	0.010–0.020	0.010–0.020	0.015–0.055
1971	120	0.010–0.020	0.010–0.020	0.015–0.055
	155	0.010–0.020	0.010–0.020	0.015–0.035
	215	0.010–0.020	0.010–0.020	0.015–0.055
	235	0.010–0.020	0.010–0.020	0.015–0.055
1972	120	0.010–0.020	0.010–0.020	0.015–0.055
	155	0.010–0.020	0.010–0.020	0.015–0.035
	165	0.010–0.020	0.010–0.020	0.015–0.065
	225	0.010–0.020	0.010–0.020	0.015–0.055
	245	0.010–0.020	0.010–0.020	0.015–0.055

Valve Specifications

Year	Engine (hp)	Seat Angle (deg.)	Face Angle (deg.)	Spring Test Pressure (lbs. @ in.)	Stem to Guide Clearance (in.)	
					Intake	Exhaust
1967	120	46	45	170–180 @ 1.26①	0.0010–0.0027	0.0015–0.0032
	155	45	45	159–169 @ 1.33	0.0012–0.0032	②
	185	46	45	170–180 @ 1.26①	0.0010–0.0027	0.0010–0.0027
	200	45	45	159–169 @ 1.34	0.0012–0.0032	②
1968	120	46	45	170–180 @ 1.26①	0.0010–0.0027	0.0015–0.0032
	155	45	45	159–169 @ 1.33	0.0012–0.0032	②
	185	46	45	170–180 @ 1.26①	0.0010–0.0027	0.0010–0.0027
	210	46	45	170–180 @ 1.26①	0.0010–0.0027	0.0010–0.0027
1969	120	46	45	170–180 @ 1.26①	0.0010–0.0027	0.0015–0.0032
	155	45	45	159–169 @ 1.33	0.0012–0.0032	②
	210	46	45	170–180 @ 1.26①	0.0010–0.0027	0.0010–0.0027
1970	120	46	45	170–180 @ 1.26①	0.0010–0.0027	0.0015–0.0032
	155	45	45	159–169 @ 1.33	0.0012–0.0032	②
	210	46	45	170–180 @ 1.26①	0.0010–0.0027	0.0010–0.0027
1971	120	46	45	170–180 @ 1.26①	0.0010–0.0027	0.0015–0.0032
	155	45	45	159–169 @ 1.33	0.0012–0.0032	②
	215	46	45	170–180 @ 1.26①	0.0010–0.0027	0.0010–0.0027
	235	46	45	170–180 @ 1.26①	0.0010–0.0027	0.0010–0.0027
1972	120	46	45	170–180 @ 1.26①	0.0010–0.0027	0.0015–0.0032
	155	45	45	159–169 @ 1.33	0.0012–0.0032	②
	165	46	45	180–192 @ 1.27①	0.0010–0.0027	0.0015–0.0032
	225	46	45	170–180 @ 1.26①	0.0010–0.0027	0.0010–0.0027
	245	46	45	170–180 @ 1.26①	0.0010–0.0027	0.0010–0.0027

①—Outer Spring.
②—Top—0.0015–0.0035; Bottom—0.002–0.004.

Torque Specifications

CAUTION: *Use a reliable torque wrench to tighten the parts listed to prevent straining or distorting the parts or possibly damaging the threads. These specifications are for clean threads only. Dirty threads produce friction which prevents accurate measurement of tight-* *ness. It is important that these torque specifications be strictly observed. Overtightening to any extent may damage threads, thus preventing proper torque from being obtained, requiring replacement or repair of the damaged part.*

General Torque Specifications

NOTE: *The following torques are for screw or bolt sizes not otherwise shown.*

Screw Size	Ft. Lbs.	In. Lbs.
#6	——	7–10
#10	2–3	25–35
#12	3–4	35–45
¼	5–7	60–80
⁵⁄₁₆	10–12	120–140
⅜	18–20	220–240

1967–72 120 HP

Part	Application	Thread	Torque Ft. Lbs.	In. Lbs.
Bolt	Camshaft Thrust Plate	¼-20		72–90
Nut	Connecting Rod	¹¹⁄₃₂-24	30–35	
Screw	Coupling, Flywheel to Crankshaft	⁷⁄₁₆-20	45–50	
Plug	Crankcase Drain	½-20	15–20	
Bolt	Cylinder Head	½-13	90–100	
Screw	Engine Mount to Cylinder Block	⅜-16	20–24	
Screw	Fill and Drain Oil Plug (outdrive)	⅜-16	4–5	
Setscrew	Gear to Clutch Spring	10–32		30–35
Screw	Gearcase to Exhaust Tube	⁵⁄₁₆-18	16–18	
Screw	Impeller Housing to Gear Housing	⅜-16	30–36	
Bolt	Main Bearing Cap (oiled)	⁷⁄₁₆-14	60–70	
Screw	Manifold to Cylinder Head	⅜-16	20–25	
Filter	Oil	½-20	Hand Tight	
Bolt	Oil Pan (end)	⁵⁄₁₆-18		120–130
Bolt	Oil Pan (side)	¼-20		72–90
Bolt	Oil Pan (to front cover)	¼-20		50–60
Screw	Oil Pump Cover to Body	¼-20		65–75
Bolt	Oil Pump Mounting	⁵⁄₁₆-18		110–120
Nut	Pinion (elastic stop nut)	¾-16	70–80	
Screw	Pulley to Balancer Hub (1)	⁵⁄₁₆-24	15–20	
	(2)	⅜-24	15–20	
Screw	Rocker Arm Cover	¼-20		50–60
Nut	Shaft and Ball Gear Assembly (upper gear box)		60–70	
Plug	Spark	14 mm	35	
Screw	Cover to Intermediate Housing	10-24		42–54
Bolt	Timing Gear Cover to Block	¼-20		72–90
Screw	Water Passage Cover	¼-20	3–7	
Bolt	Water Pump to Block	⁵⁄₁₆-18	13–17	

1967–72 155 HP

Part	Application	Torque Ft. Lbs.
Nut	Connecting Rod Bolt	30–40
Screw	Coupling, Flywheel to Crankshaft	45–50
Plug	Crankcase Drain	30–40
Bolt	Crankshaft Bearing Cap to Crankcase	95–120
Bolt	Cylinder Head to Block	65–80
Bolt	Distributor Holddown Clamp	10–15
Nut	Engine Mount to Cylinder Block Stud	40–45
Screw	Fill and Drain Oil Plug (outdrive)	4–5
Bolt	Fuel Pump Eccentric and Timing Chain Sprocket to Camshaft	40–55
Bolt	Fuel Pump to Timing Chain Cover	17–23
Setscrew	Gear to Clutch Spring	30–35 In. Lbs.
Screw	Gearcase to Exhaust Tube	16–18
Bolt	Harmonic Balancer to Crankshaft	140 Minimum
Screw	Impeller Housing to Gear Housing	30–36
Screw	Intake Manifold to Cylinder Head	45–55
Screw	Mount Bracket to Front Lateral Support	60–65
Filter	Oil	10–15
Bolt	Oil Pan to Block	9–13
Screw	Oil Pump Cover Assembly to Timing Chain Cover	8–12
Bolt	Oil Screen Housing Pipe and Flange Assembly to Block	6–9
Nut	Pinion (elastic stop nut)	70–80
Bolt	Pulley and Reinforcement to Harmonic Balancer	18–25
Bolt	Pulley to Water Pump Hub	17–23
Screw	Rear Support Bracket to Adapter	20–24
Screw	Rocker Arm Cover to Cylinder Head	3–5
Bolt	Rocker Arm Shaft Bracket to Cylinder Head	25–35
Nut	Shaft and Ball Gear Assembly (upper gear box)	60–70
Plug	Spark	35
Bolt	Special Movable Timing Chain Damper	10–15
Bolt	Starter Motor to Cylinder Block	30–40
Screw	Cover to Intermediate Housing	3–5
Bolt	Timing Chain Cover to Block	13–17
Bolt	Water Pump Cover to Timing Chain Cover	6–8

1972 1965 HP

Size	Application	Torque
¼-20	Camshaft Thrust Plate	80 in. lb.
	Crankcase Front Cover	80 in. lb.
	Flywheel Housing Pans	80 in. lb.
	Oil Pan (to crankcase)	80 in. lb.
	Oil Pan (to front cover)	50 in. lb.
	Oil Pump Cover	70 in. lb.
	Rocker Arm Cover	45 in. lb.
11⁄32-24	Connecting Rod Cap	32 ft. lb.
5⁄16-18	Clutch Pressure Plate	20 ft. lb.
	Oil Pan (to crankcase)	75 in. lb.
	Oil Pump	115 in. lb.
	Push Rod Cover	50 in. lb.
	Water Pump	15 in. lb.
⅜-16	Distributor Clamp	20 ft. lb.
	Flywheel Housing	30 ft. lb.
	Manifold (exhaust to inlet)	25 ft. lb.
	Manifold Clamp (L6 outer)	20 ft. lb.
	Manifold Clamp (all others)	30 ft. lb.
	Thermostat Housing	30 ft. lb.
7⁄16-14	Main Bearing Cap	65 ft. lb.
7⁄16-20	Flywheel	60 ft. lb.
½-13	Cylinder Head	95 ft. lb.
½-14	Temperature Sending Unit	20 ft. lb.
½-20	Oil Filter	Hand Tight
14 mm ⅝	Spark Plug	15 ft. lb.

1967–68 185 HP and 1968 210 HP

Part	Application	Torque Ft. Lbs.	In. Lbs.
Bolt	Camshaft Sprocket	15–20	
Nut	Connecting Rod	30–35	
Screw	Coupling, Flywheel to Crankshaft	45–50	
Plug	Crankcase Drain	20–25	
Bolt	Cylinder Head	60–70	
Screw	Distributor Clamp	8–12	
Screw	Engine Mount to Cylinder Block	35–45	
Screw	Fill and Drain Oil Plug (outdrive)	4–5	
Setscrew	Gear to Clutch Spring		30–35
Screw	Gearcase to Exhaust Tube	16–18	
Screw	Impeller Housing to Gear Housing	30–36	
Bolt	Main Bearing Cap (oiled)	75–85	
Screw	Intake Manifold	25–35	
Filter	Oil	Hand Tight	
Bolt	Oil Pan $5/16$-18		60–70
Bolt	Oil Pan $1/4$-20		72–96
Screw	Oil Pump Cover to Body		72–96
Bolt	Oil Pump Mounting	60–70	
Nut	Pinion (elastic stop nut)	70–80	
Screw	Pulley to Balancer Hub	15–20	
Screw	Rocker Arm Cover		50–60
Nut	Shaft and Ball Gear Assembly (upper gear box)	60–70	
Plug	Spark	25–35	
Screw	Thermostat Cover to Intermediate Casting		42–54
Bolt	Timing Chain Cover to Block		72–90
Screw	Water Passage Cover	3–7	
Bolt	Water Pump to Block	25–35	

1967 200 HP

Part	Application	Torque Ft. Lbs.
Nut	Connecting Rod Bolt	30–40
Screw	Coupling, Flywheel to Crankshaft	45–50
Plug	Crankcase Drain	25–35
Bolt	Crankshaft Bearing Cap to Crankcase	95–120
Bolt	Cylinder Head to Block	65–80
Bolt	Distributor Holddown Clamp	10–15
Nut	Engine Mount to Cylinder Block, Stud	40–45
Screw	Fill and Drain Oil Plug (outdrive)	4–5
Bolt	Fuel Pump Eccentric and Timing Chain Sprocket to Camshaft	40–55
Bolt	Fuel Pump to Timing Chain Cover	17–23
Setscrew	Gear to Clutch Spring	30–35 In. Lbs.
Screw	Gearcase to Exhaust Tube	16–18
Bolt	Harmonic Balancer to Crankshaft	140 Minimum
Screw	Impeller Housing to Gear Housing	30–36
Screw	Intake Manifold to Cylinder Head	45–55
Screw	Mount Bracket to Front Lateral Support	60–65
Filter	Oil	10–15
Bolt	Oil Pan to Block	9–13
Screw	Oil Pump Cover Assembly to Timing Chain Cover	8–12
Bolt	Oil Screen Housing Pipe and Flange Assembly to Block	6–9
Nut	Pinion (elastic stop nut)	70–80

1967 200 HP (cont.)

Part	Application	Torque Ft. Lbs.
Bolt	Pulley and Reinforcement to Harmonic Balancer	18–25
Bolt	Pulley to Water Pump Hub	17–23
Screw	Rear Support Bracket to Adapter	20–24
Screw	Rocker Arm Cover to Cylinder Head	3–5
Bolt	Rocker Arm Shaft Bracket to Cylinder Head	25–35
Nut	Shaft and Ball Gear Assembly (upper gear box)	60–70
Plug	Spark	25–35
Bolt	Starter Motor to Cylinder Block	30–40
Screw	Thermostat Cover to Intermediate Casting	3–7
Bolt	Timing Chain Cover to Block	13–17
Bolt	Water Pump Cover to Timing Chain Cover	6–8

1969–70
210 HP, 1971 215 and 235 HP
and 1972 225 and 245 HP

Part	Application	Torque	
		Ft. Lbs.	In. Lbs.
Bolt	Camshaft Sprocket	15–20	
Nut	Connecting Rod	30–35	
Screw	Coupling, Flywheel to Crankshaft	45–50	
Plug	Crankcase Drain	20–25	
Bolt	Cylinder Head	60–70	
Screw	Distributor Clamp	8–12	
Screw	Engine Mount to Cylinder Block	35–45	
Screw	Fill and Drain Oil Plug (outdrive)	4–5	
Setscrew	Gear to Clutch Spring		30–35
Screw	Gearcase to Exhaust Tube	16–18	
Screw	Impeller Housing to Gear Housing	30–36	
Bolt	Main Bearing Cap (oiled)	75–85	
Screw	Intake Manifold	25–35	
Filter	Oil	tighten snug and add ⅓ turn	
Bolt	Oil Pan ⁵⁄₁₆-18		60–70
Bolt	Oil Pan ¼-20		72–96
Screw	Oil Pump Cover to Body		72–96
Bolt	Oil Pump Mounting	60–70	
Nut	Pinion (elastic stop nut)	70–80	
Screw	Pulley to Balancer Hub	15–20	
Screw	Rocker Arm Cover		50–60
Nut	Shaft and Ball Gear Assembly (upper gear box)	60–70	
Plug	Spark	35	
Screw	Cover to Intermediate Housing		42–54
Bolt	Timing Chain Cover to Block		72–90
Screw	Water Passage Cover	3–7	
Bolt	Water Pump to Block	25–35	

Torque Sequences

Cylinder head (V6)

Cylinder head (4 cylinder)

Cylinder head (inline 6 cylinder)

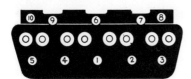

Cylinder head (200 HP V8)

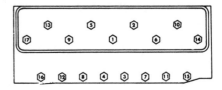

Cylinder head (185, 210, 215, 225, 235, and 245 HP)

Electrical Specifications

| Year | Engine (hp) | Battery | | Alternator Rated Output (amps) | Starter Manufacturer/Part Number | Starter | | | Brush Spring Tension (oz) |
| | | Volts | Terminal Grounded | | | No-Load Test | | | |
						Min. Amps	Volts	Min. RPM	
1967	120-L4	12	Neg.	34	Delco-Remy/1107596	65	10.6	3600	35
	155-V6	12	Neg.	34	Delco-Remy/1107596	65	10.6	3600	35
	185-V8	12	Neg.	34	Delco-Remy/1107496	49	10.6	6200	35
	200-V8	12	Neg.	34	Delco-Remy/1107596	65	10.6	3600	35
1968	120-L4	12	Neg.	34	Delco-Remy/1108366	65	10.6	3600	35
	155-V6	12	Neg.	34	Delco-Remy/1107596	65	10.6	3600	35
	185-V8	12	Neg.	34	Delco-Remy/1107496	49	10.6	6200	35
	210-V8	12	Neg.	34	Delco-Remy/1107496	49	10.6	6200	35
1969	120-L4	12	Neg.	34	Delco-Remy/1108366	65	10.6	3600	35
	155-V6	12	Neg.	34	Delco-Remy/1108366	65	10.6	3600	35
	210-V8	12	Neg.	34	Delco-Remy/1108367	49	10.6	6200	35
1970	120-L4	12	Neg.	34	OMC/384198	65	10.6	3600	35
	155-V6	12	Neg.	34	OMC/384198	65	10.6	3600	35
	210-V8	12	Neg.	34	OMC/384198	49	10.6	6200	35

Electrical Specifications (cont.)

Year	Engine (hp)	Battery			Alternator Rated Output (amps)	Starter Manufacturer/Part Number	Starter			Brush Spring Tension (oz)
		Volts	Terminal Grounded				No-Load Test			
							Min. Amps	Volts	Min. RPM	
1971	120-L4	12	Neg.		34	OMC/384198	50	9.0	5500	35
	155-V6	12	Neg.		34	OMC/384198	50	9.0	5500	35
	215-V8	12	Neg.		34	OMC/384198	50	9.0	5500	35
	235-V8	12	Neg.		34	OMC/384198	50	9.0	5500	35
1972	120-L4	12	Neg.		34	OMC/384198	50	9.0	5500	35
	155-V6	12	Neg.		34	OMC/384198	50	9.0	5500	35
	165-L6	12	Neg.		34	OMC/384198	50	9.0	5500	35
	225-V8	12	Neg.		34	OMC/384198	50	9.0	5500	35
	245-V8	12	Neg.		34	OMC/384198	50	9.0	5500	35

Carburetor Specifications

1967–71 120 HP

Model Designation .... RBS
Number of Barrels 1
Throttle Bore .... 1⁷⁄₁₆″
Main Venturi .... 1¼″
Low Speed Circuit:
  Jet .... 0.0292″ (No. 69 Dr.)
  By-pass .... 0.052″ (No. 55 Dr.)
  Economizer .... 0.0453″
  Air-Bleed .... 0.0492″ (1.25 MM Dr.)
Idle Port .... Length 0.143″—Width 0.030″
Idle Port Relation .... 0.143″–0.148″ above tightly closed valve
Main Nozzle .... Installed permanently—do not remove
Nozzle Bleed .... 0.028″ (No. 70 Dr.)
Step-up Rod Assembly:
  Economy Step .... 0.063″
  Power Step .... 0.060″
Step-up Rod Jet .... 0.089″—Installed permanently
Accelerating Pump Jet .... 0.0292″ (No. 69 Dr.)—Installed permanently
Float Level Adjustment .... 15⁄32″
Choke Setting .... Index
Choke Suction Hole .... 0.070″ (No. 50 Dr.)—In bottom of casting
Choke Unloader Adjustment .... 7⁄64″
Initial Idle Mixture .... 1 to 2 turns out
Initial Idle Speed .... 1½ to 3 turns out

1967–72
155 HP w/2GC, 1972 120 HP
w/2GC, 1972 165 HP w/2GC,
1967–68 185 HP w/2GV and 1967
200 HP w/2GC

Carburetor Make and Model .... Rochester 2GC or Rochester 2GV
Float Level .... 19⁄32″
Float Drop .... 1²⁹⁄32″
Pump Rod Adjustment .... 15⁄32″①
Choke Unloader Adjustment .... 0.110″②
Choke Setting .... Index
Initial Idle Mixture .... 1 turn out
①—⅛″ on 1967 200 HP
②—0.080″ on 1967 200 HP

1968–70
210 HP, 1971 215 and 235 HP
and 1972 225 and 245 HP

Carburetor Make and Model .... Rochester 4MV
Float Level .... ¼″
Pump Rod Location .... Inner Hole
Pump Rod Adjustment .... 9⁄32″
Choke Unloader Adjustment .... 0.300″
Choke Setting .... Index
Initial Idle Mixture .... 1 turn out
Vacuum Break Adjustment .... 13⁄64″

Wiring Diagrams

NOTE: *Wiring diagrams are typical. Small differences may exist due to varying installations.*

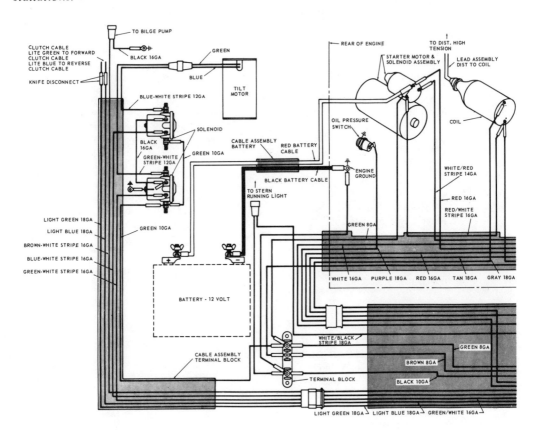

✳ Red wire used on Stewart–Warner Tachometer only.

120 HP (cont. on p. 183)

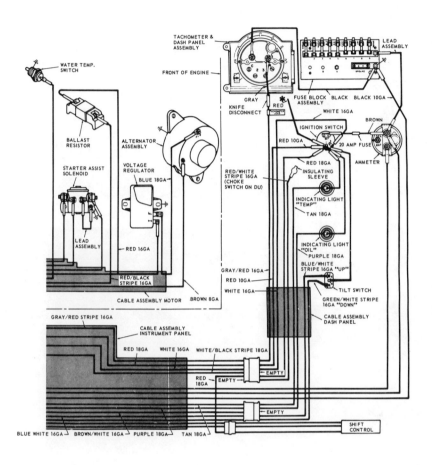

WATER TEMP.
SWITCH

TACHOMETER &
DASH PANEL
ASSEMBLY

FRONT OF ENGINE

LEAD
ASSEMBLY

BALLAST
RESISTOR

ALTERNATOR
ASSEMBLY

STARTER ASSIST
SOLENOID

VOLTAGE
REGULATOR

BLUE 18GA

GRAY

KNIFE
DISCONNECT

RED

FUSE BLOCK BLACK BLACK 10GA
ASSEMBLY

WHITE 16GA

IGNITION SWITCH

BROWN

RED 10GA

20 AMP FUSE

AMMETER

RED/WHITE
STRIPE 16GA
(CHOKE
SWITCH ON DU)

RED 18GA

INSULATING
SLEEVE

INDICATING LIGHT
"TEMP"

TAN 18GA

LEAD
ASSEMBLY

RED 16GA

INDICATING LIGHT
"OIL"

PURPLE 18GA

RED/BLACK
STRIPE 16GA

BLUE/WHITE
STRIPE 16GA "UP"

GRAY/RED 16GA

RED 10GA

TILT SWITCH

WHITE 16GA

CABLE ASSEMBLY MOTOR   BROWN 8GA

GREEN/WHITE STRIPE
16GA "DOWN"

CABLE ASSEMBLY
DASH PANEL

GRAY/RED STRIPE 16GA

CABLE ASSEMBLY
INSTRUMENT PANEL

RED 18GA   WHITE 16GA   WHITE/BLACK STRIPE 18GA

EMPTY

RED
18GA

EMPTY

EMPTY

BLUE WHITE 16GA   BROWN/WHITE 16GA   PURPLE 18GA   TAN 18GA

SHIFT
CONTROL

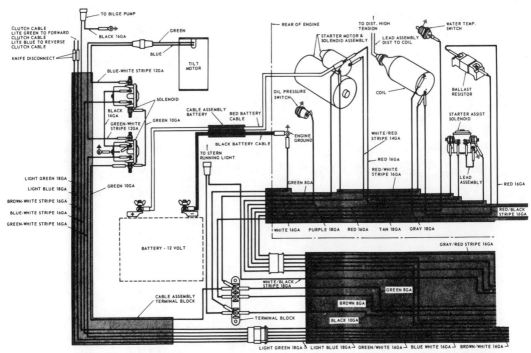

*Red wire used on Stewart-Warner Tachometer only.

155 HP (cont. on p. 185)

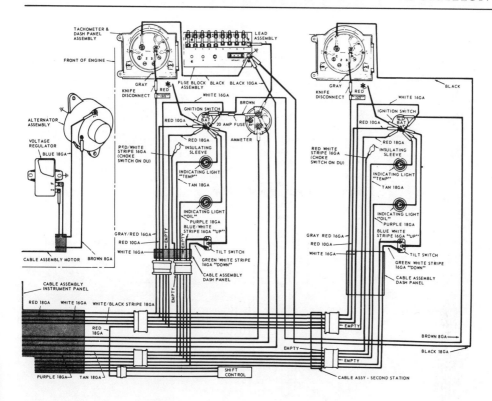

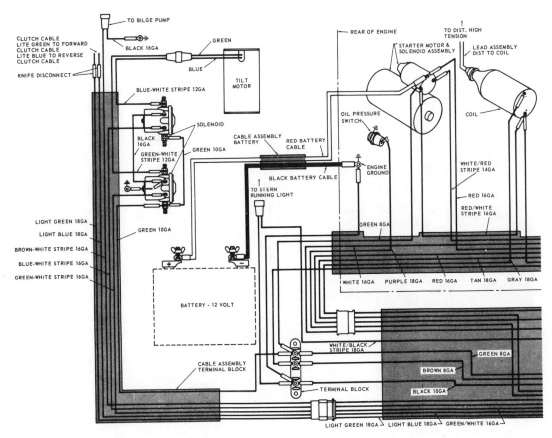

* Red wire used on Stewart-Warner Tachometer only.

185 HP (cont. on p. 187)

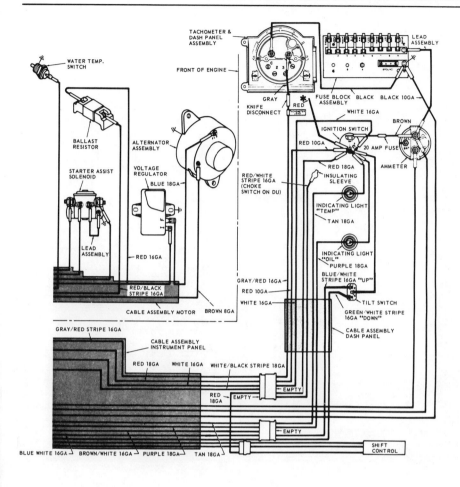

WATER TEMP. SWITCH

TACHOMETER & DASH PANEL ASSEMBLY

FRONT OF ENGINE

LEAD ASSEMBLY

BALLAST RESISTOR

ALTERNATOR ASSEMBLY

GRAY

KNIFE DISCONNECT

RED

FUSE BLOCK ASSEMBLY

BLACK   BLACK 10GA

WHITE 16GA

BROWN

IGNITION SWITCH

STARTER ASSIST SOLENOID

VOLTAGE REGULATOR

BLUE 18GA

RED 10GA

20 AMP FUSE

AMMETER

RED 18GA

INSULATING SLEEVE

RED/WHITE STRIPE 16GA (CHOKE SWITCH ON DU)

INDICATING LIGHT "TEMP"

TAN 18GA

LEAD ASSEMBLY

RED 16GA

INDICATING LIGHT "OIL"

PURPLE 18GA

RED/BLACK STRIPE 16GA

GRAY/RED 16GA

BLUE/WHITE STRIPE 16GA "UP"

CABLE ASSEMBLY MOTOR

BROWN 8GA

RED 10GA

WHITE 16GA

TILT SWITCH

GREEN/WHITE STRIPE 16GA "DOWN"

CABLE ASSEMBLY DASH PANEL

GRAY/RED STRIPE 16GA

CABLE ASSEMBLY INSTRUMENT PANEL

RED 18GA   WHITE 16GA   WHITE/BLACK STRIPE 18GA

EMPTY

RED 18GA   EMPTY

EMPTY

SHIFT CONTROL

BLUE WHITE 16GA   BROWN/WHITE 16GA   PURPLE 18GA   TAN 18GA

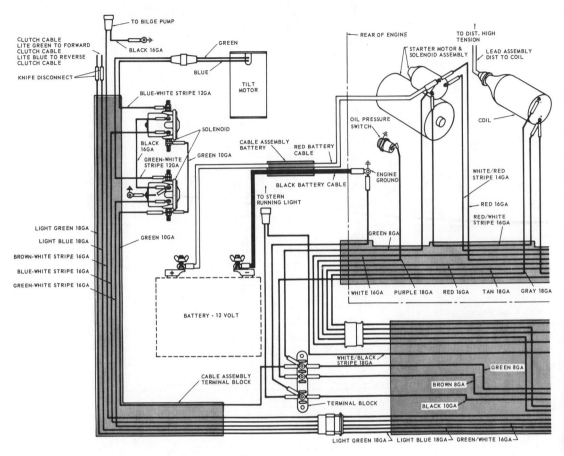

* Red wire used on Stewart-Warner Tachometer only.

200 HP (cont. on p. 189)

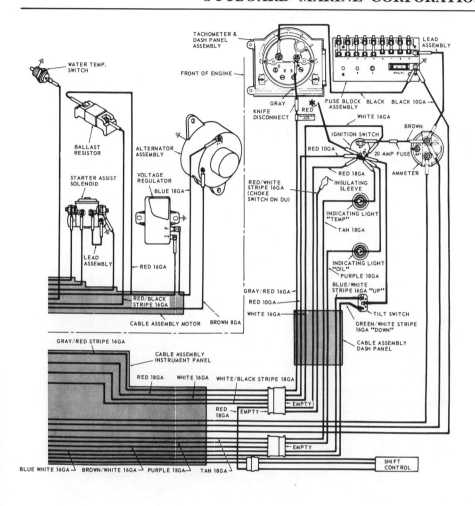

WATER TEMP.
SWITCH

TACHOMETER &
DASH PANEL
ASSEMBLY

LEAD
ASSEMBLY

FRONT OF ENGINE

BALLAST
RESISTOR

ALTERNATOR
ASSEMBLY

GRAY

KNIFE
DISCONNECT

RED

FUSE BLOCK
ASSEMBLY

BLACK

BLACK 10GA

WHITE 16GA

BROWN

IGNITION SWITCH

STARTER ASSIST
SOLENOID

VOLTAGE
REGULATOR

BLUE 18GA

RED 10GA

20 AMP FUSE

AMMETER

RED/WHITE
STRIPE 16GA
(CHOKE
SWITCH ON DU)

RED 18GA

INSULATING
SLEEVE

INDICATING LIGHT
"TEMP"

LEAD
ASSEMBLY

RED 16GA

TAN 18GA

INDICATING LIGHT
"OIL"

PURPLE 18GA

BLUE/WHITE
STRIPE 16GA "UP"

RED/BLACK
STRIPE 16GA

GRAY/RED 16GA

RED 10GA

TILT SWITCH

CABLE ASSEMBLY MOTOR

BROWN 8GA

WHITE 16GA

GREEN/WHITE STRIPE
16GA "DOWN"

CABLE ASSEMBLY
DASH PANEL

GRAY/RED STRIPE 16GA

CABLE ASSEMBLY
INSTRUMENT PANEL

RED 18GA

WHITE 16GA

WHITE/BLACK STRIPE 18GA

EMPTY

RED
18GA

EMPTY

EMPTY

SHIFT
CONTROL

BLUE WHITE 16GA

BROWN/WHITE 16GA

PURPLE 18GA

TAN 18GA

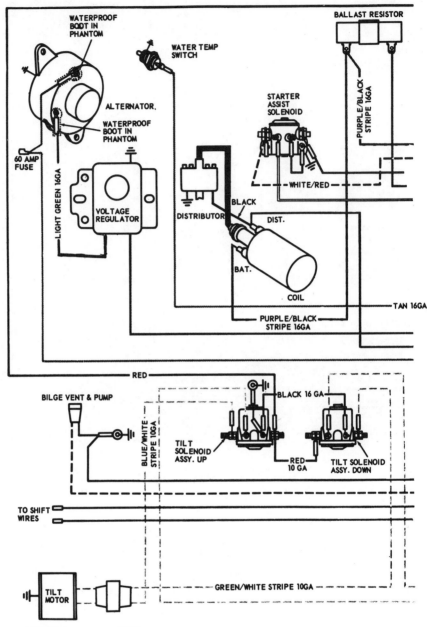

WATERPROOF
BOOT IN
PHANTOM

WATER TEMP
SWITCH

BALLAST RESISTOR

STARTER
ASSIST
SOLENOID

ALTERNATOR.

WATERPROOF
BOOT IN
PHANTOM

PURPLE/BLACK
STRIPE 16GA

60 AMP
FUSE

LIGHT GREEN 16GA

VOLTAGE
REGULATOR

DISTRIBUTOR

BLACK

WHITE/RED

DIST.

BAT.

COIL

TAN 16GA

PURPLE/BLACK
STRIPE 16GA

RED

BILGE VENT & PUMP

BLACK 16 GA

BLUE/WHITE
STRIPE 10GA

TILT
SOLENOID
ASSY. UP

RED
10 GA

TILT SOLENOID
ASSY. DOWN

TO SHIFT
WIRES

TILT
MOTOR

GREEN/WHITE STRIPE 10GA

210 HP (cont. on p. 191)

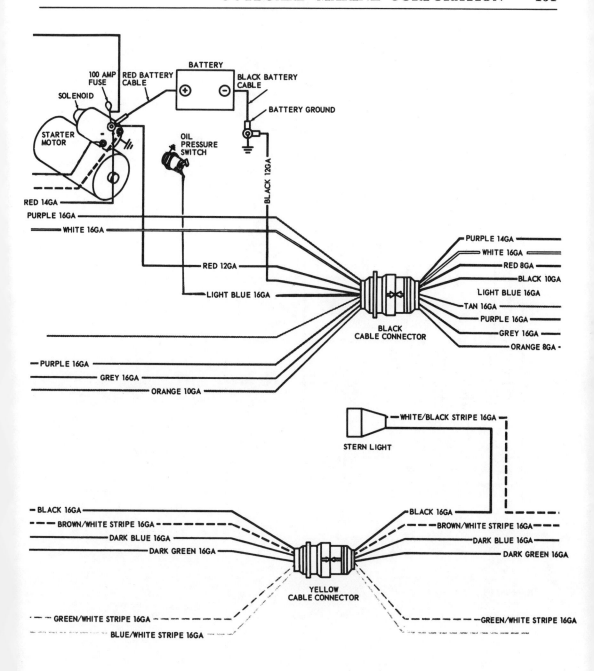

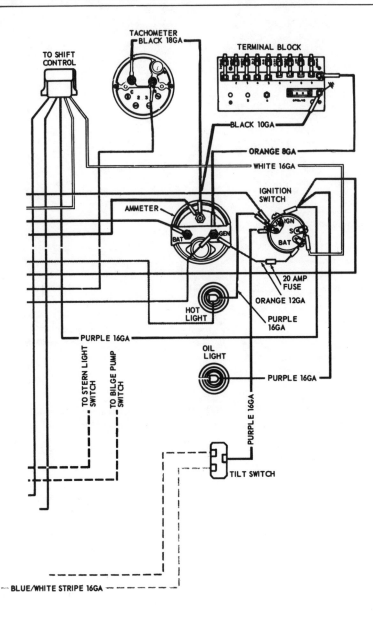

TACHOMETER
BLACK 18GA

TO SHIFT
CONTROL

TERMINAL BLOCK

BLACK 10GA

ORANGE 8GA

WHITE 16GA

IGNITION
SWITCH

AMMETER

IGN

S

BAT

BAT   GEN

20 AMP
FUSE

ORANGE 12GA

HOT
LIGHT

PURPLE
16GA

PURPLE 16GA

OIL
LIGHT

PURPLE 16GA

TO STERN LIGHT
SWITCH

TO BILGE PUMP
SWITCH

PURPLE 16GA

TILT SWITCH

BLUE/WHITE STRIPE 16GA

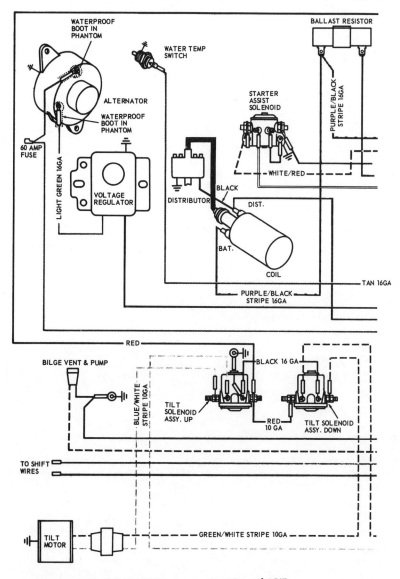

1971 120, 155, 215, 235 HP (cont. on pp. 194 and 195)

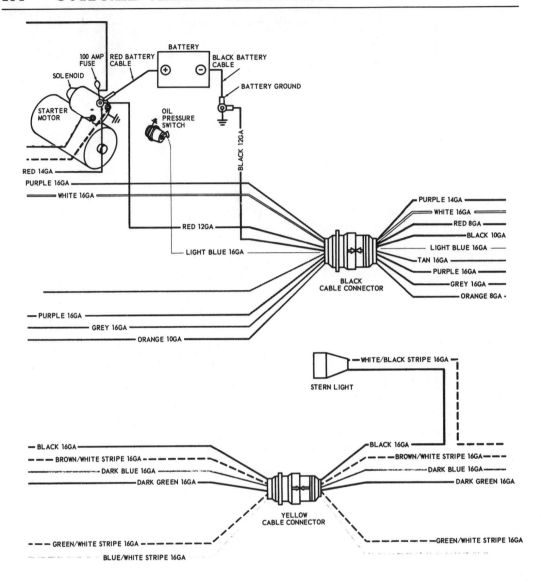

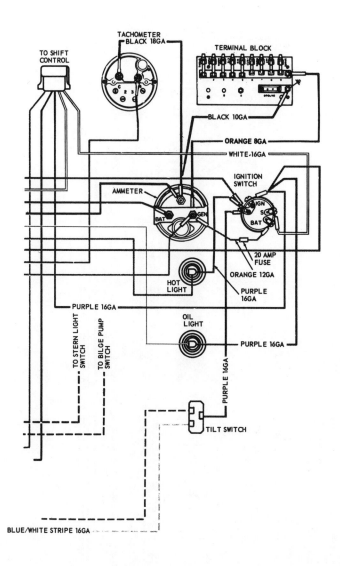

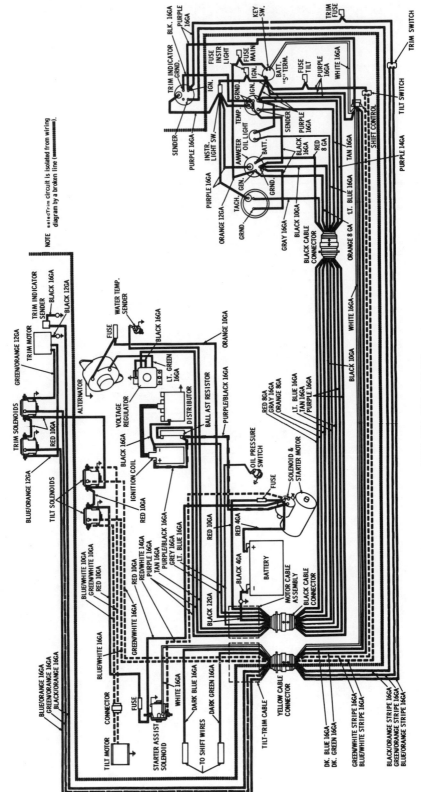

1972 165, 225, 245 HP

Propeller Recommendations

1967–71

HP	Year	Boat Size & Recommendation	Boat Speed (mph)	Part No.	Material	No. of Blades	Diameter	Pitch
120 Heavy Duty	67 Thru	Work Boats & Non-Planing Houseboats	10–24	382676	Al	3	14″	11″
		21–29′ Cruisers	22–28	382017	Al	3	14″	12″
		19–22′ Cruisers & Runabouts	26–32	381185	Al	3	14″	14″
		17–20′ Runabouts	30–36	381186	Al	3	14″	16″
		16–18′ Runabouts	33–39	381187	Al	3	14″	18″
		15–17′ Light Runabouts	37–42	383287	Al	3	14″	20″
150, 155	67 Thru	Work Boats & Non-Planing Houseboats	5–15	382676	Al	3	14″	11″
		Heavy Cruisers & Large Houseboats	14–23	382017	Al	3	14″	12″
		20–25′ Cruisers & Runabouts	22–30	381185	Al	3	14″	14″
		19–22′ Cruisers & Runabouts	28–35	381186	Al	3	14″	16″
		16–19′ Runabouts	34–41	381187	Al	3	14″	18″
		15–17′ Runabouts	38–45	383287	Al	3	14″	20″
185, 200, 219, 215, 235	67 Thru	Work Boats & Large Houseboats	10–20	382676	Al	3	14″	11″
		Houseboats & 24–30′ Cruisers	19–30	382017	Al	3	14″	12″
		19–25′ Cruisers & Runabouts	28–38	381185	Al	3	14″	14″
		17–20′ Runabouts	36–47	381186	Al	3	14″	16″
		16–18′ Runabouts	45–55	381187	Al	3	14″	18″
		16–19′ High Performance Boats	45–50	381464 * †	Br	2	13″	18″
		Dual High Performance Boats	53–60	383287	Al	3	14″	20″

*—Cupped   † V8 only
Al—Aluminum   Br—Bronze

1972

Diameter and Pitch	Part Number	Material and No. of Blades	Approx. Speed Range	Type of Boat and Approximate Length
		120 HP		
14¼ x 10	381296	3-Al	10–20	Work Boats & House Boats Non-Planing
14 x 11	382676	3-Al	10–24	Work Boats & House Boats Non-Planing
14 x 12	382017	3-Al	22–28	21'–27' Cruisers
14 x 14	381185	3-Al	26–32	19'–22' Runabouts & Cruisers
14 x 16	381186	3-Al	30–36	17'–20' Runabouts
14 x 18	381187	3-Al	33–39	16'–18' Runabouts
14 x 20	383287	3-Al	37–42	15'–17' Light Runabouts
		155–165 HP		
14¼ x 10	381296	3-Al	5–15	Work Boats Non-Planing
14 x 11	382676	3-Al	5–15	Work Boats Non-Planing
14 x 12	382017	3-Al	14–23	Large House Boats & Heavy Cruisers
14 x 14	381185	3-Al	22–30	20'–25' Runabouts & Cruisers
14 x 16	381186	3-Al	28–35	19'–22' Runabouts & Cruisers
14 x 18	381187	3-Al	34–41	16'–19' Runabouts
14 x 20	383287	3-Al	38–45	15'–17' Runabouts
		225–245 HP		
14¼ x 10	381296	3-Al	10–15	Work Boats & Large House Boats
14 x 11	382676	3-Al	10–20	Work Boats & Large House Boats
14 x 12	382017	3-Al	19–30	24'–30' Heavy Cruisers & House Boats
14 x 14	381185	3-Al	28–38	19'–25' Runabouts & Cruisers
14 x 16	381186	3-Al	36–47	17'–20' Runabouts
14 x 18	381187	3-Al	45–55	16'–18' Runabouts
13 x 18	381464 *	2-Br	45–50	16'–19' High Performance Runabouts
13¼ x 20	979896	2-Br	45–50	16'–19' High Performance Runabouts
14 x 20	383287	3-Al	53–60	Dual High Performance Runabouts

*—Cupped
Al—Aluminum
Br—Bronze

Periodic Maintenance and Lubrication

LUBRICATION

Oil Recommendations

Outboard Marine Corporation recommends that OMC Premium 4-Cycle Motor Oil be used in their engines. If this oil is not available, a reputable brand of automotive oil is satisfactory, providing it is labeled for service "SE" and meets General Motors Standard GM-6041-M. Oils conforming to this standard are satisfactory to use and contain additives.

Oil Viscosity

The grade or viscosity of the oil should be selected according to the lowest anticipated temperatures at which cold engine starts will be required. See the following temperature charts to determine the viscosity required.

1967–70

Lowest Anticipated Temperature	Use S.A.E. Viscosity Number
Over +32° F.	S.A.E. 20W or S.A.E. 10W-30
Between +32° F. and 0° F.	S.A.E. 10W or S.A.E. 10W-30
Below 0° F.	S.A.E. 5W or S.A.E. 5W-20

For sustained high speed operation when the temperature is above 90° F., S.A.E. 30 oil may be used.

1971–72

Lowest Anticipated Temperature	Use S.A.E. Viscosity Number
32° F. Up	S.A.E. 30
0° F.	S.A.E. 20W
Below 0° F.	S.A.E. 10W

For sustained high speed operation, S.A.E. 30 oil must be used.

Oil Color

The color of "SE" oil used in these engines does not indicate its condition since it is normally dark black or dark gray after a few hours of operation. This is because the detergent content of the oil traps and holds fine particles of soot and carbon which the oil filter will not remove.

Oil Changes

The oil level should be checked more frequently during the break-in period since slightly higher oil consumption is normal until the piston rings have seated. Check the oil level with the dipstick. The oil level should be maintained between the Full and Add marks. Do not fill the crankcase above the Full mark on the dipstick.

The engine oil should be changed after the first 20 hours of operation (1967–1969 engines) and the first 10 hours of operation (1970–72 engines). Thereafter the oil should be changed after every 50 hours of use at the end of each season. Whenever the oil is changed, a new filter should be installed. Refer to the following chart for Engine Oil Capacities.

Engine Oil Capacities

Engine (hp)	Capacity (qts)	
	w/o filter	w/filter
120	3.5	4.0
155	4.0	5.0
165	4.0	5.0
185	4.0	5.0
200	4.0	5.0
210	4.0	5.0
215	5.0	6.0
225	5.0	6.0
235	5.0	6.0
245	5.0	6.0

LUBRICATION

Flushing the Lower Gearcase

The lower gearcase should be drained and flushed with kerosine or fuel oil after the first ten hours of operation.

1. Place the drive unit in the down position and remove the Oil Level and Oil Drain plugs. Tilt the drive unit slightly to allow all of the oil to drain out.

2. Fill the drive unit with flushing liquid through the Oil Drain hole until liquid appears at the Oil Level hole.

3. Replace the Oil Level plug.

4. Remove the filler tube and QUICKLY replace the Oil Drain plug.

5. With the boat in water, run the engine for not more than one minute at idle speed in Neutral to thoroughly flush the gearcase components.

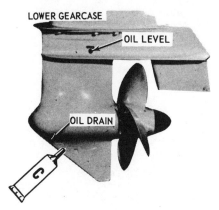

Remove the oil level and oil drain plugs

CAUTION: *Do not run the gearcase out of water.*

6. After flushing the gearcase, refill the unit with OMC Type C lubricant, using the procedure under Lower Gearcase Oil Change.

NOTE: *After the first ten hour oil change, the drive unit lower gearcase should have the oil changed twice every season or every 50 hours of use.*

TYPES OF LUBRICANT

NOTE: DO NOT USE SAE 90 IN EITHER UPPER OR LOWER GEARCASE.

OMC TYPE "A"   OMC TYPE "C"   GREASE GUN OMC TYPE "A"

Types of lubricants

Component Lubrication

ALL MODELS

Lubricate the upper gearcase and tilt shaft

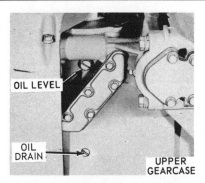

Upper gearcase lubrication

Tilt unit gearcase lubrication

Intermediate shaft and steering housing lubrication

Swivel bearing lubrication

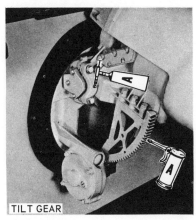

TILT GEAR

Tilt gear lubrication

Lower Gearcase Oil Change

1. When a complete oil change is required in the lower gearcase, place the drive unit in the Down position and remove the Oil Drain plug.

2. Tilt the drive unit slightly to permit the oil to drain completely.

3. Remove the plug marked Oil Level.

4. Using a tube of OMC Type C lubricant, fill the lower gearcase through the hole marked Oil Drain until lubricant appears at the Oil Level hole.

5. Replace the Oil Level plug before removing the tube of lubricant. This will create an airlock and hold the lubricant in until the Oil Drain plug can be replaced.

CAUTION: *Never lubricate the lower gearcase with anything except OMC Type C Lubricant.*

Upper Gearcase

Drain and refill the upper gearcase with the recommended lubricant every 100 hours of operation or once each season.

1. Remove the Oil Drain and Oil Level plugs on the starboard side of the upper gearcase and the Oil Fill plug on top of the upper gearcase.

2. Tilt the drive unit slightly to drain all of the lubricant from the upper gearcase.

3. Install the Oil Drain plug securely.

4. Place the drive unit in the Down position.

5. Pour OMC Type C lubricant through the filler opening on top of the drive unit.

6. When oil appears at the Oil Level opening the unit is filled to the proper level.

7. Install the Oil Fill plug on top of the drive unit upper gearcase and the Oil

Level plug on the starboard side of the upper gearcase.

CAUTION: *Use only OMC Type C lubricant in the upper gearcase.*

Intermediate Housing Ball Gear Bearing

1. Remove the fill plug and add OMC Type C lubricant through the opening until lubricant is visible at the top.

2. Replace the fill plug.

Tilt Shaft

1. Lubricate the 2 tilt shaft fittings with OMC Type A lubricant every 20 hours of operation.

Tilt Unit Gearcase

1. The tilt unit gearcase must be lubricated with OMC Type C lubricant.

2. Add oil through the opening which serves as an oil level check.

Swivel Bearing

1. Remove the plug and lubricate the swivel bearing with OMC Type A lubricant.

Tune-Up

The purpose of a tune-up is to restore the power and efficiency that have been lost through wear, corrosion and deterioration. In the normal operation of an engine, these changes take place gradually in a number of places. Because of this, it is never advisable to attempt to improve performance by servicing only one or two items. Time and money will be saved by following a definite and thorough procedure of analysis and correction of all items affecting power, performance and economy.

There are three units affecting power and performance; compression, ignition and carburetion. Tune-up procedures should cover these in the order given, but the items affecting compression and ignition can be handled according to personal preference. However, items affecting carburetion should not be corrected until all items affecting compression and ignition have been analyzed and/or corrected. Most of these procedures are covered in greater detail in this chapter.

COMPRESSION TEST

1. Remove any foreign matter from around the spark plugs with compressed air.

2. Loosen all spark plugs one turn.

3. Start the engine and accelerate it to no more than 1000 rpm. This will blow out any loose carbon.

CAUTION: *Do not run the engine without cooling water.*

4. Stop the engine and remove the spark plugs.

5. Remove the flame arrestor and block the choke in the wide open position.

6. Remove the coil-to-distributor cap wire and ground it securely to the engine to prevent sparking while cranking the engine.

7. Insert a compression gauge in the spark plug hole firmly. Crank the engine through at least 4 compression strokes to obtain the highest possible reading.

8. Check and record the compression of each cylinder.

Analyzing Compression Test Results

1. Compare the compression test results with the figures listed in the "Tune-Up Specifications."

2. Engines newly broken in may have compression considerably higher than that listed. Pressure variance among cylinders should not exceed 20 psi.

3. The compression gauge needle should jump to about 75 psi on the first compression stroke, with a few successive compression strokes giving maximum compression readings. If pressure is built up in jerky 10–20 psi steps, a leakage is indicated at some point, such as a head gasket, valves or piston rings.

4. Low compression in two adjacent cylinders indicates the possibility of a head gasket leak between the two cylinders. Engine coolant and/or oil in the cylinders could result from this problem.

5. If one or more cylinders read low, inject a tablespoon of engine oil into the low reading cylinders. Test the compression again. If compression improves, worn piston rings are indicated. If there is no improvement, the valves are sticking or seating poorly.

6. Before any attempt is made at further tune-up, the cause of poor compression should be found and corrected.

SPARK PLUGS

1. With the spark plugs removed for testing compression, inspect each plug for proper heat range, broken porcelain or badly worn electrodes.

2. Consult the "Spark Plug Diagnosis" chart for further information concerning spark plugs. This chart is located in Chapter 1.

3. If the plugs are in good condition, file the center electrode flat and adjust the gap to specifications.

4. If the plugs are not serviceable, they should be replaced with new plugs of the proper heat range. Be sure to adjust the gap on new plugs to the proper specification. Spark plugs should be replaced in sets, since they normally wear about equally. Should the plugs wear unevenly, the cause of uneven wear should be investigated and corrected.

5. Wipe the plug seats in the head clean and install new gaskets (except for taper seat plugs) and install the plugs. Torque them to the proper specification.

IGNITION SYSTEM

1. Check the spark plug leads for cracks and abrasions. Replace all leads that are not serviceable. Remove the distributor cap and inspect for cracks or carbon tracks. Replace the cap if damage is found.

2. Check the distributor centrifugal advance mechanism by turning the rotor clockwise by hand. Release the rotor and be sure that the rotor returns easily to the retarded position. If it does not return readily, disassemble the distributor to find the cause.

3. Clean the rotor and inspect for cracks or badly worn electrode. Replace the rotor if damage is found.

Breaker Points and Condenser

1. Remove the distributor cap and rotor.

2. Remove the breaker points and condenser.

3. Examine the points and clean or replace as necessary.

4. Always replace the condenser when the points are replaced.

5. Dirty contacts should be cleaned with an ignition point file. Do not use emery cloth or sandpaper, since particles imbedded in the points will cause arcing.

NOTE: *Where burned or badly pitted points are found, the cause should be*

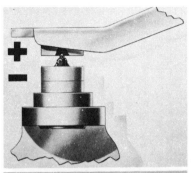

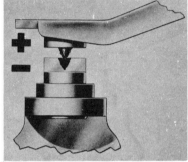

Inspect the points for burning or pitting

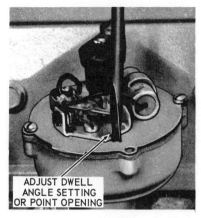

Adjusting the dwell on 120 HP

*determined and corrected before install-
ing new points. Otherwise, new points
will offer no better service than the old
ones.*

6. Clean the distributor and breaker
plate.

7. Install the points and condenser in
position and tighten the screws securing
them.

8. Tighten all connections.

9. Lubricate the distributor cam with a
thin film of high melting point, non-bleeding grease, or replace the lubricating wick.

Breaker Point Alignment

1. Check the alignment of the distributor points with the points closed. Align
new points where necessary, but do not attempt to align old points. Replace used
points where serious misalignment is observed.

2. Align the points by bending the fixed
contacts. Do not bend the breaker arm.

Dwell Angle

ADJUSTMENT

1967–72 120 HP

1. Follow the instructions that are packaged with the dwell meter.

2. If necessary, align the points by
bending the fixed contact support.

3. Position the breaker arm rubbing
block on the high point of the distributor
cam.

4. Loosen the breaker point lockscrew.

5. Use a screwdriver to move the
breaker point support to obtain the specified point opening or dwell.

6. Tighten the breaker point plate lockscrew and recheck the dwell.

7. The variation between dwell angle
readings should not be more than 3° between idle and 1750 rpm.

8. After adjusting the dwell angle, adjust the ignition timing.

1967–72 155 HP and 1967 200 HP

1. Connect dwell meter leads according
to the manufacturer's specifications.

2. Turn the selector switch on the dwell
meter to the 6-cylinder position.

Adjusting the dwell on 155 and 200 HP

3. Ground the coil high tension lead to prevent the engine from starting.

4. While cranking the engine with the starter, insert a 1/8 in. allen wrench into the adjusting screw. Set the dwell angle to specifications.

5. Disconnect the dwell meter and install the coil high tension lead.

6. Check and if necessary, adjust the ignition timing.

1967–68 185 HP and 1968 210 HP

1. Turn the distributor shaft until the breaker arm rubbing block is on the high point of the cam lobe.

2. Using a screwdriver, turn the eccentric to obtain the specified breaker point setting.

3. Tighten the contact support plate lockscrew.

4. Check the adjustment with a dwell meter.

5. Replace the distributor cap and connect all wires.

1969–72 165, 210, 215, 225, 235 and 245 HP

1. When adjusting the dwell angle with a dwell meter, always follow the manufacturer's instructions. If necessary, align the breaker points by bending the fixed contact supports. Do not attempt to align used points.

2. Turn or crank the distributor shaft until the breaker arm rubbing cam is on the high point of the distributor cam.

3. Loosen the lockscrew securing the contact support.

4. Use a screwdriver to move the breaker point support to obtain the proper gap.

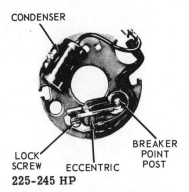

CONDENSER

LOCK SCREW   ECCENTRIC   BREAKER POINT POST

225–245 HP

Adjusting the dwell on 165, and 210–245 HP engines

5. Tighten the lockscrew and recheck the point gap.

6. After setting the point gap, check the gap and dwell angle with a dwell meter. The variation in cam angle should not be more than 3° between idle speed and 1750 rpm.

7. After adjusting the dwell angle, set the ignition timing.

Ignition Timing

1967–72 120 HP

The timing mark is a groove which is notched into the rear edge of the crankshaft pulley. The timing pointer is a part of the timing gear cover, with "0" mark being TDC and all BTDC marks falling on the A (Advance) side of the "0". The timing pointer is graduated in 2° increments.

1. Connect a timing light to No. 1 spark plug and to a suitable power source.

2. Attach a tachometer and run the engine at idle speed.

3. Aim the timing light at the timing tab and adjust the timing by loosening the distributor hold-down bolt and rotating the distributor as required.

4. Tighten the clamp bolt and recheck the timing.

5. Remove the timing light and tachometer after stopping the engine.

1967–72 155

The timing mark is a groove on the edge of the harmonic balancer. The timing indicator is a part of the timing chain cover and is graduated in 5° increments, with "0" indicating TDC. Correct timing exists when the groove is aligned with the "5" mark on the timing indicator. Do not align the groove with the number "5", but with the first mark on the indicator, which is half way between the numbers "0" and "5".

1. Connect a tachometer and timing light using an appropriate power source.

2. Start the engine and run it at idle.

3. Loosen the clamp bolt and turn the distributor by hand until the timing marks are properly aligned.

4. Tighten the clamp bolt.

5. Recheck the timing.

6. Stop the engine and remove the tachometer and timing light.

7. Check the idle speed and mixture adjustments.

1967 200 HP

The timing mark is a groove on the edge of the harmonic balancer. The timing indicator is a part of the timing chain cover. Timing is correct when the timing groove is aligned with the 2½° mark on the timing indicator.

1. The timing procedure is the same as that for the 1967–72 155 HP models.

1967–68 185 HP AND 1968 210 HP

The timing mark is a groove on the edge of the harmonic balancer. The timing indicator is part of the timing chain cover in the form of a scale indicating TDC (O) and degrees of advance (A) and Retard (R) in 2° increments.

1. Check the dwell angle before setting the ignition timing.

2. Connect a 12 volt timing light to No. 1 spark plug and an appropriate power source.

3. Connect a tachometer to the engine.

4. Start the engine and warm it thoroughly. Adjust the idle speed to 550 rpm.

5. Shine the beam of the timing light at the timing marks and loosen the distributor clamp bolt.

6. Turn the distributor slowly to adjust the ignition timing.

7. When the ignition timing is correct (see Specifications), tighten the distributor clamp bolt.

8. Recheck the timing.

9. Recheck the idle and mixture adjustments.

10. Stop the engine and remove the timing light and tachometer.

1969–72 165, 210, 215, 225, 235 AND 245 HP

The timing mark is a groove on the edge of the harmonic balancer. The timing indicator is a part of the timing chain cover and is graduated in 2° increments. The scale indicates TDC (O), degrees of advance (A) and degrees of retard (R).

1. The procedure for adjusting the timing is identical to that for 1967–68 185 HP engines and 1968 210 HP engines.

CARBURETORS

NOTE: *Idle speed and mixture adjustments should not be made until the ignition system and compression have been checked and found satisfactory. Any attempt to compensate for defective*

compression or a defective ignition system will result in decreasing performance and fuel economy.

Synchronizing Twin Carburetors

1967–71 120 HP w/CARTER RBS

1. Turn the idle mixture screws in until they seat lightly. Do not overtighten.

2. Back the screws out 1½ turns.

3. Disconnect the forward ball joint link.

4. Back out both idle stop screws fully, so that both throttle plates are fully closed.

5. Adjust the forward ball joint link so that both throttles begin to open simultaneously. Activate the throttle by pushing on the throttle connector pin where the remote control attaches.

6. Adjust the rear idle stop screw to contact the throttle arm, then turn it in 1½ turns to slightly open the throttle.

7. Start the engine and adjust the speed to 500–600 rpm in gear using the rear idle stop screw.

8. Adjust the idle mixture screws for even running.

9. Reset the idle rpm, if necessary, using the rear idle stop screw.

10. Bring the forward idle stop screw up to just touch the throttle arm.

11. Reconnect the ball joint link.

Synchronizing twin carburetors

Idle Speed and Mixture

1967–72 155 HP, 1967 200 HP, 1967–68 185 HP, AND 1972 165 HP— ALL MODELS w/ROCHESTER 2GC OR 2GV

1. Connect an accurate tachometer to the engine.

2. Start the engine and run it at fast idle until the engine is thoroughly warm.

3. With the engine at normal operating temperature, adjust the idle speed screw to obtain the specified rpm with the engine in gear.

4. Adjust the idle mixture needles alternately to obtain the highest tachometer reading.

5. Readjust the idle speed as necessary, always adjusting the idle mixture last.

6. Stop the engine and remove the tachometer.

1968–72 210, 215, 225, 235, AND 245 HP w/ROCHESTER 4MV

1. Connect an accurate tachometer to the engine.

2. Start the engine and run it at fast idle until it is thoroughly warmed.

3. With the engine at normal operating temperature, adjust the idle speed screw to the specified rpm. This setting should be made with the engine in gear.

4. Adjust the idle mixture needles alternately to obtain the highest rpm, as indicated by the tachometer.

5. Readjust the idle speed as necessary, always adjusting the idle mixture last.

Valve Lash—All Models

All OMC stern drive engines covered in this book are equipped with hydraulic valve lifters. No periodic adjustment is required and none should be attempted, unless the engine has been disassembled for rebuilding.

Stern Drive Lubrication

See "Periodic Maintenance."

Battery and Battery Cables

1. Inspect the battery and cables for wear, cracking or signs of corrosion.

2. Fill the cells to the proper level with distilled water.

3. When cleaning the battery, wash it first with a dilute ammonia or soda solution to neutralize the acid, then flush with clean water.

4. Clean the battery posts and cable connectors with a small inexpensive tool designed for this purpose. Apply a thin coating of petroleum jelly to the terminals and reinstall the cables.

5. If the battery has remained undercharged, check for a loose alternator drive belt, faulty alternator or voltage regulator.

6. If the battery is using too much water, the voltage regulator may be too high.

ALTERNATOR

1. Inspect terminals for corrosion and loose connections.

2. Check all wiring for frayed or loose insulation.

3. Check mounting bolts for tightness.

4. Adjust the alternator belt tension to $\frac{1}{2}$ in. deflection at the middle of its longest span.

COOLING SYSTEM

Inspect the cooling system for leaks, weak hoses and loose clamps. Service as required.

ENGINE LUBRICATION

1. Check the crankcase oil level.

2. Fill as required.

3. Inspect the engine for oil (or fuel) leaks.

Electrical System

IGNITION SYSTEM

Trouble Diagnosis

If engine trouble has arisen which seems to be due to improper operation of the ignition system, it may be desirable to make a quick check of the ignition system. Often, such a preliminary check will reveal the cause of the trouble.

ENGINE WILL NOT RUN

1. Make a quick check of the battery and cables, if the starter motor does not turn the engine at normal speed.

2. Pull the high tension cable from the distributor cap and hold it about $\frac{3}{16}$ in. from a good ground point on the engine. NOTE: *On capacitor discharge type ignition systems, it is advisable to hold the cable with a pair of insulated pliers.* Crank the engine and observe the spark at the ground source. If a good spark occurs, the primary and secondary ignition systems may be considered satisfactory. If poor or no spark occurs, see Step 7.

3. Remove the distributor cap and check inside for moisture, corroded termi-

nals, cracks in the housing or carbon tracks. Clean the corrosion and wipe the cap dry.

4. Inspect the ignition cables for cracked or broken cables. Remove and inspect the spark plugs. See "Spark Plug Diagnosis."

5. If the cause of trouble has not been found check ignition timing.

6. If the engine still fails to run, the trouble is most likely due to other causes, such as a malfunctioning carburetor.

7. If spark did not occur at the high tension lead (Step 2), connect a 12 volt test lamp between the distributor side of the coil and ground. Crank the engine. If the test light flickers on and off, the primary circuit is probably all right.

If the test light remains on, as the engine is cranked, the contact points are not functioning. Check the point opening and ground connection in the distributor.

If the test lamp remains off as the engine is cranked, the primary circuit is poor or the points are not opening properly. Check for loose connections, broken leads, broken switch, contact point opening and primary circuit winding in the coil.

Engine Runs, But Not Satisfactorily

1. If the engine misses, or hard starting and loss of power are present, a complete check of the ignition system is in order. The cause could be anything from a low battery to other troubles not related to the ignition system.

2. Detonation may be caused by improper timing, improper operation of the centrifugal advance mechanism, worn distributor bearings or incorrect heat range of spark plugs. It can also be caused by low octane fuel or excessive carbon in the cylinders.

3. Overheating is another cause of detonation and is caused by one or more of the causes in Step 2 as well as by improper cooling system operation.

Battery Maintenance—All Models

Good battery maintenance should include the following points.

1. Protect the battery against acid damage.

2. Clean the battery. All corrosion should be removed and a thin coat of petroleum jelly applied to the terminals. A solution of baking soda and water will usually remove most corrosion from the battery. After using solution rinse with clear water.

3. Inspect the battery cables for cracks and frayed wires.

4. Clean the battery terminals. (See Step 2.)

5. Inspect the battery hold-downs and be sure that they are tight.

6. Inspect the sealing for leaks.

7. Make a hydrometer test, to determine the state of charge of the battery.

8. Recharge the battery (trickle-charge) if the hydrometer shows less than 3/4 charge.

9. Add water as specified in the owners manual. If there are no specifications, add distilled water to the top of the plates or to the split-ring.

If the battery is not in a good state of charge, or it uses an excessive amount of water, check the charging system.

BREAKER POINT REPLACEMENT

120 HP

1. Release the distributor cap hold-down screws and remove the cap.

2. Remove the rotor.

3. Pull the primary and condenser lead wires from the breaker-point quick-disconnect terminals.

4. Remove the breaker point set attaching screw and lift the contact set from the breaker plate.

5. Clean the breaker plate of smudge and dirt.

6. Carefully remove the protecter film from the new point set.

7. Place the new point set in position and install the attaching screw.

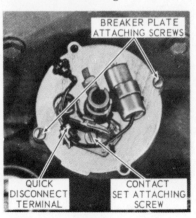

Installation of breaker points—120 HP

8. Connect the primary and condenser lead wires.

9. Check and adjust the points for proper alignment and spring tension. Use an aligning tool to bend the stationary contact, to adjust point alignment.

10. Check the breaker arm tension with a spring scale, exerting pull 90° to the lever. The breaker arm should snap back immediately when released. Spring pressure can be adjusted by *carefully* pinching or stretching the breaker spring.

11. Adjust the point opening to specifications.

12. Reinstall the rotor and check the dwell angle, with a dwell meter.

13. Install the distributor cap.

155 HP

1. Remove the distributor cap and rotor.

2. Disconnect the primary and condenser leads.

3. Loosen the 2 screws and lockwashers and remove the contact point set.

4. To install, begin by applying a thin layer of cam grease on the distributor cam.

5. Slide the contact point set over the boss on the breaker plate and under the 2 screwheads.

6. Connect the primary and condenser leads. The leads must be installed so that they will not contact the bottom of the weight base or the rotor.

7. Temporarily adjust the point opening to as close to specifications as possible with a round feeler gauge. As an alternate method, turn the adjusting screw in until the points close; then turn the screw out (counterclockwise) ½ turn (180°) to obtain an approximate point gap.

8. Start the engine and check and/or adjust the dwell angle with a dwell meter.

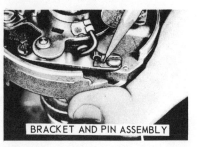

Quick disconnect terminal on 155 HP distributor

See tune-up for dwell angle adjustment.

9. Install the rotor and cap.

165 HP, 215 HP, 225 HP, 235 HP and 245 HP

1. Remove the distributor cap and rotor.

2. Disconnect the condenser and primary leads, by removing the terminal post.

3. Remove the lockscrew which holds the point set, and remove the contact points.

4. Begin installation of the new set, by applying a thin coat of the cam grease to the distributor cam.

5. Slide the contact point set over the boss on the breaker plate. The point set must lie flat on the breaker plate, with the gap adjustment eccentric screw inserted in the oval hole.

6. Tighten the screw enough to allow movement of the gap adjustment screw.

7. Install the point set, primary and condenser leads on the terminal post. The

RETAINER CLIP

LUBRICANT RESERVOIR

Distributor with breaker plate removed—6 cyl and V8 (except 200 HP)

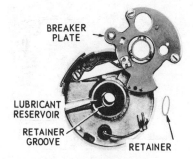

BREAKER PLATE

LUBRICANT RESERVOIR

RETAINER GROOVE

RETAINER

155 HP distributor with points removed

leads must be positioned so that they will not contact the cam or the rotor.

8. The breaker point spring tension and alignment are pre-set at the factory. Temporarily adjust the gap with a round feeler gauge.

9. Install the rotor and check the dwell angle with a dwell meter. Set the dwell to specifications. See "Tune-Up."

10. Clean and install the cap.

DISTRIBUTOR REMOVAL

120 HP and 165 HP

1. Release the distributor cap hold-down screws and remove the cap. If necessary, remove the secondary leads from the distributor cap after first marking the No. 1 tower on the cap.

2. Disconnect the distributor primary lead from the coil terminal.

3. Matchmark the distributor body and the engine block in line with the rotor.

4. Remove the distributor hold-down bolt and carefully remove the distributor from the engine.

NOTE: *Avoid rotating the engine with the distributor removed, as the ignition timing will be destroyed.*

Distributor hold-down bolt—120 HP

155 HP and 200 HP

1. Disconnect the primary wire from the coil.

2. Remove the distributor cap.

3. Crank the engine so that No. 1 cylinder is in the firing position. Matchmark the timing chain case and distributor body in line with the center of the rotor.

NOTE: *Do not rotate the engine with the distributor removed, or the engine timing will be lost.*

4. Remove the distributor hold-down bolt and lift the distributor from the timing chain cover.

185 HP, 270 HP, 215 HP, 225 HP, 235 HP and 245 HP

1. Disconnect the distributor primary wire from the coil.

2. Remove the distributor cap.

3. Crank the engine so that No. 1 cylinder is in the firing position. Matchmark the distributor base and intake manifold in line with the center of the rotor.

NOTE: *Do not rotate the engine with the distributor removed, or engine timing will be lost.*

4. Remove the distributor from the engine.

DISTRIBUTOR INSTALLATION— ENGINE NOT DISTURBED

120 HP and 165 HP

1. Turn the rotor approximately ⅛ turn clockwise past the matchmark on the distributor housing.

2. Push the distributor into the block with the distributor body in a normal installed position (matchmarks aligned).

NOTE: *It may be necessary to move the rotor slightly to facilitate the meshing of the gearteeth. After the teeth mesh, the rotor should align with the matchmarks.*

3. Tighten the distributor clampbolt and install the cap.

4. Connect the primary cable to the coil and connect all spark plug wires (if removed).

5. Check the dwell angle and ignition timing. Adjust if necessary. See "Tune-Up."

155 HP and 200 HP

1. Insert the distributor into the block so that the matchmarks on the timing chain case and distributor align and so that the rotor is aligned with the matchmarks.

2. Install and tighten the distributor clamp bolt loose enough to permit movement of the distributor under heavy hand pressure.

3. Connect the primary wire to the distributor side of the coil. Install the distributor cap.

4. If removed, install spark plug wires. See "Firing Orders."

5. Check and adjust the dwell angle and ignition timing.

185 HP, 210 HP, 215 HP, 225 HP, 235 HP, and 245 HP

1. Insert the distributor into the block so that the matchmarks on the distributor and intake manifold are aligned and so that the rotor is aligned with the matchmarks.

2. For further installation procedures use steps 2–5 of the preceding procedure.

DISTRIBUTOR INSTALLATION— ENGINE DISTURBED

All Models

1. Locate the firing position of No. 1 cylinder by removing the rocker cover and cranking the engine until No. 1 intake valve closes. An alternate method is to remove the spark plug from No. 1 cylinder and hold your thumb over the hole while cranking the engine by hand. No. 1 firing position is reached when compression is felt and the timing marks align.

2. Position the distributor in the opening position.

3. Position the rotor to point toward the front of the engine. Turn the rotor counterclockwise approximately $\frac{1}{8}$ turn and push the distributor down to mesh with the gear on the camshaft. It may be necessary to turn the rotor to facilitate meshing of the gear teeth.

4. Press firmly on the distributor and kick the engine over several times to make sure the oil pump shaft is engaged. Install the hold-down clamp and tighten it snugly.

5. Turn the distributor slightly until the points just open and fully tighten the clamp bolt.

6. Place the distributor cap in position and check to be sure that the rotor points to No. 1 terminal on the cap.

7. Install the cap and connect all wiring.

8. Check and adjust the dwell angle and ignition timing.

STARTING SYSTEM

Trouble Diagnosis

No Cranking Action

1. Make a quick check of the battery and cables. If the battery is low, the solenoid will usually produce a clattering noise.

2. If the drive pinion on the starter engages the flywheel gear, but does not drive it, the over-running clutch is slipping. The starter should be removed for service.

3. If the starter motor does not operate, note whether the solenoid plunger is pulled into the solenoid when solenoid circuit is closed. Ordinarily, the solenoid plunger makes a loud click when it is pulled in. If the plunger is pulled in, the trouble is in the solenoid switch or in the starter motor.

4. If the plunger does not pull into the solenoid when the ignition switch is turned to start, the solenoid circuit is open and the solenoid is at fault.

Cranking Speed Low

1. Low cranking speed can be caused by a low battery, defective battery cables defective starter motor, solenoid switch or an internal condition of the engine.

2. Check the battery for conditions of charge. Check the battery cables for frayed or cracked wires. Check especially for cracks in the insulation where water may have entered and corroded the wires.

3. If the battery and cables are satisfactory, test the solenoid switch and starter.

4. If the solenoid switch and starter are satisfactory, the cause of the trouble is probably due to an internal condition of the engine. Check the engine oil viscosity, which may be too heavy for prevailing conditions.

CHARGING SYSTEM

Alternator

Testing the Alternator on the Engine

1. Test connections are made as shown in the accompaning illustrations. Before making any tests, check the alternator fuse for continuity with an ohmmeter or test light. An "open" reading indicates a defective fuse.

2. Connect an ammeter between the alternator output terminal and the disconnected alternator output terminal lead. Connect a voltmeter to the voltage regulator-positive lead to the regulator "I" tertor ground. Connect a carbon pile rheostat across the battery. Be sure it is in the "off" position before connecting it.

3. Connect an accurate tachometer to register alternator speed and start the

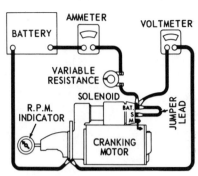

Test circuit for alternator

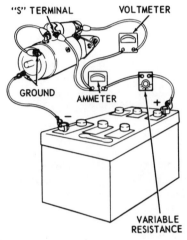

Test circuit for the alternator

engine. Adjust the alternator speed to about 4900 rpm (approx. 1970 engine rpm).

Adjust the carbon pile rheostat to obtain a 14.2 voltmeter reading and observe the ammeter reading. (Be sure that the alternator drive belt is adjusted correctly.) The ammeter reading should be at least that stated in the specifications under "Rated Output."

If the alternator fails to reach rated output, it should be removed and taken to a competent repair service, or replaced with a new unit.

REGULATOR

The regulator consists of a solid state circuit which contains no moving parts. It relies on the internal components to regulate field current to the alternator. Problems due to vibration and corrosion are minimized with this static regulator. Therefore, the regulator should last longer than most other charging system components. When searching for the cause of a charging system problem, the regulator

should be considered toward the end of the check.

Installation—All Models

To insure proper operation and to protect the charging system, the following steps should be followed during installation.

1. The regulator is for use on 12 volt negative ground systems only. Be sure that the battery negative lead is to a ground source.

2. Disconnect the battery cable at the battery terminal.

3. A ground lead should be connected between the alternator frame and the regulator mounting bolt.

4. Mount the regulator on a metal area. Be sure that regulator case is well grounded.

5. Connect the alternator field lead to the regulator "F" terminal. Then, connect the ignition lead to regulator "I" terminal.

6. Do not flash field or ground any terminal to the regulator.

7. Reconnect the battery cable.

8. Start the engine and observe the ohmmeter. A high charge rate is normal for the first few minutes of operation, but will decrease as the regulator warms up (3–5 minutes).

SERVICE—ALL MODELS

The regulator is a completely sealed unit and no adjustments or repairs are possible. It is recommended that the following procedure be followed in the event of charging system difficulties.

1. Be sure that the battery is fully charged and the battery cables are in good condition. Be sure that all connections in the system are clean and tight.

2. A voltmeter can be used to check for any excessive voltage drops in the system.

3. Test the alternator to see if it is capable of producing rated output. See "Alternator Testing." Remove and repair the alternator if necessary.

4. Test the regulator as described in the following section. See "Testing—All Models."

Testing—All Models

1. Connect an ammeter, in series, between the alternator and battery. Connect a voltmeter to the regulator "I" terminal and to the regulator case.

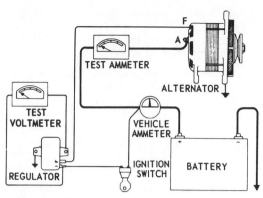

Test circuit for the regulator

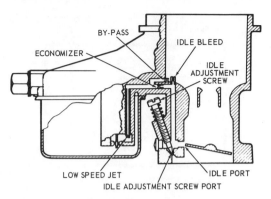

Cutaway view of Carter RBS carburetor

2. Start the engine and adjust the engine speed to about 1500–2000 engine rpm.

3. Turn on the accessories to obtain a 10–15 ampere load. Voltmeter reading should be 13.9–14.7 volts with a 10–15 amp. load.

Fuel System

CARBURETOR ADJUSTMENTS
Carter RBS (Dual Installation)
PUMP ADJUSTMENT

1. The pump adjustment must be made each time the carburetor is disassembled and must be made before the unloader adjustment.

2. Back out the throttle adjusting screw and hold the choke valve wide open. The throttle valve should seat in the bore of the carburetor.

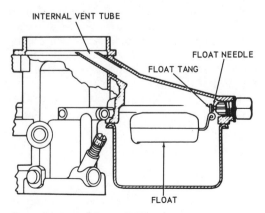

Cutaway view of Carter RBS carburetor

3. With the throttle valve closed tightly, the adjustment should be made at the connector rod nut so that there is no lag between the downward movement of the pump plunger and the opening of the throttle valve.

UNLOADER ADJUSTMENT—FORWARD CARBURETOR ONLY

1. With the throttle valve held wide open, adjust the tang on the throttle lever to obtain a $7/64$ in. clearance between the upper edge of the choke valve and the inner wall of the air horn.

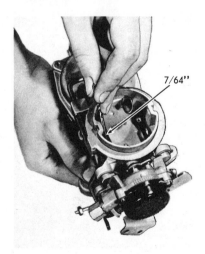

Carter RBS carburetor unloader adjustment

FLOAT LEVEL ADJUSTMENT

1. With the float chamber removed, invert the float chamber with only the weight of the float on the needle and measure the distance from the machined casting to the small bump on the outer edge of the float. The vertical distance should be $15/32$ in.

2. To adjust the float level, hold the lip end of the float bracket with needle nosed pliers and bend the float bracket at its narrowest point.

Rochester 2GC or 2GV

PUMP ROD ADJUSTMENT

1. Back out the idle stop screw and completely close the throttle valves in the bore.

2. The top of the pump rod should be $1\frac{5}{32}$ in. from the top of the carburetor air horn ring.

3. Bend the pump rod as required to obtain this dimension.

Rochester 2GC or 2GV pump rod adjustment

CHOKE UNLOADER ADJUSTMENT

1. With the throttle valves held wide open, the choke valves should open sufficiently to allow a .110 in. gauge to be inserted between it and the air horn wall.

2. Bend the unloader tang on the throttle lever to obtain this dimension.

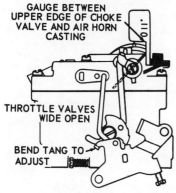

Rochester 2GC or 2GV pump rod adjustment

FLOAT LEVEL

1. With the float housing removed and inverted, the float level should be as stated

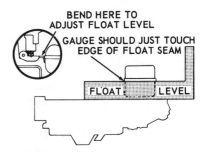

Rochester 2GC or 2GV float level adjustment

in the specifications. The distance is measured from the lower (sharp) edge of the float at the lower seam, to the air horn gasket.

2. Bend the float as required to adjust the level.

FLOAT DROP

1. With the air horn assembly held upright, the distance from the gasket to the bottom of the float pontoon should be as stated in the specifications.

2. If not, bend the float lever as required to obtain the dimension specified.

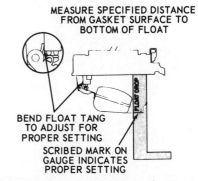

Rochester 2GC or 2GV float drop adjustment

Rochester 4MV

PUMP ROD ADJUSTMENT

1. With the throttle valves completely closed, and the pump rod in the specified hole of the pump lever, measure from the top of the choke valve wall to the top of the pump stem. The dimension should be as specified.

2. Bend the pump rod to adjust this dimension.

VACUUM BREAK ADJUSTMENT

1. Rotate the choke valve toward the closed position by pushing down on the vacuum breaker lever.

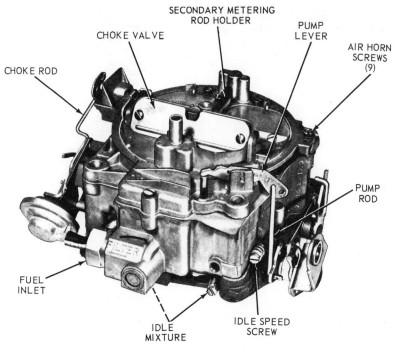

CHOKE ROD

CHOKE VALVE

SECONDARY METERING
ROD HOLDER

PUMP
LEVER

AIR HORN
SCREWS
(9)

PUMP
ROD

FUEL
INLET

IDLE
MIXTURE

IDLE SPEED
SCREW

Rochester 4MV carburetor

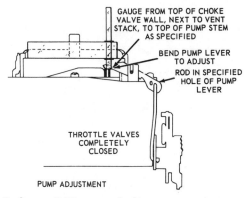

GAUGE FROM TOP OF CHOKE
VALVE WALL, NEXT TO VENT
STACK, TO TOP OF PUMP STEM
AS SPECIFIED

BEND PUMP LEVER
TO ADJUST

ROD IN SPECIFIED
HOLE OF PUMP
LEVER

THROTTLE VALVES
COMPLETELY
CLOSED

PUMP ADJUSTMENT

Rochester 4MV pump rod adjustment

2. The dimension between the lower edge of the choke valve and the choke lever end should be $^{13}/_{64}$ in.

3. To adjust this, bend the choke lever tang.

UNLOADER ADJUSTMENT

1. With the choke valve held in the closed position (rubber band on the vacuum break lever) open the primary throttle to the wide open position.

2. The dimension between the lower edge of choke valve and the air horn wall should be .300 in.

3. Bend the tang on the fast idle lever to adjust this dimension.

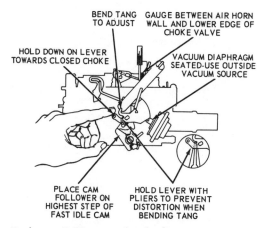

BEND TANG
TO ADJUST

GAUGE BETWEEN AIR HORN
WALL AND LOWER EDGE OF
CHOKE VALVE

HOLD DOWN ON LEVER
TOWARDS CLOSED CHOKE

VACUUM DIAPHRAGM
SEATED-USE OUTSIDE
VACUUM SOURCE

PLACE CAM
FOLLOWER ON
HIGHEST STEP OF
FAST IDLE CAM

HOLD LEVER WITH
PLIERS TO PREVENT
DISTORTION WHEN
BENDING TANG

Rochester 4MV vacuum break adjustment

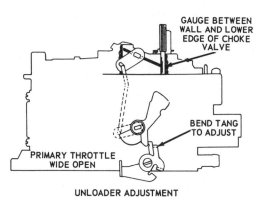

GAUGE BETWEEN
WALL AND LOWER
EDGE OF CHOKE
VALVE

BEND TANG
TO ADJUST

PRIMARY THROTTLE
WIDE OPEN

UNLOADER ADJUSTMENT

Rochester 4MV unloader adjustment

Secondary Lockout Clearance Adjustment

1. With the choke valve and both primary and secondary throttle valves closed the lockout lever should not contact the lockout pin. The clearance between the lockout lever and pin should not exceed .015 in.

2. Bend the lockout lever to adjust the tension.

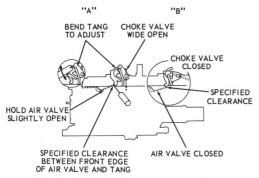

Rochester 4MV secondary lockout adjustment

Choke Coil Rod Adjustment

1. With the choke valve completely closed and the choke rod in the bottom of the choke lever slot, push the choke coil rod down to its stop. The top of the choke coil rod must be even with the bottom of the hole in the vacuum break lever.

2. To adjust this setting, bend the choke coil rod.

3. Connect the choke coil rod to the vacuum break lever and install the clip.

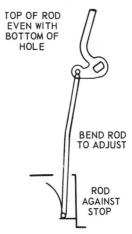

Rochester 4MV choke coil rod adjustment

4. Replace the choke bi-metal element if it is warped.

Float Level Adjustment

1. With the air horn removed, measure from the top of the float bowl gasket surface (gasket removed) to the top of the float at the toe (locate gauging point $\frac{1}{16}$ in. back from the toe).

2. The measurement should be according to specifications. If not, bend the float up or down for the proper adjustment.

Carburetor Overhaul

Carburetor repair kits are recommended for each overhaul operation. They are available from your dealer or from any reputable automotive supply house. These kits, which are usually packaged with in-

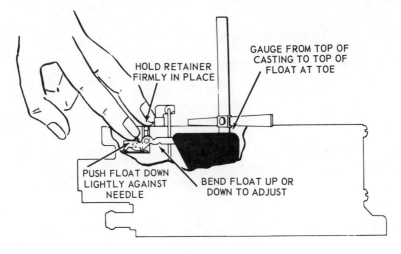

FLOAT LEVEL ADJUSTMENT

Rochester 4MV float level adjustment

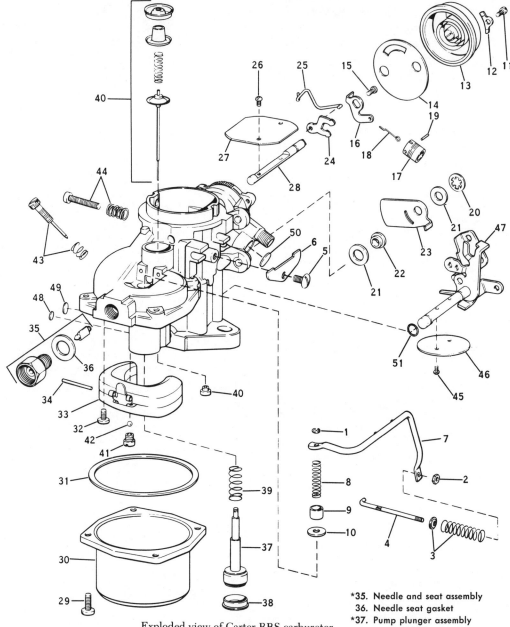

Exploded view of Carter RBS carburetor

* 1. Pump rod retainer
  2. Connector link nut
  3. Spring and retainer
  4. Connector link
  5. Pump arm retainer screw
  6. Pump arm retainer
  7. Pump arm
* 8. Upper pump spring
  9. Bushing
  10. Washer
  11. Coil housing screw
  12. Coil housing retainer
  13. Thermostatic coil and housing
*14. Coil housing gasket
  15. Lever screw
  16. Choke piston lever
  17. Choke piston

  18. Choke piston link
  19. Piston pin
  20. Cam retainer
  21. Washers
  22. Cam collar
  23. Cam
  24. Choke lever
  25. Connector Rod
  26. Choke valve screw
  27. Choke valve
  28. Choke shaft
  29. Bowl attaching screws
  30. Float bowl
*31. Bowl ring gasket
  32. Float pin screw
  33. Float
  34. Float pin

*35. Needle and seat assembly
  36. Needle seat gasket
*37. Pump plunger assembly
*38. Pump cylinder retainer
  39. Lower pump spring
*40. Step-up rod and diaphragm assembly
*41. Intake ball check
*42. Intake check ball
  43. Idle adjustment screw and spring
  44. Throttle adjusting screw and spring
  45. Throttle valve screw
  46. Throttle valve
  47. Throttle shaft
  48. Fuel well welsh plug
  49. Idle port plug
  50. Choke piston welsh plug
  51. O ring
  * Repair kit parts

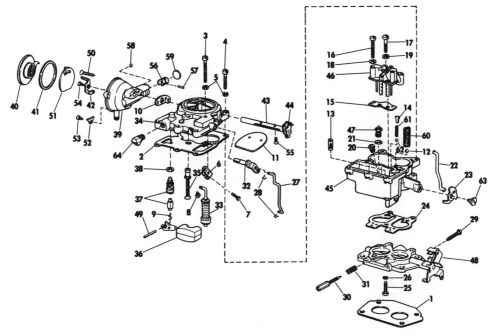

Exploded view of Rochester 2GC carburetor

1. Carburetor to manifold gasket
2. Air horn gasket
3. Long air horn screw
4. Short air horn screw
5. Air horn lockwasher
6. Pump lever
7. Pump screw
8. Pump clip
9. Pull clip
10. Choke gasket
11. Choke valve
12. Inlet check ball
13. Pump screen
14. Pump spring guide
15. Venturi gasket
16. Outer venturi screw
17. Center venturi screw
18. Outer venturi lockwasher
19. Center venturi gasket
20. Main metering jet
21. Power valve gasket
22. Choke rod
23. Idle speed screw stop

24. Throttle body gasket
25. Throttle body screw
26. Throttle body lockwasher
27. Pump rod
28. Pump rod clip
29. Idle stop screw
30. Idle adjusting needle
31. Idle needle spring
32. Pump shaft and lever assembly
33. Pump assembly
34. Air horn assembly
35. Power piston assembly
36. Float assembly
37. Needle and seat assembly
38. Needle seat gasket
39. Choke housing assembly
40. Thermostat cover
41. Thermostat cover gasket
42. Choke lever and link assembly
43. Choke shaft assembly
44. Choke lever and collar assembly
45. Float bowl assembly

46. Venturi cluster assembly
47. Power valve assembly
48. Throttle body assembly
49. Float hinge pin
50. Choke housing screw
51. Baffle plate
52. Thermostat cover retainer
53. Thermostat cover screw
54. Choke lever screw
55. Choke valve screw
56. Choke piston
57. Choke piston pin
58. Lead ball plug
59. Expansion plug
60. Pump return spring
61. Pump discharge spring
62. Pump discharge ball
63. Idle stop screw
64. Fuel line fitting

structions, contain all the necessary parts for a complete carburetor overhaul.

Disassemble the carburetor referring to the accompanying illustrations for each particular carburetor.

Dirt, gum, and varnish on the exterior moving parts of the carburetor are often responsible for poor performance and operation. For this reason, all parts, except those noted, should be cleaned in carburetor solvent.

WARNING: *Rubber parts, plastic parts, diaphragms, and pump plungers should not be immersed in carburetor cleaner or they will be destroyed. Do not soak parts in carburetor cleaner for any longer than is necessary, or the finish on certain parts will be removed by the corrosive action of the solvent.*

Inspect all parts as follows:

1. Inspect all castings for signs of corrosion or cracking.

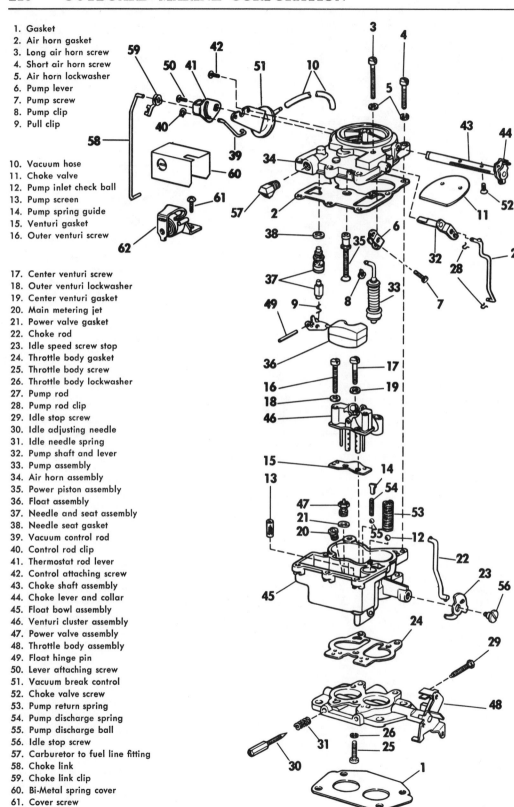

1. Gasket
2. Air horn gasket
3. Long air horn screw
4. Short air horn screw
5. Air horn lockwasher
6. Pump lever
7. Pump screw
8. Pump clip
9. Pull clip

10. Vacuum hose
11. Choke valve
12. Pump inlet check ball
13. Pump screen
14. Pump spring guide
15. Venturi gasket
16. Outer venturi screw

17. Center venturi screw
18. Outer venturi lockwasher
19. Center venturi gasket
20. Main metering jet
21. Power valve gasket
22. Choke rod
23. Idle speed screw stop
24. Throttle body gasket
25. Throttle body screw
26. Throttle body lockwasher
27. Pump rod
28. Pump rod clip
29. Idle stop screw
30. Idle adjusting needle
31. Idle needle spring
32. Pump shaft and lever
33. Pump assembly
34. Air horn assembly
35. Power piston assembly
36. Float assembly
37. Needle and seat assembly
38. Needle seat gasket
39. Vacuum control rod
40. Control rod clip
41. Thermostat rod lever
42. Control attaching screw
43. Choke shaft assembly
44. Choke lever and collar
45. Float bowl assembly
46. Venturi cluster assembly
47. Power valve assembly
48. Throttle body assembly
49. Float hinge pin
50. Lever attaching screw
51. Vacuum break control
52. Choke valve screw
53. Pump return spring
54. Pump discharge spring
55. Pump discharge ball
56. Idle stop screw
57. Carburetor to fuel line fitting
58. Choke link
59. Choke link clip
60. Bi-Metal spring cover
61. Cover screw
62. Thermostat assembly

Exploded view of Rochester 2GV carburetor

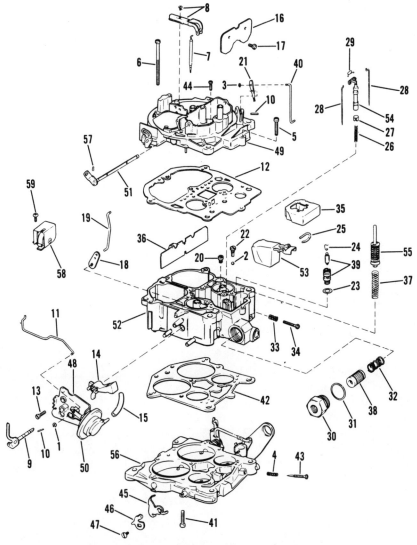

Exploded view of Rochester 4MV carburetor

1. Vacuum and choke rod clip	21. Pump actuating lever	41. Throttle body screw
2. Pump discharge ball	22. Pump discharge ball retainer	42. Throttle body gasket
3. Pump rod clip	23. Needle seat gasket	43. Idle needle
4. Idle needle spring	24. Float needle pull clip	44. Air horn screw
5. Air horn screw	25. Float assembly hinge pin	45. Cam lever
6. Air horn screw	26. Power piston spring	46. Fast idle lever
7. Secondary metering rod	27. Power piston retainer	47. Idle lever screw
8. Secondary metering rod holder	28. Primary metering rod	48. Vacuum break control bracket
9. Air valve lockout lever	29. Primary metering rod spring	49. Air horn assembly
10. Roll pin	30. Fuel inlet filter nut	50. Vacuum break control assembly
11. Vacuum break rod	31. Filter nut gasket	51. Choke shaft & lever assembly
12. Air horn gasket	32. Fuel filter gasket	52. Float bowl assembly
13. Control attaching screw	33. Idle stop screw spring	53. Float assembly
14. Fast idle cam	34. Idle screw	54. Power piston assembly
15. Vacuum hose	35. Float bowl insert	55. Pump assembly
16. Choke valve	36. Float bowl baffle	56. Throttle body assembly
17. Choke valve screw	37. Pump return spring	57. Choke link clip
18. Intermediate choke lever	38. Fuel inlet filter	58. Choke thermostat assembly
19. Choke rod	39. Needle and seat assembly	59. Choke screw
20. Primary jet	40. Pump rod	

2. Blow out all passages in the castings with compressed air and allow the parts to air dry. Do not attempt to clean small passages with a piece of wire.

3. Carefully inspect all parts for wear and replace those that are worn.

4. Remove carbon from the throttle shafts with sandpaper. Never use emery cloth.

5. Inspect the float needles and seats for wear. If either is worn, replace both the needles and seats.

6. Inspect the float pins for excessive wear.

7. Inspect the floats for dents or holes. Check the inside of the floats for liquid by shaking the float.

8. Inspect the throttle shafts for excessive wear (looseness or rattle in the body flange casting). Replace the flange assembly if it is excessively worn.

9. Inspect the idle mixture screws for burrs and replace if any are found.

10. Examine the fast idle cam for wear or damage.

11. Check all throttle levers or valves for binding or other damage.

12. Check all filters for dirt or clogging and replace as necessary.

Assemble the carburetor, referring to the accompanying illustrations for each particular carburetor. Use all of the parts contained in the rebuilding kit, especially the gaskets. Install and adjust the carburetor.

FUEL PUMP

Testing

1. Be sure that there is fuel in the tank.

2. With the engine running, check for leaks at all gasoline feed line connections. Inspect all lines for kinks which could restrict the flow of fuel.

3. Inspect the fuel pump filter for excessive dirt, gum or varnish. Replace the filter at least once a year and clean as often as necessary.

4. Inspect for leaks at the fuel pump diaphragm. If leaks persist, remove and replace the fuel pump.

5. Disconnect the feed hose at the carburetor. Ground the distributor terminal of the coil so that the engine can be cranked without starting. Place a container at the end of the hose and crank the engine through a few revolutions. If little or no gasoline flows, either the fuel pump is inop-

erative or the lines are clogged. Before assuming the pump is bad, disconnect the fuel line at the other end and blow through it with compressed air, to be sure it is clear.

6. If gasoline flows in good volume, you can assume that the fuel pump and lines are all right. However, it is advisable to make a static pressure test. (See Step 7.)

7. Insert a "Tee" connector and gauge into the fuel line at the outlet side of the pump. Reconnect all fuel lines, start the engine and allow it to run at idle. If the pump is operating properly, the pressure will be as specified.

8. If not, remove and replace the fuel pump.

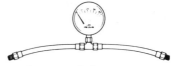

"Tee" gauge for testing fuel pump pressure

Engine Mechanical

OMC engines covered in this book are of four-cylinder, six-cylinder or V8 design. All engines are not necessarily used in any model year.

IN-HULL SERVICE

NOTE: *The operations listed in this section can be accomplished with the engine mounted in the hull. Since "Engine Removal" and the operations which can only be done with the engine removed from the hull are dependent upon "Outdrive Removal," these operations are not included in this book. "Outdrive Removal" is a very complex operation requiring a great many special tools which would normally only be found in a well-equipped repair facility, such as a dealership.*

INTAKE MANIFOLD
Removal and Installation

4 AND 6 CYLINDER

The four-cylinder and six-cylinder intake and exhaust manifolds are removed as a unit.

1. Disconnect the exhaust pipe flange

and remove all connections to the carburetor.

2. Take off all the vacuum lines at the manifold and carburetor.

3. Remove the carburetor.

4. Remove the retaining bolts from the side of the cylinder head.

5. To separate the intake and exhaust manifolds, remove the one retaining bolt and two nuts at the center.

6. Install the manifold in the reverse order of the removal procedure.

V8 (EXCEPT V6 AND 300 CU IN. V8)

1. Remove the flame arrestor.

2. Drain the cooling system.

3. Disconnect the:

a. Battery cables at the battery;

b. Upper coolant hoses at the manifold;

c. Crankcase ventilation hoses as required;

d. Fuel line at the carburetor;

e. Accelerator linkage at the carburetor;

f. Vacuum hose at the distributor;

g. Power brake hose at the carburetor base or manifold, if applicable;

h. Ignition coil and temperature sending switch wires.

4. Remove the distributor cap and scribe the rotor position relative to the distributor body.

5. Remove the distributor.

6. If applicable, remove the Delcotron upper bracket.

7. Remove the manifold-to-head attaching bolts, then remove the manifold and carburetor as an assembly.

8. If the manifold is to be replaced, transfer the carburetor (and mounting studs), water outlet, and thermostat (use a new gasket), and, if applicable, the choke coil.

9. Before installing the manifold, thoroughly clean the gasket and seal surfaces of the cylinder heads and manifold.

10. Install the manifold end seals, folding the tabs if applicable, and the manifold/head gaskets, using a sealing compound around the water passages.

11. When installing the manifold, care should be taken not to dislocate the end seals. It is helpful to use a pilot in the distributor opening. Tighten the manifold bolts to 30 ft lbs in the sequence illustrated.

12. Install the ignition coil.

13. Install the distributor with the rotor in its original location as indicated by the scribe line. If the engine has been disturbed, refer to the distributor R & R procedures.

14. If applicable, install the Delcotron upper bracket and adjust the belt tension.

15. Connect all components disconnected in Step 3 above.

16. Fill the cooling system, start the engine, check for leaks, and adjust the ignition timing and carburetor idle speed and mixture.

V6 AND 200 HP V8

1. Drain water from the engine.

2. Remove the flame arrestor and disconnect all hoses and tubes from the carburetor.

3. Disconnect the throttle linkage at the carburetor. Disconnect the PCV hose.

4. Drain the water from the manifold by removing the clamp at the hose and removing the bypass hose.

5. Remove the bolts attaching the manifold to the cylinder heads.

6. Remove the carburetor and intake manifold as an assembly.

7. Remove the intake manifold gasket clamps and remove the gasket and rubber gasket seal.

8. Installation is the reverse of removal.

EXHAUST MANIFOLD

Removal and Installation

4 AND 6 CYLINDER

See the "Removal and Installation" procedures listed for the intake manifold of four-cylinder and six-cylinder engines because the manifolds are removed as a unit.

V8 (EXCEPT V6 AND 200 HP V8)

1. If equipped with A.I.R., remove the air injector manifold assembly. The ¼ in. pipe

V8 intake manifold (except 300 cu in. V8)

threads in the manifold are straight threads. Do not use a ¼ in. tapered pipe tap.

2. Disconnect the battery.

3. If applicable, remove the air cleaner preheater shroud.

4. Remove the exhaust pipe flange nuts, then hang the pipe with wire.

5. Remove the manifold mounting bolts (end bolts first), then remove the manifold.

6. To install, clean the mating surfaces, then install the manifold with the center bolts first. Install the end bolts, then tighten all bolts to 20 ft lbs.

7. To complete installation, reverse steps 1 through 3.

V6 AND 200 HP V8

This is a general procedure for all models.

1. Remove exhaust manifold-to-exhaust pipe attaching bolts.

2. On the right side, remove Delcotron, as necessary.

3. Unlock and remove exhaust manifold-to-cylinder head bolts. Remove the manifold.

4. Installation is the reverse of removal.

CYLINDER HEAD

Removal and Installation

4 AND 6 CYLINDER

1. Drain the cooling system and remove the flame arrestor. Disconnect the PCV hose.

2. Disconnect the accelerator rod at the bellcrank on the manifold and the fuel and vacuum lines at the carburetor.

3. Disconnect the exhaust pipe at the manifold flange, then remove the manifold bolts and clamps and remove the manifolds and carburetor as an assembly.

4. Remove the fuel and vacuum line retaining clip from the water outlet. Disconnect the wire harness from the heat sending unit and coil, leaving the harness clear of the clips on the rocker arm cover.

5. Disconnect the radiator hose at the water outlet housing and the battery ground strap at the cylinder head.

6. Disconnect the wires and remove the spark plugs. On the six-cylinder engine, disconnect the coil-to-distributor primary wire lead at the coil and remove the coil.

7. Remove the rocker arm cover. Back off the rocker arm nuts, pivot the rocker

arms to clear the pushrods, and remove the pushrods.

8. Remove the cylinder head bolts, the cylinder head, and the gasket.

To install:

1. Place a new cylinder head gasket over the dowel pins in the cylinder block.

2. Guide the lower cylinder head into place over the dowels and gasket.

3. Oil the cylinder head bolts, install them, and run them down snug.

4. Tighten the cylinder head bolts a little at a time with a torque wrench in the correct sequence. Final torque should be as specified.

REFERENCE PICTURE

4 and 6 cylinder engine cylinder head

5. Install valve pushrods down through the cylinder head openings and seat them in their lifter sockets.

6. Install the rocker arms, balls, and nuts and tighten the rocker arm nuts until all pushrod play is taken up.

7. Install the thermostat, thermostat housing, and water outlet, using new gaskets. Connect the coolant hose.

8. Install the heat sending switch and torque it to 15–20 ft lbs.

9. Clean the old spark plugs or install new ones. Set the gaps to 0.035 in.

10. Use new plug gaskets and torque to 20–25 ft lbs.

11. Install the coil (on six-cylinder engines) and then connect the heat sending unit and coil primary wires, and connect the battery ground cable at the cylinder head.

12. Clean the surfaces and install a new gasket over the manifold studs. Install the manifold. Install the bolts and clamps and torque them as specified.

13. Connect the throttle linkage.

14. Connect the PCV, fuel, and vacuum lines and secure the lines in a clip at the water outlet.

15. Fill the cooling system and check for leaks.

16. Adjust the valve lash.

17. Install the rocker arm cover and position the wiring harness in the clips.

18. Clean and install the flame arrestor.

V8 (EXCEPT V6 AND 200 HP V8)

1. Remove the intake manifold as previously outlined.

2. Remove the exhaust manifolds as previously outlined and tie them out of the way.

3. Back off the rocker arm nuts and pivot the rocker arms out of the way so the pushrods can be removed. Identify the pushrods so they can be installed in their original positions.

4. Remove the cylinder head bolts and remove the heads.

5. Install the cylinder heads using new gaskets. Install the gaskets with the bead up.

NOTE: *Coat a steel gasket with sealer on both sides. If a composition gasket is used, do not use sealer.*

6. Clean the bolts, apply sealer to the threads, and install them hand tight.

7. Tighten the head bolts a little at a time in the sequence shown. Head bolt torque is listed in the specifications.

8. Install the intake and exhaust manifolds.

9. Adjust the valves as previously described.

V6 AND 200 HP V8

1. Drain coolant and disconnect battery ground strap.

2. Remove intake manifold.

3. For right head only: Remove Delcotron.

4. For left head only: Remove the dipstick.

5. Disconnect exhaust pipe from manifold, remove manifold.

6. Remove rocker cover, rocker shaft assembly, and pushrods. The pushrods should be reinstalled in their original locations. It is important to protect the hydraulic lifters from dirt.

7. Loosen all head bolts, then remove all bolts and remove head and gasket.

8. Installation is the reverse of removal.

CYLINDER HEAD OVERHAUL

See the procedures listed in the "Engine Rebuilding Section."

ROCKER ARMS AND PUSHRODS

Removal and Installation

ALL ENGINES EXCEPT 302 CU IN.

1. Remove the valve covers.

2. Remove the rocker arm nuts, rocker arm balls, and rocker arms.

3. Remove the pushrods.

4. Segregate the rocker arms, balls, and pushrods so that they can be installed in their original locations.

5. Install the pushrods. Be sure that the pushrods seat in the lifter sockets.

6. Install the rocker arms, rocker arm balls, and rocker arm nuts. Tighten the rocker arms until all lash is removed. When installing new rocker arms, coat the rocker arms and balls with Molykote or its equivalent.

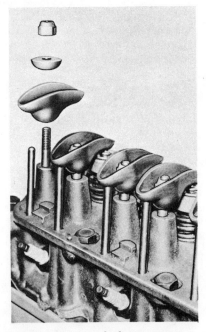

Installing rocker arms and adjusting nuts

Valve Adjustment

NOTE: *This procedure is not a normal running adjustment. Under normal operating conditions the valves should not require adjustment. This procedure should only be used in the event that the valve train is removed or disturbed.*

4 AND 6 CYLINDER

1. Perform the following adjustment with the engine stopped.

2. Remove the valve cover.

3. Adjust the valves when the lifter is

on the base circle of the camshaft lobe.

4. Mark the distributor housing with chalk at No. 1 and 6 firing positions (plug wires).

5. Remove the plug wires at the spark plugs and remove the coil wire.

6. Remove the distributor cap and plug wires.

7. Crank the engine until the distributor rotor points to No. 1 firing position and the breaker points are open. In this position the following valves can be adjusted:

No. 1 Cylinder—Exhaust and Intake
No. 2 Cylinder—Intake
No. 3 Cylinder—Exhaust
No. 4 Cylinder—Intake
No. 5 Cylinder—Exhaust
No. 6 Cylinder—Exhaust

Back out the adjusting nut until lash is felt at the pushrod. This can be determined by checking the pushrod side-play while moving the nut. Turn the nut down until all lash is removed. When play is removed, turn the nut down an additional ¾ turn.

8. Crank the engine until the distributor rotor points to No. 6 firing position and the breaker points are open. In this position, the following valves can be adjusted:

No. 2 Cylinder—Exhaust
No. 3 Cylinder—Intake
No. 4 Cylinder—Exhaust
No. 5 Cylinder—Exhaust
No. 6 Cylinder—Intake and Exhaust

Adjust the valves as outlined in the preceding step.

9. Install the distributor cap and connect the plug wires and coil wire.

4 and 6 cylinder valve adjustment

10. Install the rocker arm cover and adjust the carburetor.

V8 (EXCEPT V6 AND 200 HP V8)

1. Remove the valve cover and adjust the valves with the lifter on the base circle of the camshaft lobe.

V8 rocker arm, pushrod, and valve lifter

Adjusting the hydraulic valve lifters—V8 except 200 HP

2. Crank the engine with the starter or by hand (spark plugs removed) until the mark on the damper aligns with the "0" mark on the timing tab. This can be determined by placing your finger on no. 1 spark plug port until compression is felt. This is no. 1 firing position.

3. With the engine in no. 1 firing position, the following valves can be adjusted:

Left-Hand Rotation Engines—
  Exhaust: 1-3-4-8
  Intake: 1-2-5-7

Right-Hand Rotation Engines—
Exhaust: 1-2-5-7
Intake: 1-3-4-8

Back off the adjusting nut until lash is felt. This can be determined by checking the pushrod side-play as the nut is turned. Turn the adjusting nut down until all play is removed. Tighten the nut an additional $\frac{3}{4}$ turn. No other adjustment is required.

4. Crank the engine ONE more revolution until the "0" mark and the pointer align again. This is no. 6 firing position. In this position, the following valves can be adjusted:

Left-Hand Rotation Engines—
Exhaust: 2-5-6-7
Intake: 3-4-6-8

Right-Hand Rotation Engines—
Exhaust: 3-4-6-8
Intake: 2-5-6-7

5. Install the rocker arm covers.

6. Adjust the carburetor idle speed and mixture.

WATER PUMP

**Removal and Installation—
All Models**

1. Drain the water from the cooling system.

2. If equipped, remove the shroud covering the alternator belt.

3. Release the tension on the belt and slide the alternator inward.

4. Remove the pulley from the water pump shaft.

5. Remove the pump and gasket from the timing case cover.

6. Disconnect the water pump hoses and remove the water pump.

7. Installation is the reverse of removal.

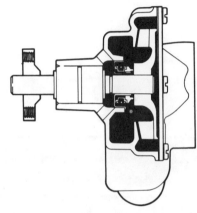

Cutaway view of the water pump (typical)

4 · Volvo Penta (Chrysler Marine Division)

General Information and Specifications

INTRODUCTION

The Volvo inboard/outdrive unit was introduced in 1959 and was installed in a wide range of craft all over the world. Newer units are characterized by such features as bevel gears, silent, cone-type clutches and silent exhaust. Corrosion protection is of the highest quality and surface treatment can require as many as seven or nine separate processes. Stainless steel thread inserts, zinc rings and zinc anodes are used to deter electrolysis.

Maintenance is relatively simple on Volvo units as the oil dipstick is located in an easily accessible place. An adjustable trim tab guarantees steady running on a set course. Steering torque can be readily adjusted with the trim tab.

General Engine Specifications

Model	Engine Cu In. Displacement	Carburetor Type	Advertised Horsepower @ rpm	Maximum rpm	Bore and Stroke (in.)	Advertised Compression Ratio	Oil Pressure @ rpm (psi)
95/100	108.6	①	95	N.A.	3.313 x 3.150	10.0 : 1	36–85 @ 2000
95A/100	108.6	①	95	N.A.	3.313 x 3.150	9.7 : 1	36–85 @ 2000
100/100	108.6	①	100	N.A.	3.313 x 3.150	9.5 : 1	36–85 @ 2000
110/100	108.6	①	110	N.A.	3.313 x 3.150	10.0 : 1	36–85 @ 2000
110/200	108.6	①	110	N.A.	3.313 x 3.150	10.0 : 1	36–85 @ 2000
120/200	108.6	①	120	N.A.	3.313 x 3.150	9.7 : 1	36–85 @ 2000
105A	121.0	①	105 @ 5100	5100②	3.500 x 3.150	9.5 : 1	36–85 @ 2000

General Engine Specifications (cont.)

Model	Engine Cu In. Displacement	Carburetor Type	Advertised Horsepower @ rpm	Maximum rpm	Bore and Stroke (in.)	Advertised Compression Ratio	Oil Pressure @ rpm (psi)
115A	121.0	①	115 @ 5100	5100②	3.500 x 3.150	9.5 : 1	36–85 @ 2000
130A	121.0	①	130 @ 5100	5100②	3.500 x 3.150	9.5 : 1	36–85 @ 2000
130B	121.0	①	115 @ 5100	5100②	3.500 x 3.150	8.4 : 1	36–85 @ 2000
130C	121.0	①	130 @ 5100	5100②	3.500 x 3.150	9.5 : 1	36–85 @ 2000
165A	182.0	①	165 @ 5000	5000	3.500 x 3.150	9.2 : 1	36–85 @ 2000
170A	182.0	①	170 @ 5000	5000	3.500 x 3.150	9.5 : 1	36–85 @ 2000

① 95/100, 95A/100—1 Zenith Stromberg 150 CD
   110/100, 110/200—2 Zenith Stromberg 150 CD
   100/100, 110/100—2 Zenith 36 VNP
   120/200—2 Zenith Stromberg 175 CD
   115A—1 Solex 44 PAI
   130C—2 Solex 44 PAI
   170A—3 Solex 44 PAI
   105A—1 Zenith Stromberg 150 CD
   130A, 130B—2 Zenith Stromberg 175 CDSE
   165A—3 Zenith Stromberg 175 CDSE
② On light boats with a speed exceeding 30 knots, maximum rpm of the 4-cylinder engine can reach 5500 rpm.

Tune-Up Specifications

When analyzing compression-test results, look for uniformity among cylinders rather than specific pressures.

Model	Horse-power	SPARK PLUGS Type	Gap (in.)	DISTRIBUTOR Point Dwell (deg)	Point Gap (in.)	IGNITION TIMING (deg)	Fuel Pump Pressure (psi)	IDLE SPEED (rpm)
95/100	95	W225T1	0.028	60	0.016–0.020	See Chart	1.5–3.5	900–1000
95A/100	95	W225T1	0.028	60	0.016–0.020	See Chart	1.5–3.5	900–1000
100/100	100	W225T1	0.028	60	0.016–0.020	See Chart	1.5–3.5	600
110/100	110	W225T1	0.028	60	0.016–0.020	See Chart	1.5–3.5	600
110/200	110	W225T1	0.028	60	0.016–0.020	See Chart	1.5–3.5	900–1000
120/200	120	W225T1	0.028	60	0.016–0.020	See Chart	1.5–3.5	900–1000
105A	105	W225T35	0.028	59–65	0.016–0.020	9B①	3.0–3.5	900–1000
115A	115	W225T35	0.028	59–65	0.016–0.020	9B②	3.0–3.5	900–1000
130A	130	W225T35	0.028	59–65	0.016–0.020	9B③	3.0–3.5	900–1000

Tune-Up Specifications (cont.)

When analyzing compression test results, look for uniformity among cylinders rather than specific pressures.

Model	Horse-power	SPARK PLUGS		DISTRIBUTOR		IGNITION TIMING (deg)	Fuel Pump Pressure (psi)	IDLE SPEED (rpm)
		Type	Gap (in.)	Point Dwell (deg)	Point Gap (in.)			
130B	115	W225T35	0.028	59–65	0.016–0.020	12B④	3.0–3.5	900–1000
130C	130	W225T35	0.028	59–65	0.016–0.020	12B③	3.0–3.5	900–1000
165A	165	W225T35	0.028	37–43	0.010–0.014	12B⑤	3.0–3.5	800–900
170A	170	W225T35	0.028	37–43	0.010–0.014	12B⑤	3.0–3.5	900–1000

① 22–24 @ 2000
② 24–26 @ 2000
③ 27–29 @ 2000
④ 26–28 @ 2000
⑤ 15B when equipped with thick cylinder head gasket.
　165A—22–24 @ 2000 with vacuum disconnected and plugged.
　170A—28–30 @ 2000 with vacuum disconnected and plugged.

Ignition Timing Specifications
95/100—120/200

Engine	Carburetor	Distributor	Basic Setting	Stroboscope Setting
120/200	Stromberg 175 CD	0231153003 or 0231153007	10° BTDC	18–20° BTDC/1500 rpm
95A/100	Stromberg 150 CD	0231153003 or 0231153007	8° BTDC	15–17° BTDC/1500 rpm
110/100 110/200 95/100	Stromberg 150 CD	0231110038 (VJ4BL32TMK)	2° ATDC	31–33° BTDC/3500 rpm
110/100 110/200 95/100	Stromberg 150 CD	0231153003 or 0231153007	4° BTDC	31–33° BTDC/4500 rpm
110/100 110/200	Zenith 36 VNP	0231110038 (VJ4BL32TMK)	2° ATDC	28–30° BTDC/3500 rpm
110/100 110/200	Zenith 36 VNP	0231153007	TDC	28–30° BTDC/4500 rpm
100/100	Zenith 36 VNP	0231110038 (VJ4BL32TMK)	2° ATDC	28–30° BTDC/3500 rpm
100/100	Zenith 36 VNP	0231153007	TDC	28–30° BTDC/4500 rpm

Firing Orders

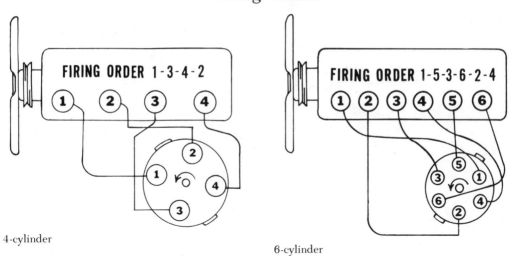

4-cylinder

6-cylinder

Crankshaft and Connecting Rod Specifications

All measurements are given in in.

Engine Model	Engine (hp)	CRANKSHAFT			CONNECTING ROD		
		Main Brg. Journal Dia	Main Brg. Oil Clearance	Shaft End-Play	Journal Diameter	Oil Clearance	Side Clearance
95/100	95						
95A/100	95						
100/100	100	2.4977–	0.0015–	0.0007–	2.1295–	0.0015–	0.006–
110/100	110	2.4982	0.0035	0.0042	2.1300	0.0032	0.014
110/200	110						
120/200	120						
105A	105						
115A	115						
130A	130						
130B	115	2.4981–	0.0011–	0.0019–	2.1650–	0.0011–	0.006–
130C	130	2.4986	0.0034	0.0054	2.1304	0.0028	0.014
165A	165						
170A	170						

Ring Gap Specifications

Engine Model	Engine (hp)	Top Compression	Bottom Compression	Oil Control
95/100	95			
95A/100	95			
100/100	100	0.010–	0.010–	0.010–
110/100	110	0.020	0.020	0.020
110/200	110			
120/200	120			
105A	105			
115A	115			
130A	130			
130B	115	0.0158–	0.0158–	0.0158–
130C	130	0.0217	0.0217	0.0217
165A	165			
170A	170			

Ring Side Clearance Specifications

Engine Model	Engine (hp)	Top Compression	Bottom Compression	Oil Control
95/100	95			
95A/100	95			
100/100	100	0.0021–	0.0021–	0.0017–
110/100	110	0.0032	0.0032	0.0028
110/200	110			
120/200	120			

Ring Side Clearance Specifications (cont.)

Engine Model	Engine (hp)	Top Compression	Bottom Compression	Oil Control
105A	105			
115A	115			
130A	130			
130B	115	0.0018–	0.0018–	0.0018–
130C	130	0.0028	0.0028	0.0028
165A	165			
170A	170			

Valve Specifications

Engine Model	Engine (hp)	Seat Angle (deg)	Face Angle (deg)	Spring Test Pressure (lbs. @ in.)	Stem to Guide Clearance (in.)		Stem Diameter (in.)	
					Intake	Exhaust	Intake	Exhaust
95/100	95	45	44½	182–192 @ 1.18	0.0010–0.0022	0.0026–0.0037	0.3419–0.3425	0.3403–0.3409
95A/100	95	45	44½	182–192 @ 1.18	0.0012–0.0027	0.0026–0.0037	0.3094–0.3099	0.3403–0.3409
100/100	100	45	44½	182–192 @ 1.18	0.0010–0.0022	0.0026–0.0037	0.0026–0.0037	0.3403–0.3409
110/100	110	45	44½	182–192 @ 1.18	0.0010–0.0022	0.0026–0.0037	0.0026–0.0037	0.3403–0.3409
110/200	110	45	44½	182–192 @ 1.18	0.0010–0.0022	0.0026–0.0037	0.0026–0.0037	0.3403–0.3409
120/200	120	45	44½	182–192 @ 1.18	0.0012–0.0027	0.0026–0.0037	0.3094–0.3099	0.3403–0.3409
105A	105	45	44½	138–193 @ 1.18	0.0012–0.0022	0.0024–0.0038	0.3132–0.3138	0.3122–0.3128
115A	115	45	44½	138–193 @ 1.18	0.0012–0.0022	0.0024–0.0038	0.3132–0.3138	0.3122–0.3128
130A	130	45	44½	138–193 @ 1.18	0.0012–0.0022	0.0024–0.0038	0.3132–0.3138	0.3122–0.3128
130B	115	45	44½	138–193 @ 1.18	0.0012–0.0022	0.0024–0.0038	0.3132–0.3138	0.3122–0.3128

Valve Specifications (cont.)

Engine Model	Engine (hp)	Seat Angle (deg)	Face Angle (deg)	Spring Test Pressure (lbs. @ in.)	Stem to Guide Clearance (in.)		Stem Diameter (in.)	
					Intake	Exhaust	Intake	Exhaust
130C	130	45	44½	138–193 @ 1.18	0.0012–0.0022	0.0024–0.0038	0.3132–0.3138	0.3122–0.3128
165A	165	45	44½	138–193 @ 1.20	0.0012–0.0022	0.0024–0.0038	0.3132–0.3138	0.3122–0.3128
170A	170	45	44½	138–193 @ 1.20	0.0012–0.0022	0.0024–0.0038	0.3132–0.3138	0.3122–0.3128

Torque Specifications
—All readings in ft lbs—

Engine Model	Engine (hp)	Cylinder Head Bolts	Rod Bearing Bolts	Main Bearing Bolts	Crankshaft Pulley Bolt	Flywheel to Crankshaft Bolts	Camshaft Nut	Spark Plugs
95/100	95	65	40	90	51–58	35	95–108	30
95A/100	95	65	40	90	51–58	35	95–108	30
100/100	100	65	40	90	51–58	35	95–108	30
110/100	110	65	40	90	51–58	35	95–108	30
110/200	110	65	40	90	51–58	35	95–108	30
120/200	120	65	40	90	51–58	35	95–108	30
105A	105	65	40	90	51–58	35	95–108	30
115A	115	65	40	90	51–58	35	95–108	30
130A	130	65	40	90	51–58	35	95–108	30
130B	115	65	40	90	51–58	35	95–108	30
130C	130	65	40	90	51–58	35	95–108	30
165A	165	65	40	90	51–58	35	95–108	30
170A	170	65	40	90	51–58	35	95–108	30

Torque Sequences

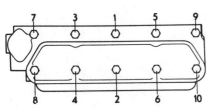

Cylinder head—4-cylinder

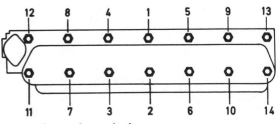

Cylinder head—6-cylinder

Wiring Diagrams

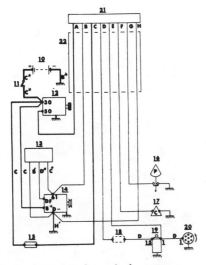

4-cylinder and 6-cylinder with alternator

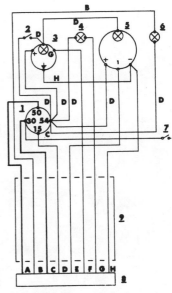

Instrument panel—all engines

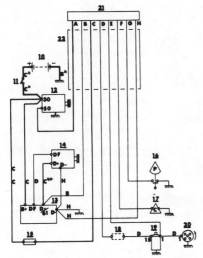

4-cylinder with DC generator

Cable markings		
Mark	Color	1. Key switch with starter contact
A	Ivory	2. Instrument light switch
B	Black	3. Temperature gauge
B'	Black	4. Warning lamp for "low oil pressure"
B+	Black	5. Tachometer
C	Red	6. Charging control lamp
C+	Red	7. Extra switch
C++	Red	8. Connection terminal
C"	Red	9. Cable harness
D	Green	10. Battery
D+	Green	11. Master switch
E	Grey	12. Starter motor
F	Yellow	13. Charging regulator
G	Brown	14. Alternator (or D.C. generator)
H	Blue	15. Fuse
H'	Blue	16. Oil pressure sender
		17. Temperature sender
		18. Advance engaging resistor
		19. Ignition coil
		20. Distributor
		21. Connector
		22. Cable harness

Routine Maintenance

OIL FILTER

The oil filter should be replaced every 100 hours of operation, and when changing the oil. With a new or reconditioned engine, the oil filter should also be changed after the first 50 hours of operation.

Replacement

1. Drain the engine oil.
2. Screw off the old filter. It may be necessary to loosen the filter with an oil filter wrench.
3. Smear a thin coat of engine oil on the rubber gasket of the new filter.

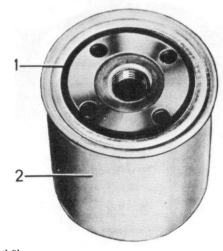

Oil filter

1. Gasket (oiled)   2. Filter

D. LUBRICATING SYSTEM

DESCRIPTION

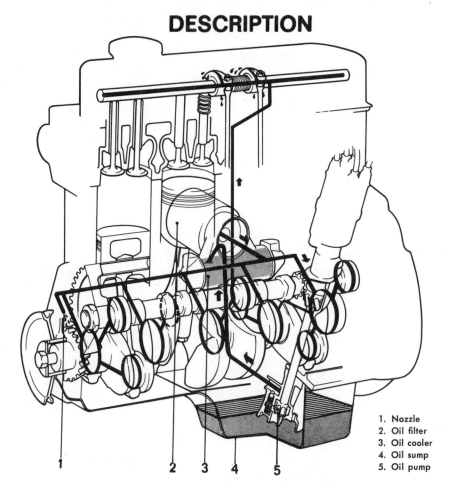

1. Nozzle
2. Oil filter
3. Oil cooler
4. Oil sump
5. Oil pump

Engine lubrication system

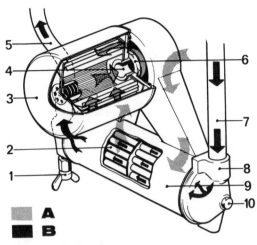

Oil filter and oil cooler

A=Lubricating oil	B=Cooling water
1. Drain cock	6. Nut
2. Cooling tubes	7. Water intake
3. Oil filter	8. End cover
4. Nipple	9. Oil cooler
5. Water outlet	10. Center bolt

4. Screw the new filter on by hand until it just touches the oil cooler. Tighten the oil filter another ½ turn by hand. Do not use a wrench to tighten the filter. Fill the engine with fresh oil and start the engine.

5. Run the engine at idle and check for leaks.

6. Check the engine oil level.

Removing the oil filter

FLAME ARRESTOR

Every 100 hours of operation, or once a season, clean the flame arrestor. The flame arrestor should be cleaned in a non-flammable solvent and allowed to air dry.

OUTDRIVE

Oil Level

The oil level should be checked periodically, at least once every 10 hours. Check

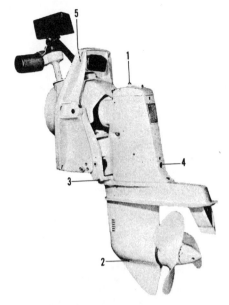

Outdrive lubrication points

1. Oil dipstick
2. Drain hole
3. Steering shaft lubrication fitting
4. Oil filter hole
5. Steering arm lubrication fitting (inside mounting collar)

the oil level by unscrewing the dipstick and pushing it all the way down. Do not screw it down. Remove the dipstick and read the oil level. If necessary, top up the oil reservoir with the recommended oil.

NOTE: *On all outdrives except the 270 model, it is necessary to use SAE 90 gear oil.*

Replace the dipstick and check the oil level again. Screw the dipstick down when finished. Do not forget the small seal under the head of the dipstick.

OIL RECOMMENDATIONS

The following companies have recommended the oils shown below for lubricating the outdrive unit.

All Except the 270

Lubriplate	Marine 90
BP	BP-EP 90
Caltex	Caltex Universal Thuban 90
Esso	Esso Hypoid Oil EP 90
Gulf	Gulf Multipurpose Gear Lubricant SAE 90
Mobil	Mobilube GX 90
Shell	Shell Spira 90 EP

270

Any good quality SAE 10W-30 or SAE 20W-40 oil which is designated for service "SE" is satisfactory for this unit.

OIL CHANGES

Use the following procedure to drain the oil from the outdrive.

1. Loosen the dipstick to relieve pressure inside the system.
2. Place a container of sufficient volume under the drain plug.
3. Remove the drain plug from the housing and allow all of the oil to drain from the outdrive.

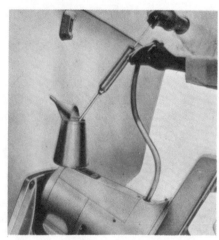

Lubricating the outdrive

4. Replace the drain plug and fill the unit with approved oil through the dipstick opening. Add enough oil to obtain a correct reading on the dipstick.

Tune-Up

SPARK PLUGS

Removal

1. Locate all of the spark plugs.
2. If the spark plug wires are not numbered as to cylinder, mark each wire with a small piece of masking tape.
3. Grasp each wire by the rubber boot. Pull all of the wires from the spark plugs. If the wires do not readily come off, remove them with a slight twisting motion. Never pull the wires off by the wires themselves.

4. If compressed air is available, blow out the recesses around the spark plugs to remove accumulated dirt.
5. Using a spark plug socket and extension, (if necessary), loosen each spark plug a few turns.
6. Blow out the accumulated dirt again, or, if compressed air is not available, wipe the dirt away with a clean cloth. The object is not to allow any foreign material to enter the cylinder.
7. Unscrew the plugs the rest of the way and remove them from the engine.

Inspection

1. Compare the condition of the spark plugs to the plugs shown in the accompanying illustration (see "Troubleshooting," subject 4.6). It should be remembered that any type of deposit will decrease the efficiency of the plug. If the plugs are not to be replaced, they should be thoroughly cleaned before installation. If the electrode ends of the plugs are not worn or damaged and if they are to be reused, wipe off the porcelain insulator on each plug and check for cracks or breaks. If either condition exists, the plug must be replaced.
2. If the plugs are judged reusable, have them cleaned on a plug cleaning machine (found in most service stations) or remove the deposits with a stiff wire brush.
3. Check the plug gap on both new and used plugs before installing them in the engine. The ground electrode must be parallel to the center electrode and the specified size wire gauge should pass through the opening with a slight drag. If the center or ground electrode has worn unevenly, level them off with a file. If the air gap between the two electrodes is not correct, open or close the ground electrode, with the proper tool, to bring it to specifications. Such a tool is usually provided with a gap gauge.

Installation

1. Insert the plugs into the engine and tighten them finger-tight.
2. Be sure that the plugs are not cross-threaded. If the plugs use metal gaskets, new gaskets should be installed each time the plugs are removed and installed.
3. Tighten the spark plugs to 30 ft lbs.
4. Install the spark plug wires on their respective plugs. Be sure that each wire is firmly connected.

5. While you are about the task of checking the spark plugs, the spark plug wires should also be checked. Any wires that are cracked or brittle should be replaced.

BREAKER POINTS AND CONDENSER

Replacement

1. Remove the distributor cap and rotor from the top of the distributor, taking note of their placement.

2. Place a screwdriver against the breaker points and examine the condition of the contacts. Replace the points if the contacts are blackened, pitted, or worn excessively, if the breaker arm has lost its tension, or if the fiber rubbing block on the breaker has become worn or loose. Contact points that have become slightly burned (light gray) may be cleaned with a point file.

3. To replace the points and condenser, disconnect the electrical leads for both at the primary connection.

4. Remove the lockscrew for the contact breakers and lift them straight up.

5. Loosen the condenser bracket retaining screw and slide out the condenser.

6. While the points are out, lubricate the breaker cam with a very light coating of silicone-based grease. Clean the distributor base with alcohol to free it of any oil film that might affect completion of the ground circuit. Also clean the contact point surfaces with the solvent.

7. Install the new points and new condenser and tighten their retaining screws. Connect the electrical leads for both at the primary connection. Make sure that the point contacts are aligned horizontally and vertically.

8. If the points are not aligned properly, bend the stationary arm.

9. The breaker points must be correctly gapped before proceeding any further. Turn the engine until the rubbing block on the point assembly is resting on the high point of a breaker cam lobe. Loosen the point hold-down screw slightly and insert a feeler gauge of the proper thickness between the point contacts. Fine adjustment is made by inserting a screwdriver into the adjusting recess and turning the screwdriver until the proper size feeler gauge passes between the point contacts with a

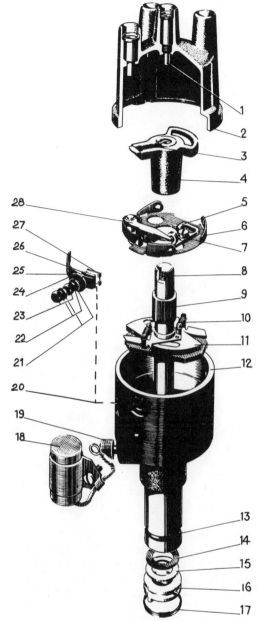

Exploded view of the distributor

1. Rod brush	15. Steel washer
2. Cap	16. Flange
3. Built-in resistor	17. Snap-ring
4. Distributor rotor arm	18. Capacitor
5. Contact plate	19. Lubricating cup
6. Breaker plate	20. Primary terminal
7. Lock screw	21. Flat washer
8. Lubricating wick	22. Snap-ring
9. Breaker cam	23. Nut
10. Spring	24. Fiber washer
11. Governor flyweight	25. Insulating strip
12. Distributor housing	26. Fiber washer
13. Rubber seal	27. Flat washer
14. Fiber washer	28. Breaker arm

slight drag. Without disturbing the setting, tighten the breaker point retaining screw.

10. If a dwell meter is available, proceed to "Dwell Angle Setting." A dwell meter is considered a more accurate means of measuring point gap. If the meter is not available, proceed to replace the rotor in top of the distributor shaft, making sure that the tab inside the rotor aligns with the slot on the distributor. Place the distributor cap on top of the distributor and snap the cap clasps into the slots on the cap.

11. Make sure that all the spark plug wires fit snugly into the cap. Proceed to "Ignition Timing Adjustment" Dwell Angle.

DWELL ANGLE ADJUSTMENT

The dwell angle is the number of degrees of distributor cam rotation through which the breaker points remain fully closed (conducting electricity). Increasing the point gap decreases dwell, while decreasing the point gap increases dwell.

1. Using a dwell meter of known accuracy, connect the red lead (positive) wire of the meter to the distributor primary wire connection on the positive (+) side of the coil, and the black ground (negative) wire of the meter to a good ground on the engine (e.g. thermostat housing nut).

2. The dwell angle may be checked either with the distributor cap and rotor installed and the engine running, or with the cap and rotor removed and the engine cranking at starter speed. The meter gives a constant reading with the engine running. Never attempt to change dwell angle while the ignition is on. *Touching the point contacts or primary wire connection with a metal screwdriver may result in a 12 volt shock.*

3. To change the dwell angle, loosen the point retaining screw slightly and make the approximate correction.

4. Tighten the retaining screw and test the dwell with the engine at idle. If the dwell appears to be correct, install the breaker point protective cover (if so equipped), the rotor and distributor cap and test the dwell with the engine running. Take the engine through its entire range and observe the dwell meter. The dwell should remain within specifications at all times. Great fluctuation of dwell at different engine speeds indicates worn distributor parts.

5. Following the dwell angle adjustment, the ignition timing must be checked. A 1° increase in dwell results in the ignition timing being retarded 2° and vice versa.

IGNITION TIMING

1. Clean the crankshaft damper and pointer on the water pump housing with a solvent-soaked rag so that the marks can be seen.

2. Connect a stroboscopic timing light to the No. 1 cylinder spark plug and to the battery, according to the manufacturer's instructions.

3. Scribe a mark on the crankshaft damper and on the marker with chalk or luminescent (day-glo) paint to highlight the correct timing setting. On carbureted models, disconnect the vacuum advance line from the intake manifold at the distributor and plug it with a pencil, golf tee, or some other suitably small object.

4. Attach a tachometer to the engine and set the idle speed to specifications. With the engine running, aim the timing light at the pointer and the marks on the damper. If the marks made with the chalk or paint coincide when the timing light flashes, the engine is timed correctly. If the marks do not coincide, stop the engine, loosen the distributor attaching belt, and start the engine again. While observing the timing light flashes on the markers, grasp the distributor vacuum regulator—

4-cylinder engine timing marks

not the distributor cap—and rotate the distributor until the marks do coincide.

5. Stop the engine and tighten the distributor attaching bolt, taking care not to disturb the setting.

6. As a final check, start the engine once more to make sure that the timing marks align.

7. Reconnect all disconnected hoses and remove the timing light and tachometer from the engine.

VALVE LASH ADJUSTMENT

1. Remove the valve cover and crank the engine until number one cylinder is at Top Dead Center (TDC). TDC is the point at which both intake and exhaust valves are fully closed and the piston is on its compression stroke.

2. To find TDC, crank the engine, preferably with a remote starter switch, until the pushrods for both valves on the subject cylinder stop falling. Stop cranking the engine.

3. At this point, it will be easier to find TDC by turning the engine over manually. To accomplish this, remove all of the spark plugs so the compressions and resistance to cranking are diminished, and remove the distributor cap so the position of the rotor may be observed.

4. To crank the engine manually, position a socket or closed-end wrench—with a long handle for greater leverage—on the crankshaft damper bolt and turn the crankshaft in the required direction.

5. At TDC, the piston for the subject cylinder should be at its highest point of travel. Make a visual check or insert a screwdriver through the spark plug hole to make sure that the piston is no longer traveling upward. As an additional check, the distributor rotor should be pointed to the spark plug wire for the subject cylinder at TDC.

6. Number one cylinder is at TDC when the 0 degree mark on the crankshaft damper aligns with the pointer on the water pump housing. On four-cylinder models, with number one cylinder at TDC, valves (counting from the front) 1, 2, 3, and 5 may be adjusted. On six-cylinder models, with number one cylinder at TDC, valves 1, 2, 3, 6, 7, and 10 may be adjusted.

7. Insert a step-type (go and no-go) feeler gauge of the specified thickness between the rocker arm and the valve stem.

Adjust each rocker arm so that the thinner gauge slides in easily but the thicker gauge cannot be inserted. Adjustment is accomplished by loosening the locknut and turning the adjusting screw and then, without disturbing the adjustment, retightening the locknut.

8. The remainder of the valves may be adjusted in the following manner. On four-cylinder models, with no. 4 cylinder at TDC, valves (counting from the front) 4, 6, 7, and 8 may be adjusted. On six-cylinder models, with no. 6 cylinder at TDC, valves 4, 5, 8, 9, 11, and 12 may be adjusted.

9. Make sure that the feeler gauge of the minimum thickness may pass between the rocker arm and the valve stem easily. Excessive clearance may cause greater valve train noise but insufficient clearance may burn a valve. When in doubt, be generous with the clearance adjustment to avoid costly valve work.

10. After adjusting the valves, replace the valve cover with a new gasket, if needed, and install the spark plugs and distributor cap if they were removed. Start the engine. Listen for excessive valve train noise and check for oil leaks.

CARBURETOR

Adjustment

ZENITH 36 VNP

1. Run the engine to operating temperature.

2. Disconnect the control cable from the rear carburetor. Remove the flame arrestors.

Zenith 36 VNP carburetor idle adjustment

1. Idle adjusting screw
2. Choke control
3. Fast idle adjusting screw
4. Control shaft
5. Adjusting screw for control cable
6. Control cable

3. Adjust the idle speed with both screws on the respective carburetors.

4. Adjust the fuel/air mixture with the adjusting screw for each carburetor to obtain the best and smoothest idle. First, turn the screw inwards (leaner) until the engine starts to run unevenly. Then turn the screw out, until the best idle speed is obtained. Adjust the idle screws if necessary.

5. Adjust the length of the control rod shaft, so that the spring is tensioned about .08 in. with the control rod connected.

STROMBERG 150CD AND 175CD

1. Run the engine to normal operating temperature. Remove the flame arrestor and disconnect the control wire.

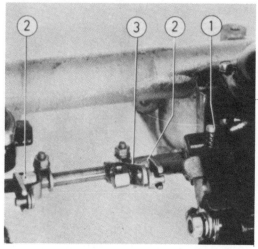

Stromberg 150 CD and 175 CD carburetor adjustment

1. Idle adjusting screw
2. Lever
3. Lever

2. Screw in the idle adjusting screw so it touches the underside of the air valve. Raise the jet and drop it. It should seat with a distinct click.

3. Screw out the adjusting screw 2½–2¾ turns.

4. Check that the intermediate shaft on the carburetors does not bind.

5. Check the oil level in the dampers. It should be ⅜ in. from the upper edge of the center spindle. Fill with engine oil.

6. Start the engine and adjust the idle speed to specifications.

7. On dual carburetor installations, the carburetors should be balanced with a synchronizer.

8. Adjust the fuel mixture by screwing up the adjusting screw until the engine begins to stall. Loosen the adjusting screw ¼ turn.

9. Adjust the levers so that they are flush against the throttle shafts.

10. Install the flame arrestors and check the idle speed again.

Engine Electrical

DISTRIBUTOR

Removal

1. Unsnap the distributor cap clasps and remove the cap.

2. Crank the engine until No. 1 cylinder is at Top Dead Center (TDC). At this point the rotor should point to the spark plug wire socket for No. 1 cylinder, and the 0° timing mark on the crankshaft dam-

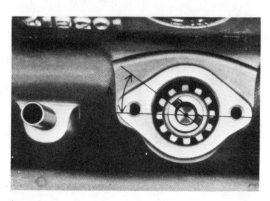

Distributor drive location where A = approximately 35°

per should be aligned with the pointer. For ease of assembly, scribe a chalk mark on the distributor housing to note the position of the rotor.

3. Disconnect the primary lead from the coil at its terminal on the distributor housing.

4. Remove the vacuum hose(s) from the regulator. Take care not to damage the bakelite connection during removal.

5. Slacken the distributor attaching screw and hold-down clamp enough to slide the distributor up and out of position.

6. When ready to install the distributor, if the engine has been disturbed

(cranked), find TDC for No. 1 cylinder as outlined under "Valve Lash Adjustment". If the engine has not been disturbed, install the distributor with the rotor pointing to the No. 1 cylinder spark plug wire socket, or the chalk mark made prior to removal. To approximate ignition timing,

Distributor drive location where A = approximately 35°

position the vacuum regulator to the rear of the distributor. If the distributor is installed incorrectly, the rotor will be 180° (of distributor rotation) out of place, incorrectly pointing at No. 4 spark plug wire on four-cylinder engines and incorrectly pointing at No. 6 spark plug wire on six-cylinder engines. Do not tighten the distributor attaching screw at this time.

7. Connect the primary lead to its terminal on the distributor housing.

8. Connect the vacuum hose(s) to the bakelite connection(s) on the vacuum regulator.

9. If the distributor was disassembled, or if the contact point setting was disturbed, proceed to set the point gap and/or dwell angle.

10. Install the distributor cap and secure the clasps. Proceed to set the ignition timing. Tighten the distributor attaching screw.

ALTERNATOR

The alternator converts the mechanical energy which is supplied by the drive belt into electrical energy by electromagnetic induction. When the ignition switch is turned on, current flows from the battery, through the charging system light or ammeter, to the voltage regulator, and finally to the alternator. When the engine is started, the drive belt turned the rotating

field (rotor) in the stationary windings (stator), inducing alternating current. This alternating current is converted into usable direct current by the diode rectifier. Most of this current is used to charge the battery and power the electrical components of the vehicle. A small part is returned to the field windings of the alternator enabling it to increase its output. When the current in the field windings reaches a predetermined control voltage, the voltage regulator grounds the circuit, preventing any further increase. The cycle is continued so that the voltage remains constant.

Alternator Precautions

Several precautions must be observed when performing work on alternator equipment.

1. If the battery is removed for any reason, make sure that it is reconnected with the correct polarity. Reversing the battery connections may result in damage to the one-way rectifiers.

2. Never operate the alternator with the main circuit broken. Make sure that the battery, alternator, and regulator leads are not disconnected while the engine is running.

3. Never attempt to polarize an alternator.

4. When charging a battery that is installed in the boat, disconnect the negative battery cable.

5. When utilizing a booster battery as a starting aid, always connect it in parallel; negative to negative, and positive to positive.

6. When arc welding is to be performed on any part of the vehicle, disconnect the negative battery cable, disconnect the alternator leads, and unplug the voltage regulator.

Removal

1. Disconnect the negative battery cable.

2. Disconnect the electrical leads to the alternator.

3. Remove the adjusting arm-to-alternator bolt and the adjusting arm-to-engine bolt.

4. Remove the alternator-to-engine mounting bolt.

5. Remove the fan belt and lift the alternator forward and out.

6. Reverse the above procedure to install, taking care to tension the fan (drive) belt.

STARTER

105A-170A

REMOVAL

1. Disconnect the battery leads from the battery.

2. Disconnect and tag the cables from the starter motor.

3. Remove the bolts holding the starter motor to the flywheel housing and remove the starter motor.

INSTALLATION

1. Installation is the reverse of removal.

Engine Fuel

CARBURETOR

Removal

ALL MODELS

The procedure for removing the carburetors is basically identical. Cleanliness is very important, so all parts should be cleaned before removal. This will prevent dirt from entering the intake manifold.

1. Remove all dirt from the carburetors.

2. Remove the flame arrestor.

3. Disconnect the fuel lines and plug them to prevent leakage.

4. Disconnect the throttle and idle linkage from the carburetors.

5. Remove the attaching nuts.

6. Lift the carburetor from the manifold.

Installation

ALL MODELS

1. Installation is the reverse of removal.

Overhaul

ALL TYPES

Efficient carburetion depends greatly on careful cleaning and inspection during overhaul since dirt, gum, water, or varnish in or on the carburetor parts are often responsible for poor performance.

Overhaul your carburetor in a clean, dust-free area. Carefully disassemble the

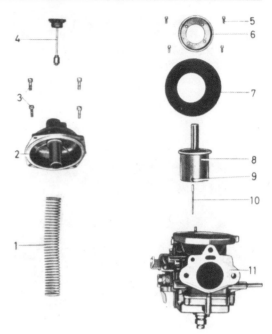

Upper section of Zenith Stromberg carburetor

1. Spring
2. Suction chamber
3. Screw
4. Damper piston
5. Screw
6. Washer
7. Diaphragm
8. Air valve
9. Lock screw, metering needle
10. Metering needle
11. Intermediate section

carburetor, referring often to the exploded views. Keep all similar and look-alike parts segregated during disassembly and cleaning to avoid accidental interchange during assembly. Make a note of all jet sizes.

When the carburetor is disassembled, wash all parts (except diaphragms, electric choke units, pump plunger, and any other plastic, leather, fiber, or rubber parts) in clean carburetor solvent. Do not leave parts in the solvent any longer than is necessary to sufficiently loosen the deposits. Excessive cleaning may remove the special finish from the float bowl and choke valve bodies, leaving these parts unfit for service. Rinse all parts in clean solvent and blow them dry with compressed air or allow them to air dry. Wipe clean all cork, plastic, leather, and fiber parts with a clean, lint-free cloth.

Blow out all passages and jets with compressed air and be sure that there are no

Exploded view of Zenith Stromberg float bowl

1. Lock spring (marked "TOP")
2. Float
3. Emulsion block
4. Air jet for idling
5. Barrel
6. Outlet valve
7. Acceleration jet
8. Spring
9. Screws
10. Accelerator plunger
11. Float chamber
12. Intake valve
13. Stop screw

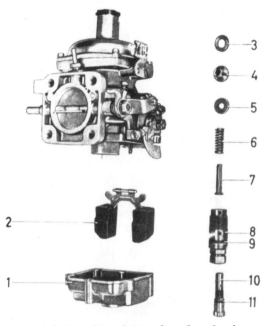

Exploded view of Zenith Stromberg float chamber

1. Float chamber
2. Float
3. Washer
4. Guide with O-ring
5. Washer
6. Spring
7. Jet
8. Holder
9. O-ring
10. Adjusting screw
11. O-ring

restrictions or blockages. Never use wire or similar tools to clean jets, fuel passages, or air bleeds. Clean all jets and valves separately to avoid accidental interchange.

Check all parts for wear or damage. If wear or damage is found, replace the defective parts. Especially check the following:

1. Check the float needle and seat for wear. If wear is found, replace the complete assembly.

2. Check the float hinge pin for wear and the float(s) for dents or distortion. Replace the float if fuel has leaked into it.

3. Check the throttle and choke shaft bores for wear or an out-of-round condition. Damage or wear to the throttle arm, shaft, or shaft bore will often require replacement of the throttle body. These parts require a close tolerance of fit; wear may allow air leakage, which could affect starting and idling.

NOTE: *Throttle shafts and bushings are not included in overhaul kits. They can be purchased separately.*

4. Inspect the idle mixture adjusting needles for burrs or grooves. Any such condition requires replacement of the needle, since you will not be able to obtain a satisfactory idle.

5. Test the accelerator pump check valves. They should pass air one way but not the other. Test for proper seating by blowing and sucking on the valve. Replace the valve if necessary. If the valve is satisfactory, wash the valve again to remove breath moisture.

6. Check the bowl cover for warped surfaces with a straightedge.

7. Closely inspect the valves and seats for wear and damage, replacing as necessary.

8. After the carburetor is assembled, check the choke valve for freedom of operation.

Carburetor overhaul kits are recommended for each overhaul. These kits contain all gaskets and new parts to replace those that deteriorate most rapidly. Failure to replace all parts supplied with the kit (especially gaskets) can result in poor performance later.

Some carburetor manufacturers supply overhaul kits of three basic types: minor repair; major repair; and gasket kits. Basically, they contain the following:

Minor Repair Kits:
　All gaskets
　Float needle valve
　Volume control screw
　All diaphragms
　Spring for the pump diaphragm
Major Repair Kits:
　All jets and gaskets
　All diaphragms
　Float needle valve
　Volume control screw
　Pump ball valve
　Main jet carrier
　Float
　Complete intermediate rod
　Intermediate pump lever
　Complete injector tube
　Some cover hold-down screws and
　washers
Gasket Kits:
　All gaskets

After cleaning and checking all components, reassemble the carburetor, using new parts and referring to the exploded view. When reassembling, make sure that all screws and jets are tight in their seats, but do not overtighten, as the tips will be distorted. Tighten all screws gradually, in rotation. Do not tighten needle valves into their seats; uneven jetting will result. Always use new gaskets. Be sure to adjust the float level when reassembling.

S.U. (SKINNERS UNION CARBURETORS ONLY)

The preceding information applies to S.U. carburetors also, but the following, additional suggestions should be followed.

1. Soak the small cork gaskets (jet gland washers) in penetrating oil or hot water for at least a half-hour prior to assembly, or they will invariably split.

2. When the jet is fully assembled, the jet tube should be a close fit without any lateral play, but it should be free to move smoothly. A few drops of oil or polishing

of the tube may be necessary to achieve this.

3. If the jet sealing ring washer is made of cork, soak it in hot water for a minute or two prior to installation.

4. Adjust the float height.

5. Center the jet so that the piston will fall freely (when raised) and seat with a distinct click. If the jet is not centered properly, it will hang up in the tube. Refer to the procedure for centering the jet in the adjustments section of the text.

Engine Mechanical

The engines used in inboard/outdrive installations are basically the same as Volvo automotive engines. The early 4 cylinder is similar to the B18B, the later 4 cylinder engine is basically the same as the B20B and the 6 cylinder engine is very similar to the B30A. However, because of the complex procedures and tools necessary to remove and install the engine, only those procedures which can be accomplished in the boat are given here.

CYLINDER HEAD

Removal and Installation

NOTE: *To prevent warpage of the head, removal should be attempted only on a cold engine.*

1. Drain the cooling system.

2. Disconnect the choke control cables at the carburetors. Remove the vacuum hoses for the distributor advance.

3. Remove the throttle control shaft, link rods, and bracket.

4. Remove the flame arrestor, intake hose, and heat control valve hose from the engine.

5. Remove and plug the fuel line at the carburetors.

6. Label the spark plug wires and disconnect them from the plugs.

7. Remove the exhaust manifold preheating plate. Remove the nuts and disconnect the exhaust pipe from the exhaust manifold.

8. Unbolt the alternator adjusting arm from the head.

9. Remove the valve cover. Remove the rocker shaft and arm assembly as a

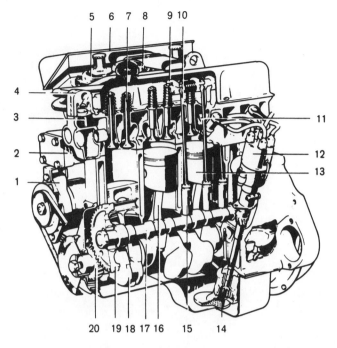

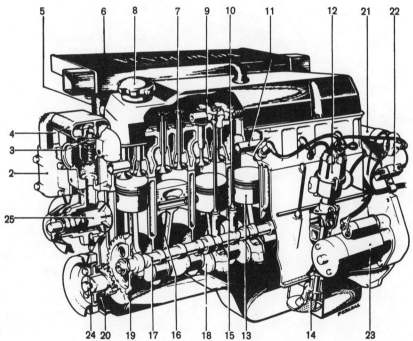

Cut-away view of 4- and 6-cylinder engines

1. Alternator
2. Water-cooled exhaust manifold
3. Thermostat
4. Water distribution housing
5. Carburetor
6. Flame arrester
7. Valve
8. Oil filler cap
9. Rocker arm
10. Pushrod
11. Water distribution pipe
12. Distributor
13. Piston
14. Oil pump
15. Valve lifter
16. Connecting rod
17. Camshaft
18. Crankshaft
19. Camshaft gear
20. Crankshaft gear
21. Ignition coil
22. Pre-engaging resistance
23. Starter motor
24. Vibration damper
25. Circulation pump

unit and draw out the pushrods, keeping them in order.

10. Loosen the head bolts gradually, in the same order as their tightening sequence. Remove the head bolts, noting their locations, and lift off the head. Do not attempt to pry off the head. The head may be tapped lightly with a rubber mallet to break the gasket seal. If any residual water in the cooling passages of the head falls into the combustion chambers during removal, remove it immediately and coat the cylinder walls with oil.

11. Remove the integrally cast intake and exhaust manifold from the cylinder head.

12. Remove the old head gasket, flange gasket, and rubber sealing rings for the water pump.

13. Inspect the condition of the valves in the combustion chambers, and the intake and exhaust ports in the head. Small deposits may be removed with rotating brushes. If large deposits are present, however, proceed to "Cylinder Head Reconditioning" in the "Engine Rebuilding" section of this chapter. Make sure that no foreign matter has fallen into the cylinders or onto the tops of the pistons. Thoroughly clean the mating surfaces of the cylinder head and block and remove any traces of the old head gasket. Check the mating surfaces for warpage. There is an oil feed hole for the rocker arm assembly on the tappet side, in the middle of the head. Make sure it is clean. A clogged oil feed hole may be opened with a length of thin gauge metal wire and some kerosene to dissolve some of the deposits. Clean and oil the head bolts.

14. Install the combination intake and exhaust manifold on the head with new gaskets.

15. Install new sealing rings for the water pump.

16. Use a pair of guide studs for proper alignment of the cylinder head, head gasket, and block. Guide studs can be easily made by cutting the heads off a pair of spare head bolts. The tops of the bolts are then filed to a tapered edge and slotted so that they may be installed and removed with a screwdriver. The guide studs should be installed in the cylinder block; one in the front right-hand head bolt hole, and the other in the rear left-hand head bolt hole.

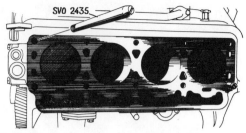

Guide pins for installing the cylinder head

17. Fit a new head gasket on the cylinder block with the lettering "TOP" (wide edge) facing up. Slide the gasket down over the two guide studs.

18. Carefully lower the cylinder head over the guide studs onto the block. Install, but do not tighten, two head bolts at opposite ends to secure the gasket, and remove the guide studs. Install the remaining head bolts fingertight. Torque the head bolts in proper sequence.

19. Roll the pushrods on a level surface to inspect them for straightness. Replace any bent pushrods. Install the pushrods in their original positions and install the rocker shaft and arm assembly.

20. Adjust the valve clearance. Install the valve cover with a new gasket.

21. Install the alternator adjusting arm and adjust the fan belt tension.

22. Install the following: exhaust manifold preheating plate, exhaust pipe and flange nuts (with new gaskets), spark plug wires, coolant temperature sensor, fuel line, flame arrestor, intake hose, heat control valve hose, choke and throttle linkage, vacuum hoses for the distributor and the positive crankcase ventilation hoses.

23. Close the drain plug and fill the cooling system.

24. Run the engine for 10 minutes so that it reaches operating temperature. Stop the engine.

25. Remove the valve cover and torque the head bolts in proper sequence. Adjust the valve clearance to specifications. Install the valve cover.

Cylinder Head Overhaul

Refer to "Cylinder Head Reconditioning" in the "Engine Rebuilding" section of this chapter.

Rocker Shaft and Arm Assembly Removal and Installation

1. Remove the four retaining screws and the valve cover and gasket.

2. Remove the rocker shaft-to-cylinder head bolts and lift out the shaft and rocker arms as a unit.

3. Lift out the pushrods, keeping them in order, and check them for straightness by rolling them on a flat surface. Replace any bent pushrods.

4. Inspect the rocker shaft and arms. If the shaft and rockers are coated with baked-on sludge, oil may not be reaching them. Clean out the oil feed holes in the rocker shaft with 0.020 in. wire (piano wire). If the clearance between the rocker arms and shaft exceeds 0.004 in., the rocker arm needs to be rebushed. The rocker arm bushings are press fitted, and are removed with a drift. When pressing in a new bushing, make sure that the oil hole in the bushing aligns with the hole in the arm.

5. Position the pushrods on their respective lifters. Install the rocker shaft and arm assembly on the head, and install the retaining bolts. Step-tighten the bolts, moving front to rear.

6. Check to see that valve lash has remained within specifications. Adjust valve lash, if necessary.

7. Install the valve cover and gasket, and snugly tighten the valve cover retaining screws.

INTAKE AND EXHAUST MANIFOLDS

On all late model carbureted engines, the intake and exhaust manifolds are cast integrally. A preheating chamber is located within the combination manifold. The chamber's function is to transfer the heat from the exhaust ports to the fuel-air mixture in the intake manifold for improved cold-weather operation.

Removal and Installation

1. Remove the exhaust manifold pre-heating place. Remove the nuts and disconnect the exhaust pipe from the exhaust manifold.

2. Remove the flame arrestor. Disconnect the throttle and choke, if so equipped. Disconnect the positive crankcase ventilation hoses, and the vacuum hoses for the distributor advance.

3. Remove the nuts and slide the combination intake and exhaust manifold off the studs. Remove and discard the old manifold gasket.

4. To install, reverse the above procedure. Remember to use a new manifold gasket and exhaust pipe flange gasket in assembly. Torque the manifold retaining nuts to 13–16 ft lbs.

Engine Cooling

The engine is cooled by sea water and equipped with a thermostat which controls the temperature of the engine. Cooling water is circulated by means of a sea water pump on the timing gear cover. This pump is driven by the camshaft gear through a rubber flange.

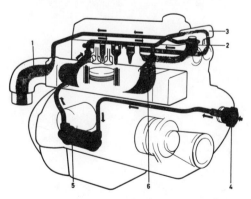 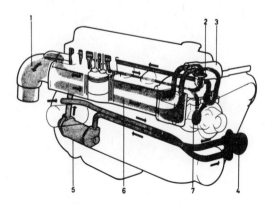

Cooling system schematic for 4- and 6-cylinder engines

1. Cooling water outlet in exhaust elbow	3. Distribution housing
2. Thermostat (open)	4. Sea-water pump
	5. Oil cooler
	6. Water-cooled exhaust pipe
	7. Circulation pump

SEA WATER PUMP IMPELLER

Replacement

1. Remove the cover on the sea water pump.
2. Pull the shaft and impeller far enough from the housing to unscrew the impeller from the shaft.

Removing the impeller for the sea water pump

3. Pull the impeller from the shaft.
4. Clean the impeller housings.
5. Replace the impeller with a genuine Volvo new part.

6. Install the securing screw.
7. Push the shaft and impeller into the housing and install the cover.

Outdrive

NOTE: *Any service to the outdrive except the propeller should be referred to an authorized shop equipped with the specialized tools and knowledge to handle this type of work. The only exception to this is "Propeller Removal" which can be done as follows.*

PROPELLER

Removal

1. Bend up the tabs on the lockwasher.
2. Unscrew the tapered nut on the end of the propeller shaft.
3. Remove the lockwasher, propeller and spacer sleeve.

Installation

1. Installation is the reverse of removal.

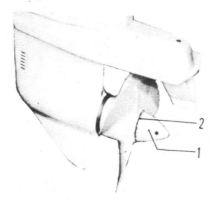
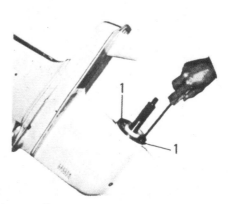

Removing the propeller

1. Tapered nut
2. Lock washer

Appendix

General Conversion Table

Multiply by	To Convert	to	
2.54	Inches	Centimeters	0.3937
30.48	Feet	Centimeters	0.0328
0.914	Yards	Meters	1.094
1.609	Miles	Kilometers	0.621
0.645	Square Inches	Square cm	0.155
0.836	Square Yards	Square meters	1.196
16.39	Cubic Inches	Cubic cm	0.061
28.3	Cubic Feet	Liters	0.0353
1.152	Knots/Hour	MPH	0.8684
2.113	Liters	US Pints	0.473
1.057	Liters	US Quarts	1.06
0.21998	Liters	Imp. Gallons	4.54
0.2642	Liters	US Gallons	3.785
0.4536	Pounds	Kilograms	2.2045
0.068	PSI	Atmospheres	14.7
	To Obtain	from	Multiply by

NOTE: 1 cm = 10 mm; 1 mm = 0.0394 in.
1 Imp. Gallon = 1.2 US Gallons = 4.5459 liters
1 US Gallon = 0.833 Imp. Gallon = 3.78543 liters

Conversion—Common Fractions to Decimals and Millimeters

INCHES			INCHES			INCHES		
Common Fractions	Decimal Fractions	Millimeters (approx.)	Common Fractions	Decimal Fractions	Millimeters (approx.)	Common Fractions	Decimal Fractions	Millimeters (approx.)
1/128	0.008	0.20	11/32	0.344	8.73	43/64	0.672	17.07
1/64	0.016	0.40	23/64	0.359	9.13	11/16	0.688	17.46
1/32	0.031	0.79	3/8	0.375	9.53	45/64	0.703	17.86
3/64	0.047	1.19	25/64	0.391	9.92	23/32	0.719	18.26
1/16	0.063	1.59	13/32	0.406	10.32	47/64	0.734	18.65
5/64	0.078	1.98	27/64	0.422	10.72	3/4	0.750	19.05
3/32	0.094	2.38	7/16	0.438	11.11	49/64	0.766	19.45
7/64	0.109	2.78	29/64	0.453	11.51	25/32	0.781	19.84
1/8	0.125	3.18	15/32	0.469	11.91	51/64	0.797	20.24
9/64	0.141	3.57	31/64	0.484	12.30	13/16	0.813	20.64
5/32	0.156	3.97	1/2	0.500	12.70	53/64	0.828	21.03
11/64	0.172	4.37	33/64	0.516	13.10	27/32	0.844	21.43
3/16	0.188	4.76	17/32	0.531	13.49	55/64	0.859	21.83
13/64	0.203	5.16	35/64	0.547	13.89	7/8	0.875	22.23
7/32	0.219	5.56	9/16	0.563	14.29	57/64	0.891	22.62
15/64	0.234	5.95	37/64	0.578	14.68	29/32	0.906	23.02
1/4	0.250	6.35	19/32	0.594	15.08	59/64	0.922	23.42
17/64	0.266	6.75	39/64	0.609	15.48	15/16	0.938	23.81
9/32	0.281	7.14	5/8	0.625	15.88	61/64	0.953	24.21
19/64	0.297	7.54	41/64	0.641	16.27	31/32	0.969	24.61
5/16	0.313	7.94	21/32	0.656	16.67	63/64	0.984	25.00
21/64	0.328	8.33						

Decimal Equivalent Size of the Number Drills

Drill No.	Decimal Equivalent	Drill No.	Decimal Equivalent	Drill No.	Decimal Equivalent
80	0.0135	53	0.0595	26	0.1470
79	0.0145	52	0.0635	25	0.1495
78	0.0160	51	0.0670	24	0.1520
77	0.0180	50	0.0700	23	0.1540
76	0.0200	49	0.0730	22	0.1570
75	0.0210	48	0.0760	21	0.1590
74	0.0225	47	0.0785	20	0.1610
73	0.0240	46	0.0810	19	0.1660
72	0.0250	45	0.0820	18	0.1695
71	0.0260	44	0.0860	17	0.1730
70	0.0280	43	0.0890	16	0.1770
69	0.0292	42	0.0935	15	0.1800
68	0.0310	41	0.0960	14	0.1820
67	0.0320	40	0.0980	13	0.1850
66	0.0330	39	0.0995	12	0.1890
65	0.0350	38	0.1015	11	0.1910
64	0.0360	37	0.1040	10	0.1935
63	0.0370	36	0.1065	9	0.1960
62	0.0380	35	0.1100	8	0.1990
61	0.0390	34	0.1110	7	0.2010
60	0.0400	33	0.1130	6	0.2040
59	0.0410	32	0.1160	5	0.2055
58	0.0420	31	0.1200	4	0.2090
57	0.0430	30	0.1285	3	0.2130
56	0.0465	29	0.1360	2	0.2210
55	0.0520	28	0.1405	1	0.2280
54	0.0550	27	0.1440		

Tap Drill Sizes

National Fine or S.A.E			National Coarse or U.S.S.		
Screw & Tap Size	Threads Per Inch	Use Drill Number	Screw & Tap Size	Threads Per Inch	Use Drill Number
No. 5	44	37	No. 5	40	39
No. 6	40	33	No. 6	32	36
No. 8	36	29	No. 8	32	29
No. 10	32	21	No. 10	24	25
No. 12	28	15	No. 12	24	17
$\frac{1}{4}$	28	3	$\frac{1}{4}$	20	8
$\frac{5}{16}$	24	1	$\frac{5}{16}$	18	F
$\frac{3}{8}$	24	Q	$\frac{3}{8}$	16	$\frac{5}{16}$
$\frac{7}{16}$	20	W	$\frac{7}{16}$	14	U
$\frac{1}{2}$	20	$\frac{29}{64}$	$\frac{1}{2}$	13	$\frac{27}{64}$
$\frac{9}{16}$	18	$\frac{33}{64}$	$\frac{9}{16}$	12	$\frac{31}{64}$
$\frac{5}{8}$	18	$\frac{37}{64}$	$\frac{5}{8}$	11	$\frac{17}{32}$
$\frac{3}{4}$	16	$\frac{11}{16}$	$\frac{3}{4}$	10	$\frac{21}{32}$
$\frac{7}{8}$	14	$\frac{13}{16}$	$\frac{7}{8}$	9	$\frac{49}{64}$
$1\frac{1}{8}$	12	$1\frac{3}{64}$	1	8	$\frac{7}{8}$
$1\frac{1}{4}$	12	$1\frac{11}{64}$	$1\frac{1}{8}$	7	$\frac{63}{64}$
$1\frac{1}{2}$	12	$1\frac{27}{64}$	$1\frac{1}{4}$	7	$1\frac{7}{64}$
			$1\frac{1}{2}$	6	$1\frac{11}{32}$

Decimal Equivalent Size of the Letter Drills

Letter Drill	Decimal Equivalent	Letter Drill	Decimal Equivalent	Letter Drill	Decimal Equivalent
A	0.234	J	0.277	S	0.348
B	0.238	K	0.281	T	0.358
C	0.242	L	0.290	U	0.368
D	0.246	M	0.295	V	0.377
E	0.250	N	0.302	W	0.386
F	0.257	O	0.316	X	0.397
G	0.261	P	0.323	Y	0.404
H	0.266	Q	0.332	Z	0.413
I	0.272	R	0.339		

Conversion—Millimeters to Decimal Inches

mm	inches	mm	inches	mm	inches	mm	inches	mm	inches
1	0.039 370	31	1.220 470	61	2.401 570	91	3.582 670	210	8.267 700
2	0.078 740	32	1.259 840	62	2.440 940	92	3.622 040	220	8.661 400
3	0.118 110	33	1.299 210	63	2.480 310	93	3.661 410	230	9.055 100
4	0.157 480	34	1.338 580	64	2.519 680	94	3.700 780	240	9.448 800
5	0.196 850	35	1.377 949	65	2.559 050	95	3.740 150	250	9.842 500
6	0.236 220	36	1.417 319	66	2.598 420	96	3.779 520	260	10.236 200
7	0.275 590	37	1.456 689	67	2.637 790	97	3.818 890	270	10.629 900
8	0.314 960	38	1.496 050	68	2.677 160	98	3.858 260	280	11.032 600
9	0.354 330	39	1.535 430	69	2.716 530	99	3.897 630	290	11.417 300
10	0.393 700	40	1.574 800	70	2.755 900	100	3.937 000	300	11.811 000
11	0.433 070	41	1.614 170	71	2.795 270	105	4.133 848	310	12.204 700
12	0.472 440	42	1.653 540	72	2.834 640	110	4.330 700	320	12.598 400
13	0.511 810	43	1.692 910	73	2.874 010	115	4.527 550	330	12.992 100
14	0.551 180	44	1.732 280	74	2.913 380	120	4.724 400	340	13.385 800
15	0.590 550	45	1.771 650	75	2.952 750	125	4.921 250	350	13.779 500
16	0.629 920	46	1.811 020	76	2.992 120	130	5.118 100	360	14.173 200
17	0.669 290	47	1.850 390	77	3.031 490	135	5.314 950	370	14.566 900
18	0.708 660	48	1.889 760	78	3.070 860	140	5.511 800	380	14.960 600
19	0.748 030	49	1.929 130	79	3.110 230	145	5.708 650	390	15.354 300
20	0.787 400	50	1.968 500	80	3.149 600	150	5.905 500	400	15.748 000
21	0.826 770	51	2.007 870	81	3.188 970	155	6.102 350	500	19.685 000
22	0.866 140	52	2.047 240	82	3.228 340	160	6.299 200	600	23.622 000
23	0.905 510	53	2.086 610	83	3.267 710	165	6.496 050	700	27.559 000
24	0.944 880	54	2.125 980	84	3.307 080	170	6.692 900	800	31.496 000
25	0.984 250	55	2.165 350	85	3.346 450	175	6.889 750	900	35.433 000
26	1.023 620	56	2.204 720	86	3.385 820	180	7.086 600	1000	39.370 000
27	1.062 990	57	2.244 090	87	3.425 190	185	7.283 450	2000	78.740 000
28	1.102 360	58	2.283 460	88	3.464 560	190	7.480 300	3000	118.110 000
29	1.141 730	59	2.322 830	89	3.503 903	195	7.677 150	4000	157.480 000
30	1.181 100	60	2.362 200	90	3.543 300	200	7.874 000	5000	196.850 000

To change decimal millimeters to decimal inches, position the decimal point where desired on either side of the millimeter measurement shown and reset the inches decimal by the same number of digits in the same direction. For example, to convert 0.001 mm into decimal inches, reset the decimal behind the 1 mm (shown on the chart) to 0.001; change the decimal inch equivalent (0.039" shown) to 0.00039".